Numerical Methods

IN ENGINEERING

PRENTICE-HALL CIVIL ENGINEERING
AND ENGINEERING MECHANICS SERIES

N. M. NEWMARK, *Editor*

Numerical Methods
IN ENGINEERING

Mario G. Salvadori

PROFESSOR OF CIVIL ENGINEERING
COLUMBIA UNIVERSITY

AND

Melvin L. Baron

ADJUNCT ASSOCIATE PROFESSOR OF CIVIL ENGINEERING
COLUMBIA UNIVERSITY

Englewood Cliffs, N. J.
PRENTICE-HALL, INC.
1961

Library of Congress Catalog Card Number: 61-15760

PRINTED IN THE UNITED STATES OF AMERICA

62679-C

To our wives

Preface to the Second Edition

The ever-increasing interest in numerical procedures, the favor encountered by the English, Portuguese, Russian, and Chinese editions of this book, and the preparation of its Spanish, Japanese, and Italian editions have convinced us of the timeliness of a revision. In preparing it we have maintained unchanged the elementary character of the book, while widening its scope and correcting the minor errors and misprints of the first edition.

In the first chapter we have added a treatment of quartic equations by Brown's method, a simple presentation of Graeffe's method for complex roots of algebraic equations, a method for the calculation of inverse matrices, and a method for the solution of simultaneous nonlinear equations. A new section is given to the solution of linear programming problems by the simplex method.

In the second chapter we have introduced sections on Sterling's interpolation formula and on Lagrangian interpolation and have considerably extended the treatment of quadrature formulas, as well as of central differences in table checking.

In the third chapter predictor-corrector methods have been included for first- and second-order differential equations, and Noumerov's method has been extended to higher-order equations. A separate section is dedicated to the integration of difference equations in order to improve the understanding of error accumulation in step-by-step integration.

While the structure of the fourth chapter was left practically untouched, the fifth chapter has been completely rewritten. The essential differences in the integration procedures for hyperbolic, parabolic, and elliptic equations have been emphasized. The section on double integration has been extended to consider integrals with variable limits. Improved Poissonian operators in Cartesian and triangular coordinates have been derived, and the stability of the numerical solution of parabolic equations has been analyzed.

New problems involving techniques presented for the first time in this book have been added, with alternate solutions. The total number of problems is now approximately 500.

We wish to express our appreciation to Mrs. Alva Matthews Solomon and to Mr. Raymond Parnes, who carefully solved all the new problems, and to Dr. T. L. Liu, who drew some of the new figures.

MARIO G. SALVADORI
MELVIN L. BARON

New York, N. Y.

Preface to the First Edition

The interest of the applied mathematician and of the scientist in numerical methods has grown considerably during the last decades for many reasons. Electric desk calculators, mass-produced at reasonable prices, and electronic super-computers of the digital and the analogue type make possible today computations which could not have been tackled a few years ago. Technical problems, for which an analytical solution is unobtainable, more complicated and more numerous than ever, require an immediate answer, while technical personnel capable of working out complex analytical problems is scarce. The numerical approach permits the use of workers with a limited knowledge of mathematics.

These conditions explain the popularity of numerical methods, and indicate the increasing need for personnel with numerical skills and for courses on numerical methods in our colleges and universities.

This book has evolved from a set of mimeographed lecture notes used in a one-semester course offered in the School of Engineering at Columbia University. The course is the last of a sequence of five inaugurated by the author several years ago in order to widen the mathematical background of undergraduate and graduate students and to fill the gap between a knowledge of theoretical mathematics and the technique of solving physical problems by mathematical methods.

It would be obviously impossible to encompass the whole wide and growing field of numerical methods in a book of moderate size. It is the purpose of this presentation to introduce both the student and the practicing scientist, and in particular the engineer, to those elementary techniques which are needed more often in the solution of technical problems. The book is therefore addressed to students of engineering, physics, chemistry, mathematics, and to any individual desiring to become acquainted with numerical methods in order to apply them in his professional work. It is assumed that the reader has a knowledge of the calculus and a smattering of differential equations.

The five chapters of the book deal with:

1. The solution of algebraic equations of high degree and of simultaneous linear algebraic equations.

2. The elementary theory of finite differences and its application to numerical differentiation, integration, interpolation, and extrapolation.

3. The solution of ordinary initial-value problems.

4. The solution of ordinary boundary and characteristic-value problems.

5. The solution of problems involving partial differential equations of the boundary, characteristic, and mixed types.

In the presentation of the material, finite difference theory is made the unifying basis of all the numerical techniques. This makes the treatment of the various subjects economical and avoids unnecessary repetition. It also allows a simple evaluation of errors throughout the book and, perhaps for the first time, the systematic use of efficient extrapolation procedures.

The various numerical techniques are either introduced by, or applied to, a simple illustrative problem taken from the various fields of engineering, (mechanics, strength of materials, electricity, elasticity, plasticity, heat flow, vibrations, elastic stability, etc.) in order to give as wide a range of applications as possible within the limits of space and prerequisites. But the reader does not need to be familiar with the particular field of knowledge involved in the illustrative problem to grasp the meaning of the numerical technique.

The choice of techniques was based upon their simplicity and efficiency: some have been known for over two centuries; others have been advanced in the recent past. The numerical tools to which these techniques can be applied are, usually, the electric desk calculator and, in many cases, the slide rule. Modern electronic calculators, to which most of these techniques can also obviously be applied, are not mentioned since their theory constitutes an entire new field of applied mathematics.

The problems at the end of each chapter are essentially of two types: purely numerical exercises and applied problems. Many of the numerical exercises represent actual physical problems and can be interpreted analogically in a variety of ways. The mathematical formulation of the applied problems is given or can be derived from the text or from the numerous references in the footnotes. Answers are given to alternate problems and to all problems whose answers are of general interest.

Melvin L. Baron undertook, under my supervision, the painstaking and laborious task of assembling and solving the 400 problems contained in this book. He also checked the problems in the text and drew sketches for the figures. I am glad to express here my deep appreciation for his efficient efforts.

The books and individuals from which I have learned numerical mathematics are too many to be listed here, but I take this opportunity to express my gratitude to Prof. Mauro Picone, Director of the Istituto Nazionale per le Applicazioni del Calcolo (the national Italian computational laboratory, seat of the recently established International Center of Mechanical Calculus), who first taught me the love of numbers while I was his student at the University of Rome 20 years ago.

I am indebted to my friends and colleagues. Prof. R. J. Schwartz, for his critical reading of the manuscript, and Prof. F. H. Lee, for the care he gave to the drawing of the figures.

Mrs P. Arno Moriarty has given renewed proof of her exceptional skill in typing the manuscript.

MARIO G. SALVADORI

New York, N. Y.

Note: The following books are referred to in the footnotes by their abbreviated titles.

Engineering Problems for *The Mathematical Solution of Engineering Problems,* by M. G. Salvadori and K. S. Miller, Columbia University Press, New York, 1953.

Differential Equations for *Differential Equations in Engineering Problems,* by M. G. Salvadori and R. J. Schwarz, Prentice-Hall, Inc., Englewood Cliffs, N. J., 1954.

Contents

Chapter I

The Practical Solution of Algebraic and Transcendental Equations

Chapter II

FINITE DIFFERENCES AND THEIR APPLICATIONS

Chapter III

THE NUMERICAL INTEGRATION OF INITIAL VALUE PROBLEMS

Chapter IV

THE NUMERICAL INTEGRATION OF ORDINARY BOUNDARY VALUE PROBLEMS

Chapter V

THE NUMERICAL SOLUTION OF PARTIAL DIFFERENTIAL EQUATIONS

Numerical Methods
IN ENGINEERING

I

The Practical Solution of Algebraic
and Transcendental Equations

1.1 Introduction

The solution of algebraic and transcendental equations, and of systems of simultaneous linear equations, is one of the numerical tasks encountered most frequently in applied mathematics. Although many methods have been devised to obtain these solutions, and some of them are extremely ingenious from a theoretical viewpoint, the task of solving equations remains burdensome.

In what follows, methods are presented for the evaluation of the real and complex roots of algebraic equations of high degree, of real roots of transcendental equations, and of roots of simultaneous linear algebraic equations. These procedures are well adapted to slide-rule use and to use on desk electric calculators. They allow an accuracy of 5 to 10 significant figures and the solution of systems of between 40 and 100 simultaneous linear equations. Modern electronic calculators may extend considerably the use of these methods.

The general procedures outlined below attempt to combine various methods so as to reduce the amount of labor involved in the solution, but the reader may prefer other classical procedures or formulas since the choice of method is often a matter of training and personal preference.

1.2 Real Roots of Algebraic Equations

The algebraic equation of degree n

$$f(x) = a_n x^n + a_{n-1} x^{n-1} + \ldots + a_1 x + a_0 = 0 \qquad (1.2.1)$$

has n roots, some of which may be real and different or real and repeated, and the rest of which appear in couples of complex conjugate numbers.

In solving an algebraic equation of high degree it is advisable to locate first its real roots, in order of decreasing absolute value. This is best done by trial and error, evaluating remainders by synthetic division.

The possible number of positive and negative roots may be determined by Descartes' rule of sign: *the number of positive roots is equal to the number of sign changes in the coefficients of the equation (or less than that by an even number); the number of negative roots is equal to the number of sign repetitions in the coefficients (or less than that by an even number).* Zero coefficients are ignored in this count.

If n is odd, Eq. (1.2.1) has at least one real root of sign opposite to the sign of a_0/a_n.

To scan for the real roots of Eq. (1.2.1) less than 1 in absolute value, evaluate $f(x)$ for $-1 \leq x \leq 1$ in steps of 0.2 or 0.1. To scan for the roots of Eq. (1.2.1) larger than 1 in modulus, let

$$x = \frac{1}{\xi} \qquad (a)$$

and evaluate for $-1 \leq \xi \leq 1$ the equation

$$a_0 \xi^n + a_1 \xi^{n-1} + \ldots + a_{n-1} \xi + a_n = 0. \qquad (1.2.1a)$$

The largest root of Eq. (1.2.1) may frequently be approximated by the root of the linear equation

$$a_n x + a_{n-1} = 0 \qquad (1.2.2)$$

or by the root larger in absolute value of the quadratic equation

$$a_n x^2 + a_{n-1} x + a_{n-2} = 0. \qquad (1.2.3)$$

Whenever the largest root of Eq. (1.2.1) is much larger in absolute value than all the others, these approximations are accurate.

The smallest root of Eq. (1.2.1) may similarly be approximated by the root of the equation

$$a_1 x + a_0 = 0 \qquad (1.2.4)$$

or by the smaller root in absolute value of the quadratic equation

$$a_2 x^2 + a_1 x + a_0 = 0, \tag{1.2.5}$$

whenever the smallest root is much smaller than the others.

The roots x_i $(i = 1, 2, \ldots, n)$ of Eq. (1.2.1) may be checked by means of Newton's relations:

$$\sum_{i=1}^{n} x_i = -\frac{a_{n-1}}{a_n} \tag{1.2.6a}$$

$$\sum_{(i,j)=1}^{n} x_i x_j = \frac{a_{n-2}}{a_n} \tag{1.2.6b}$$

$$\sum_{(i,j,k)=1}^{n} x_i x_j x_k = -\frac{a_{n-3}}{a_n} \tag{1.2.6c}$$

$$\cdots\cdots\cdots\cdots\cdots$$

$$x_1 \cdot x_2 \cdot x_3 \cdot \ldots \cdot x_n = (-1)^n \frac{a_0}{a_n} \tag{1.2.6d}$$

in which $i \neq j \neq k \neq \ldots$.

The evaluation of a polynomial $f(x)$ and of its successive derivatives for a value x_0 of x is easily performed by successive applications of *synthetic substitution* (or *division*), as shown in Table 1.1.

Table 1.1
Synthetic Substitution

a_n	a_{n-1}	a_{n-2}	$\ldots$	a_2	a_1	a_0
	$b_n x_0$	$b_{n-1} x_0$	$\ldots$	$b_3 x_0$	$b_2 x_0$	$b_1 x_0$
$b_n \equiv a_n$	b_{n-1}	b_{n-2}	$\ldots$	b_2	b_1	$b_0 \equiv f(x_0)$
	$c_n x_0$	$c_{n-1} x_0$	$\ldots$	$c_3 x_0$	$c_2 x_0$	
$c_n \equiv b_n$	c_{n-1}	c_{n-2}	$\ldots$	c_2	$c_1 \equiv \dfrac{1}{1!} f'(x_0)$	
	$d_n x_0$	$d_{n-1} x_0$	$\ldots$	$d_3 x_0$		
$d_n \equiv c_n$	d_{n-1}	d_{n-2}	$\ldots$	$d_2 \equiv \dfrac{1}{2!} f''(x_0)$		

The coefficients of the powers of x not appearing in the equation must be labeled zero in the synthetic division scheme.

A general procedure for the location of real roots will now be applied to the equation

$$y = f(x) = x^3 - 12.2 x^2 + 7.45 x + 42 = 0, \tag{b}$$

which, by Descartes' rule of signs, may have either two positive roots or none, and only one negative root.

An approximate value of the largest root is given by the equation

$$x - 12.2 = 0$$

or by the equation

$$x^2 - 12.2x + 7.45 = 0.$$

The first equation gives $x_1 = 12.2$; the second gives

$$x_1 = 6.1 + \sqrt{(6.1)^2 - 7.45} = 11.55,$$

if the $+$ sign is chosen in front of the square root to obtain the larger root. Applying synthetic division with a trial value $x_1 = 12$, we obtain

		-12.2	7.45	42
12		12.0	-2.40	60.6
	1	-0.2	5.05	$\lvert 102.6$

The magnitude of the remainder may lead the reader to believe that 12 is a poor approximation to x_1. This is not so, because *whenever a root is much larger than unity, the remainder is sensitive to changes in the value of the root.* In fact, a second trial, with $x_2 = 10$, gives

		-12.2	7.45	42
10		10.0	-22.00	-145.50
	1	-2.2	-14.55	$\lvert -103.50$

The values $x_1 = 12$ and $x_2 = 10$ approximate the root from above and from below, respectively, and a better approximation may be obtained by *linear interpolation.* The intersection with the x-axis ($y = 0$) of the straight line

$$\frac{x - x_1}{y - y_1} = \frac{x_2 - x_1}{y_2 - y_1}$$

connecting the two points $P_1(x_1,y_1)$ and $P_2(x_2,y_2)$,

$$x_3 = \frac{x_1 y_2 - x_2 y_1}{y_2 - y_1} \qquad (1.2.7)$$

gives the value of the linearly interpolated approximation x_3 (Fig. 1.1). The right side of Eq. (1.2.7) can be evaluated by a single machine operation. An application of Eq. (1.2.7) to the approximations $x_1 = 12$, $y_1 = 103$, and $x_2 = 10$, $y_2 = -103$ gives

$$x_3 = \frac{12(-103) - 10(103)}{-103 - 103} = 11,$$

and synthetic division gives a remainder $y_3 = -21.25$. We can now interpolate linearly between 11 and 12, obtaining $x_4 = 11.17$ with a remainder of $-3\,55$, and a final guess 11.20 gives

$$
\begin{array}{r}
 \quad 1 \qquad -12.2 \qquad\quad 7.45 \qquad\quad 42 \\
11.20 \qquad\qquad\qquad 11.2 \qquad -11.20 \qquad -42.0 \\
\hline
1 \qquad -\ 1.0 \qquad -\ 3.75 \qquad\quad 0
\end{array}
$$
(c)

which shows $x = 11.2$ to be the required root.

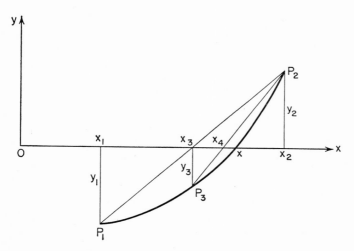

Fig. 1.1.   Linear interpolation.

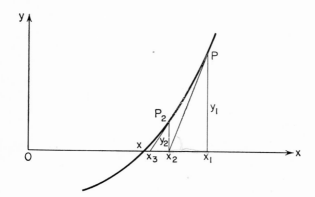

Fig. 1.2.   Newton's method of tangents.

Alternatively, and usually with definite advantage, one may use *Newton's method of tangents* (Fig. 1.2) to improve a first approximation to the root.

The intersection x_{n+1} with the x-axis ($y = 0$) of the tangent to a curve $y = f(x)$ at $x = x_n$ is given by

$$x_{n+1} = x_n - \frac{f(x_n)}{f'(x_n)}. \tag{1.2.8}$$

Applying synthetic substitution twice in succession, we obtain directly $f(x_n)$ and $f'(x_n)$ and evaluate the next approximation x_{n+1} of the root.

Thus with $x_1 = 12$ we obtain, in two steps,

	1	-12.2	7.45	42
$x_1 = 12$		12.0	-2.40	61
	1	-0.2	5.05	$103 = f(x_1)$
$x_1 = 12$		12.0	142	
	1	11.8	$147 = f'(x_1)$	

$$x_2 = 12 - \frac{103}{147} = 12 - 0.7 = 11.3.$$

Using the newly found value $x_2 = 11.3$, we have

	1	-12.2	7.45	42.0
$x_2 = 11.3$		11.3	-10.17	-30.7
	1	-0.9	-2.72	$11.3 = f(x_2)$
$x_2 = 11.3$		11.3	117.52	
	1	10.4	$114.80 = f'(x_2)$	

$$x_3 = 11.3 - \frac{11}{115} = 11.3 - 0.1 = 11.2,$$

which is the value of the root obtained before.

Faster convergence at the cost of slightly increased labor is obtained by *Newton's second-order method*. Expanding $f(x)$ into a Taylor series about $x = x_n$ up to its third term and letting

$$x_{n+1} - x_n = h, \tag{1.2.9}$$

we obtain

$$f(x_{n+1}) = f(x_n) + f'(x_n)h + \frac{f''(x_n)}{2}h^2 + \ldots = 0,$$

or

$$f(x_n) + h\left[f'(x_n) + \frac{f''(x_n)}{2}h\right] = 0. \tag{d}$$

Approximating h inside the bracket by Eq. (1.2.8), i.e., letting $h = -f(x_n)/f'(x_n)$, Eq. (d) gives

$$\frac{1}{h} = -\frac{f'(x_n)}{f(x_n)} + \frac{f''(x_n)/2}{f'(x_n)}. \tag{1.2.10}$$

Thus starting with $x_1 = 12$, Eq. (b) gives

$$
\begin{array}{c|rrrr}
 & 1 & -12.20 & 7.45 & 42.00 \\
x_1 = 12 & & 12.00 & -2.40 & 60.60 \\
\hline
 & 1 & -0.20 & 5.05 & \boxed{102.60 = f(x_1)} \\
x_1 = 12 & & 12.00 & 141.60 & \\
\hline
 & 1 & 11.80 & \boxed{146.65 = f'(x_1)} & \\
x_1 = 12 & & 12.00 & & \\
\hline
 & 1 & \boxed{23.80 = (1/2)f''(x_1)} & &
\end{array}
$$

$$
\frac{1}{h} = -\frac{146.65}{102.6} + \frac{23.8}{146.65} = -1.27; \qquad h = -0.79;
$$

$$
x_2 = x_1 + h = 12.00 - 0.79 = 11.21.
$$

One of the principal advantages of synthetic division lies in the fact that it gives directly the coefficients of the *reduced equation*, whose roots are the remaining roots of the original equation. Thus synthetic division of Eq. (b) by $x - 11.2$ gives the quadratic whose coefficients appear in the last row of scheme (c):

$$
x^2 - x - 3.75 = 0,
$$

which may be solved by formula, giving the other two roots of Eq. (b):

$$
x = 0.5 \pm \sqrt{0.25 + 3.75} = \left\{ \begin{array}{l} +2.5 \\ -1.5. \end{array} \right.
$$

Generalizing the results of the present example, the m real roots of any algebraic equation may be obtained one at a time, using synthetic division by $(x - x_1)$, $(x - x_2)$, ..., $(x - x_m)$, to any required accuracy.

Particular care must be taken in evaluating real roots if two roots are almost equal, that is, if the equation has an almost repeated root. A root *repeated k times* is a root of the equation $f(x) = 0$ and of its first $k - 1$ derivatives. For example, using synthetic division by $x - 3$ on the equation

$$
x^3 - 5x^2 + 3x + 9 = 0,
$$

we find that

$$
\begin{array}{c|rrrr}
 & 1 & -5 & 3 & 9 \\
3 & & 3 & -6 & -9 \\
\hline
 & 1 & -2 & -3 & \boxed{0 = f(3)} \\
3 & & 3 & 3 & \\
\hline
 & 1 & 1 & \boxed{0 = f'(3)} & \\
3 & & 3 & & \\
\hline
 & 1 & \boxed{4 = (1/2)f''(3)} & &
\end{array}
$$

and hence that $x = 3$ is a double root.

Whenever $f'(x)$ is very small in the neighborhood of a root $\bar{x}$, Eqs. (1.2.8) and (1.2.10) become extremely sensitive to changes in x. In this case it is practical to evaluate first the root a of $f'(x) = 0$ near the root $\bar{x}$, to compute $f''(a)$, and to expand $f(x)$ in a Taylor series around $x = a$, neglecting terms of order higher than the third:

$$f(\bar{x}) = f(a) + f'(a)(\bar{x} - a) + \tfrac{1}{2}f''(a)(\bar{x} - a)^2 + \ldots$$
$$\doteq f(a) + \tfrac{1}{2}f''(a)(\bar{x} - a)^2.$$

To find the roots of $f(x)$ near $x = a$, we solve the quadratic equation

$$f(a) + \tfrac{1}{2}f''(a)(x - a)^2 = 0,$$

obtaining
$$\bar{x}_{1,2} = a \pm \sqrt{\frac{-f(a)}{\tfrac{1}{2}f''(a)}}. \tag{1.2.11}$$

For example, using synthetic division with $x = 1$ on the equation

$$f(x) = x^3 - x^2 - 1.0001x + 0.9999 = 0$$

we obtain

	1	-1	-1.0001	0.9999
1		1	0	-1.0001
	1	0	-1.0001	$\boxed{-0.0002 = f(1)}$
1		1	1.0000	
	1	1	$\boxed{-0.0001 = f'(1)}$	

Since both $f(1)$ and $f'(1)$ are small, we solve first the equation

$$f'(x) = 3x^2 - 2x - 1.0001 = 0$$

starting with $x = 1$:

	3	-2	-1.0001
1		3	1.0000
	3	1	$\boxed{-0.0001 = f'(1)}$
1		3	
	3	$\boxed{4 = f''(1)}$	

and we obtain the root

$$a = 1 - \frac{-0.0001}{4} = 1.000025.$$

Evaluating $f(a)$ and $\tfrac{1}{2}f''(a)$ by synthetic division;

	1	$-1.$	-1.000100	0.999900
1.000025		1.000025	0.000025	-1.000095
	1	0.000025	-1.000075	$\boxed{-0.000195 = f(a)}$
1.000025		1.000025	1.000075	
	1	1.000050	$\boxed{0 = f'(a)}$	
1.000025		1.000025		
	1	$\boxed{2.000075 = (1/2)f''(a)}$		

we obtain, by Eq. (1.2.11),

$$\bar{x}_{1,2} = 1.000025 \pm \sqrt{-\frac{-0.000195}{2.000075}} = \begin{cases} 1.009899 \\ 0.990151. \end{cases}$$

The true roots of the equation are 1.01, 0.99, and -1.00.

Once all the real roots have been divided out of the equation, the last reduced equation contains only pairs of complex conjugate roots.

When the reduced equation is a quadratic, the two complex conjugate roots are immediately obtained by formula. When the reduced equation is of fourth, sixth, or even higher degree, it is convenient to isolate in the equation the quadratic factors which are responsible for each pair of complex conjugate roots.

1.3 Brown's Method for Quartic Equations

The two quadratic factors into which a quartic equation may be separated can be obtained directly by Brown's method.*

Given the quartic equation

$$x^4 + a_3 x^3 + a_2 x^2 + a_1 x + a_0 = 0, \tag{1.3.1}$$

evaluate the coefficients

$$b_1 = a_3 a_1 - 4a_0; \qquad b_0 = a_0(4a_2 - a_3^2) - a_1^2 \tag{1.3.2}$$

and compute the *algebraically* largest *real* root z_3 of the cubic equation

$$z^3 - a_2 z^2 + b_1 z + b_0 = 0. \tag{1.3.3}$$

Compute the coefficients

$$c_{1,2} = \frac{a_3}{2} \pm \sqrt{\left(\frac{a_3}{2}\right)^2 - a_2 + z_3} \tag{1.3.4}$$

$$d_{i,j} = \frac{z_3}{2} \pm \sqrt{\left(\frac{z_3}{2}\right)^2 - a_0} \quad (i,j = 1 \text{ or } 2), \tag{1.3.5}$$

and check which of the two values d_i, d_j is d_1 and which is d_2 by means of the relationship

$$c_1 d_2 + c_2 d_1 = a_1. \tag{1.3.6}$$

The two quadratic factors of Eq. (1.3.1) are

$$x^2 + c_1 x + d_1 = 0; \qquad x^2 + c_2 x + d_2 = 0. \tag{1.3.7}$$

* W. S. Brown, "Solution of Biquadratic Equations," *Aircraft Engineering*, **16,** 14 (1944).

For example, given

$$x^4 - 6x^3 + 18x^2 - 24x + 16 = 0, \tag{a}$$

we obtain

$$a_3 = -6; \quad a_2 = 18; \quad a_1 = -24; \quad a_0 = 16;$$

$$b_1 = (-6)(-24) - 4(16) = 80;$$

$$b_0 = 16[(4)(18) - (-6)^2] - (-24)^2 = 0;$$

$$z^3 - 18z^2 + 80z = 0;$$

$$z_1 = 0; \quad z_2 = 8; \quad z_3 = 10;$$

$$c_{1,2} = \frac{-6}{2} \pm \sqrt{9 - 18 + 10} = \left\{ \begin{array}{c} -2; \\ -4; \end{array} \right.$$

$$d_{i,j} = \frac{10}{2} \pm \sqrt{25 - 16} = \left\{ \begin{array}{c} 8; \\ 2; \end{array} \right.$$

$$c_1 d_2 + c_2 d_1 = -2(2) - 4(8) = -36;$$

$$c_1 d_2 + c_2 d_1 = -2(8) - 4(2) = -24;$$

$$d_2 = 8; \quad d_1 = 2;$$

$$x^2 - 2x + 2 = 0; \quad x^2 - 4x + 8 = 0$$

$$x_{1,2} = 1 \pm i; \quad x_{3,4} = 2(1 \pm i).$$

1.4 Graeffe's Method

Given an algebraic equation $f(x) = 0$ with roots $|x_1| > |x_2| > |x_3| > \ldots > |x_n|$, the equation

$$F(-x^2) = 0$$

with the roots $-x_1^2$, $-x_2^2$, $-x_3^2$, $\ldots$, $-x_n^2$ has coefficients b_j obtained by means of the scheme of Table 1.2.

Table 1.2
Graeffe's Scheme

a_n	a_{n-1}	a_{n-2}	a_{n-3}	$\ldots$	a_3	a_2	a_1	a_0
a_n^2	a_{n-1}^2	a_{n-2}^2	a_{n-3}^2	$\ldots$	a_3^2	a_2^2	a_1^2	a_0^2
	$-2a_n a_{n-2}$	$-2a_{n-1}a_{n-3}$	$-2a_{n-2}a_{n-4}$	$\ldots$	$-2a_4 a_2$	$-2a_3 a_1$	$-2a_2 a_0$	
		$+2a_n a_{n-4}$	$+2a_{n-1}a_{n-5}$	$\ldots$	$+2a_5 a_1$	$+2a_4 a_0$		
			$-2a_n a_{n-6}$	$\ldots$	$-2a_6 a_0$			
				$\ldots$				
b_n	b_{n-1}	b_{n-2}	b_{n-3}	$\ldots$	b_3	b_2	b_1	b_0

Applying the same process to $F(-x^2) = 0$, an equation is obtained with roots $-x_i^4$; repeating the process a sufficiently high number of times r, the last equation has roots $-x_i^{2r}$, such that

$$|x_1^{2r}| \gg |x_2^{2r}| \gg |x_3^{2r}| \gg \ldots \gg |x_n^{2r}|.$$

Hence, indicating the coefficients of this equation by c_j and letting $2r = m$, by Newton's relations [Eqs. (1.2.6)],

$$\sum_{i=1}^{n} - x_i^m \approx -x_1^m = - \frac{c_{n-1}}{c_n}$$

$$\sum_{(i\,j)=1}^{n} x_i^m x_j^m \approx x_1^m x_2^m = + \frac{c_{n-2}}{c_n}$$

$$\sum_{(i,j,k)=1}^{n} - x_i^m x_j^m x_k^m \approx -x_1^m x_2^m x_3^m = - \frac{c_{n-3}}{c_n}$$

$$\ldots \ldots \ldots \ldots \ldots \ldots \ldots \ldots \ldots \ldots \ldots \ldots$$

and dividing the second by the first, the third by the second, etc.,

$$x_1^m = + \frac{c_{n-1}}{c_n}; \quad x_2^m = + \frac{c_{n-2}}{c_{n-1}}; \quad x_3^m = + \frac{c_{n-3}}{c_{n-2}}; \quad \ldots \qquad (1.4.1)$$

We must distinguish three cases:

(a) When all the roots are real, the double products in Table 1.2 eventually become negligible in comparison with the a_j^2 and all the c_j become "pure squares." The process is stopped at this point, and the roots are computed as $\pm \sqrt[m]{x_i^m}$. Their sign is determined by substitution in the original equation.

(b) When one of the c_j, say c_s, does not become a pure square but is flanked by two pure squares c_{s-1}, c_{s+1}, the ratio

$$r^{2m} = \frac{c_{s-1}}{c_{s+1}} \qquad (1.4.2)$$

gives the $2m$th power of the modulus of a pair of complex roots $\alpha_s \pm \beta_s i$, or of two equal real roots ($\beta_s = 0$) of the original equation. The real and imaginary parts α_s, β_s of these roots are determined by means of Newton's relations, once all the other real roots and all the moduli of the complex roots are known, as shown below.

(c) When $2k - 1$ nonsquares are flanked by two pure squares c_s, c_{s-2k}, there are k pairs of complex roots with identical modulus r, given by

$$r^{2km} = \frac{c_{s-2k}}{c_s}. \qquad (1.4.3)$$

To determine the complex roots once the real roots have been eliminated, one makes use of Newton's relations.

For example, for a fourth-degree equation, knowing the two moduli r_1, r_2,

$$r_1^2 = \alpha_1^2 + \beta_1^2 \tag{a}$$

$$r_2^2 = \alpha_2^2 + \beta_2^2, \tag{b}$$

we obtain

$$\sum_{i=1}^{4} x_i = x_1 + x_2 + x_3 + x_4 = 2\alpha_1 + 2\alpha_2 = -\frac{a_{n-1}}{a_n} \tag{c}$$

$$\sum_{(i,j)=1}^{4} x_i x_j = r_1^2 + r_2^2 + 4\alpha_1\alpha_2 = \frac{a_{n-2}}{a_n}. \tag{d}$$

The four unknowns α_1, α_2, β_1, β_2 are the roots of the four equations (a), (b), (c), and (d).

The following equation has real and complex roots and is solved as shown in scheme (f), where the superscripts indicate powers of 10.

$$x^4 - 15x^3 + 138x^2 - 324x + 200 = 0 \tag{e}$$

a_4	a_3	a_2	a_1	a_0	m	
1^0	-1.5^1	$+1.38^2$	-3.24^2	$+2.00^2$	1	
1^0	2.25^2	1.9044^4	10.4976^4	4.00^4		
	-2.76^2	-0.9720^4	-5.5200^4			
		0.0400^4				
1^0	-0.51^2	0.9724^4	4.9776^4	4.00^4	2	
1^0	0.2601^4	0.9456^8	2.4777^9	1.60^9		(f)
	-1.9448^4	0.0508^8	-0.7779^9			
		0.0008^8				
1^0	-1.6847^4	0.9772^8	1.6997^9	1.60^9	4	
1^0	2.8382^8	0.9944^{16}	2.8890^{18}	2.56^{18}		
	-1.9944^8	0.0057^{16}	-0.3191^{18}			
		0.0000^{16}				
1^0	0.8438^8	1.0001^{16}	2.5699^{18}	2.56^{18}	8	
c_4	c_3	c_2	c_1	c_0		

Only c_3 is not a pure square. Hence there are two real roots and two complex conjugate roots. Thus, with two-decimal-figure accuracy,

$$x_1^8 = \frac{c_0}{c_1} = 1.00; \qquad x_1 = \pm 1.00; \qquad x_2^8 = \frac{c_1}{c_2} = 257; \qquad x_2 = \pm 2.00$$

$$(r_{3,4}^2)^8 = \frac{c_2}{c_4} = 1.00 \times 10^{16}; \qquad r_{3,4}^2 = 100.$$

Substitution in the equation shows that $x_1 = 1.00$, $x_2 = 2.00$, and by

Newton's relations,

$$\sum_{i=1}^{4} x_i = 1.00 + 2.00 + 2\alpha = -(-15), \qquad \alpha = 6$$

$$\alpha^2 + \beta^2 = r^2 = 100; \qquad \beta^2 = 100 - 36 = 64; \qquad \beta = 8$$

$$x_{3,4} = 6 \pm 8i$$

The following equation has roots with identical moduli:

$$x^4 - 6x^3 + 18x^2 - 30x + 25 = 0 \tag{g}$$

and is solved as shown below

1	-6	18	-30	25	$m = 1$
1	36	324	900	625	
	-36	-360	-900		
		$+50$			
1	0	14	0	6.25^2	$m = 2$
1	0	0.0196^4	0	39.0625^4	
	-0.2800^2	0	-1.7500^4		
		0.1250^4			
1	-0.2800^2	0.1446^4	-1.7500^4	39.0625^4	$m = 4$

$c_4 = 1$, $c_0 = 39.0625^4$ are pure squares; c_1, c_2, c_3 are not; $(2k - 1 = 3)$. There are $k = 2$ pair of roots:

$$x_{1,2} = \alpha_1 \pm \beta_1 i; \qquad x_{3,4} = \alpha_2 \pm \beta_2 i$$

with equal modulus r such that

$$r^{2(2\cdot4)} = 39.0625 \times 10^4 \quad \therefore \quad r^2 = 5.$$

By solving the equations [(a), (b), (c), (d) of this section]

$$\alpha_1^2 + \beta_1^2 = 5; \qquad \alpha_2^2 + \beta_2^2 = 5; \qquad 2\alpha_1 + 2\alpha_2 = -(-6);$$

$$5 + 5 + 4\alpha_1\alpha_2 = 18,$$

we obtain:

$$\alpha_1 = 1; \qquad \alpha_2 = 2; \qquad \beta_1 = 2; \qquad \beta_2 = 1;$$

and

$$x_{1,2} = 1 \pm 2i; \qquad x_2 = 2 \pm i.^*$$

1.5 Complex Roots by Iteration

The separation of an equation into quadratic factors may also be obtained by synthetic division of the equation by trial quadratic

---

* Graeffe's method is explained in detail in J. B. Scarborough, *Numerical Mathematical Analysis*, Johns Hopkins Press, Baltimore, 1930, pp. 198 ff., and in R. E. Doughterty and E. G. Keller, *Mathematics of Modern Engineering*, John Wiley & Sons, Inc., New York, 1936, pp. 98 ff.

factors until the remainder, which is a binomial $s_1 x + s_0$, becomes equal to zero or negligible.

A first approximation to the quadratic factor responsible for the roots of largest modulus in Eq. (1.2.1) is the factor

$$x^2 + a_{n-1}/a_n x + a_{n-2}/a_n, \tag{1.5.1}$$

while a first approximation to the quadratic factor responsible for the roots of smallest modulus is

$$x^2 + \frac{a_1}{a_2} x + \frac{a_0}{a_2}. \tag{1.5.2}$$

Table 1.3

Synthetic Division by $x^2 + px + q$ (in descending powers of x)

$$f(x) = x^n + a_{n-1}x^{n-1} + a_{n-2}x^{n-2} + \ldots + a_1 x + a_0$$

$$= (x^2 + px + q)\left(x^{n-2} + s_{n-1}x^{n-3} + s_{n-2}x^{n-4} + \ldots + s_3 x + s_2 + \frac{s_1 x + s_0}{x^2 + px + q}\right)$$

$-q$	$-p$	1	→						
	1	a_{n-1}	a_{n-2}	a_{n-3}	$\ldots$	a_2	a_1	a_0
		$-p \cdot 1$	$-ps_{n-1}$	$-ps_{n-2}$	$\ldots$	$-ps_3$	$-ps_2$	
		$-q \cdot 1$	$-qs_{n-1}$	$-qs_{n-2}$	$\ldots$	$-qs_4$	$-qs_3$	$-qs_2$
	1	s_{n-1}	s_{n-2}	s_{n-3}	$\ldots$	s_2	s_1	s_0

In order to reduce the linear remainder $s_1 x + s_0$ to zero, we may either proceed by trial and error or by iteration. Both processes will be demonstrated on the following fourth-degree equation:

$$f(x) = x^4 + 27.4x^3 + 307.44x^2 - 873.7x + 1503.11 = 0. \tag{a}$$

An approximation to the smaller quadratic factor of this equation is given by

$$x^2 - \frac{873.7}{307.44} x + \frac{1503.11}{307.44} = x^2 - 2.84x + 4.89 \doteq x^2 - 3x + 5.$$

To evaluate the remainder due to the factor $x^2 + px + q$, we use first the scheme of synthetic division of Table 1.3, where

$$s_{n-1} = a_{n-1} - p; \qquad s_{n-2} = a_{n-2} - ps_{n-1} - q, \qquad \ldots$$

With an approximate factor $x^2 - 3x + 5$, this scheme applied to Eq. (a) with rounded-off coefficients gives:

-5	3	1	→		
	1	27.4	307	-874	1503
		3.0	91.2	1179.6	
			-5.0	-152.0	-1966
	1	30.4	393.2	153.6	-463

(b)

The remainder is $153.6x - 463$, and the quotient is $x^2 + 30.4x + 393.2$. We try division by $x^2 - 2x + 5$, obtaining

-5	2	1	→			
	1	27.4	307	-874	1503	
		2.0	58.8	721.6		
			-5.0	-147.0	-1804	
	1	29.4	360.8	-299.4	-301	

The coefficient s_1 of x in the remainder has changed sign, and the constant s_0 is slightly reduced in value. We try division by $x^2 - 3x + 4$:

-4	3	1	→			
	1	27.4	307	-874	1503	
		3.0	91.2	1182.6		
			-4.0	-121.6	-1576.8	
	1	30.4	394.2	187.0	-73.8	

The coefficient s_1 is now positive and larger than in the first trial, and the constant s_0 is smaller. We divide by $x^2 - 2.5x + 4$, obtaining a remainder of $-49.1x - 8.2$, while a final guess $x^2 - 2.6x + 3.9$ gives a remainder of $0.2x + 17$, which may be considered small, and a quotient $x^2 + 30x + 381.10$. The four roots of Eq. (a) are thus approximately

$$x_{1,2} = 1.3 \pm \sqrt{(1.3)^2 - 3.9} = 1.3 \pm 1.49i;$$

$$x_{3,4} = -15 \pm \sqrt{(15)^2 - 381.10} = -15 \pm 12.5i.$$

The correct values of the roots are $x_{1,2} = 1.3 \pm 1.5i$ and $x_{3,4} = -15 \pm 12.5i$.

The *iteration process of Friedman** (which is more rapidly convergent than the better-known Barstow-Lin process) eliminates the necessity of guesses, but may converge very slowly or may not converge at all, if the moduli of the complex roots are almost equal. In general, it is advisable to work by iteration and trial and error at the same time.

The Friedman procedure consists in dividing the left-hand member $f(x)$ of the equation by a trial quadratic factor *in descending powers of x*, as was done in Table 1.3, and in obtaining an improved factor by division of $f(x)$ by the quotient of the previous division, both arranged *in ascending powers of x*, as shown in Table 1.4. The remainders of these divisions are not computed, since they are not needed if the process converges.

* B. Friedman, "Note on Approximating Complex Zeros of a Polynomial," *Communications on Pure and Applied Mathematics*, **II**, 195 (June–September, 1949).

Table 1.4
Synthetic Division by $1 + p'x + q'x^2$ (in ascending powers of x)

						←	1	$-p'$	$-q'$
a_n	a_{n-1}	a_{n-2}	. . .	a_3	a_2	a_1	a_0		
	$-p's'_{n-2}$	$-p's'_{n-3}$	. . .	$-p's'_2$	$-p's'_1$	$-p's'_0$			
$-q's'_{n-2}$	$-q's'_{n-3}$	$-q's'_{n-4}$	. . .	$-q's'_1$	$-q's'_0$				
s'_n	s'_{n-1}	s'_{n-2}	. . .	s'_3	s'_2	s'_1	$s'_0 \equiv a_0$		

Thus, starting with the trial factor $x^2 - 3x + 5$ and dividing $f(x)$ in descending powers, we obtain [scheme (b), p. 14] the quotient

$$x^2 + 30.4x + 393.2 = 393.2(1 + 0.077x + 0.0025x^2).$$

Division of

$$f(x) = 1503.11 - 873.7x + 307.44x^2 + 27.4x^3 + x^4$$

by

$$1 + 0.077x + 0.0025x^2$$

(division in ascending powers) gives, by the scheme of Table 1.4;

	←	1	-0.077	-0.0025
307.44		-873.70	1503.11	
76.19		-115.74		
-3.76				
379.87		-989.44	1503.11	

that is, a quotient

$$1503.11 - 989.44x + 379.87x^2 = 379.87(x^2 - 2.60x + 3.78).$$

Repeating these two operations once more and assembling the two divisions in a single table, with the division in descending powers on the left and the division in ascending powers on the right, we obtain:

-3.78	2.6	1	→			←	1	-0.0786	-0.00262
	1	27.4	307.44	307.44		-873.70	1503.11		
		2.6	78.00	77.96		-118.14			
			-3.78	-3.94					
	1	30.0	381.66*	381.46*		-991.84	1503.11		

that is, a quotient

$$x^2 + 30x + 381.66 = 381.66(1 + 0.0786x + 0.00262x^2)$$

for the division in descending powers, and a quotient

$$381.46x^2 - 991.84x + 1503.11 = 381.46(x^2 - 2.60x + 3.94)$$

for the division in ascending powers. The near equality of the starred numbers indicates that the process converges and that the two factors of the equation are approximately $x^2 - 2.6x + 3.94$ and $x^2 + 30x + 381.66$, whose roots are

$$x_{1,2} = -1.3 \pm 1.5i; \qquad x_{3,4} = -15 \pm 12.5i.$$

These factors are correct to the number of figures computed.

The largest quadratic factor may be evaluated by the Friedman procedure starting with a division in ascending powers rather than with a division in descending powers. Thus, given

$$f(x) = x^6 - 16x^5 + 128x^4 - 504x^3 + 1156x^2 - 1360x + 800 = 0, \quad (c)$$

we start with the division in ascending powers of x by the largest factor

$$x^2 - 16x + 128 = 128(1 - 0.125x + 0.008x^2),$$

obtaining the quotient

$$74x^4 - 370x^3 + 993x^2 - \ldots = 74x^2(x^2 - 5x + 13.4) + \ldots.$$

The process is continued with a division in descending powers of x by $x^2 - 5x + 13.4$, and by alternate divisions, as shown in scheme (d).

	1	−16	128 ‖	128	−504	1156	−1360	800	
−13.4	5	1 →				←	1	0.125	−0.008
		5	−55	−46	124	−158	100		
		−13	−8	10	−6				
	1	−11	60 ‖	74	−370	992	−1260	800	
−17.03	5.83	1 →				←	1	0.183	−0.017
		6	−58	−58	168	−222	146		
		−17	−16	21	−14				
	1	−10	53 ‖	54	−315	920	−1214	800	(d)
−17.35	5.85	1 →				←	1	0.189	−0.019
		5.9	−59.1	−58.1	173.4	−228.5	151.2		
		−17.4	−17.3	23.0	−15.1				
	1	−10.1	51.5 ‖	52.6	−307.6	912.4	1208.8	800	
−17.64	5.92	1 →				←	1	0.196	−0.019
		5.9	−59.2	−59.5	177.4	−235.8	156.8		
		−17.6	−17.2	22.9	−15.2				
	1	−10.1	51.2* ‖	51.3*	−303.7	905.0	−1203.2	800	

The two approximate factors of Eq. (c) are

$$x^2 - 10.1x + 51.2 = 0$$

$$51.3(x^4 - 5.92x^3 + 17.64x^2 - 23.45x + 15.59).$$

The roots of the first factor are

$$x_{1,2} = +5.05 \pm 5.07i.$$

Their correct values are $x_{1,2} = 5 \pm 5i$.

1.6 Transcendental Equations

Any nonalgebraic equation is called a *transcendental equation*. A transcendental equation may have a finite or an infinite number of real roots and may have no real roots at all. For example, the equation

$$\sin x = 2$$

has no real roots (Fig. 1.3) but an infinity of complex roots; the equation

$$\sin x = \tfrac{1}{2}$$

has an infinite number of real roots (Fig. 1.3); the equation

$$\sin x = \tfrac{1}{2}x$$

has three real roots (Fig. 1.3).

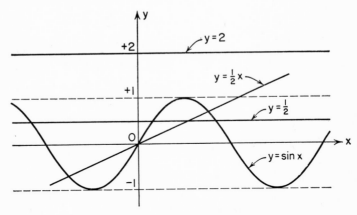

Fig. 1.3. Transcendental equations.

Once a real root of a transcendental equation has been approximated from above and below, either graphically or by trial and error, linear interpolation can be used to improve the value of the root by use of Eq. (1.2.7). For example, the equation

$$y = f(x) = e^x - 3x = 0 \qquad\qquad \text{(a)}$$

has two real roots, one of which lies between 0.4 and 0.9 (Fig. 1.4).

With $x_1 = 0.9$, $y_1 = -0.24$ and $x_2 = 0.4$, $y_2 = 0.29$, Eq. (1.2.7) gives

$$x_3 = \frac{0.9(0.29) - 0.4(-0.24)}{0.29 - (-0.24)} = 0.67$$

and $y_3 = -0.06$. Proceeding in the same way we obtain successively $x_4 = 0.627$, $y_4 = -0.009$ and $x_5 = 0.619$, $y_5 = 0.0001$.

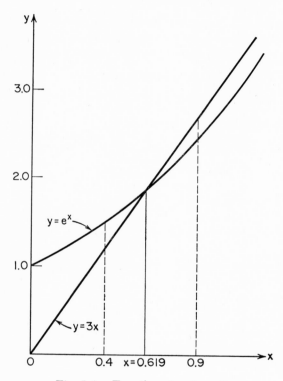

Fig. 1.4.   Equation $e^x - 3x = 0$.

Alternately, by Newton's method of tangents [Eq. (1.2.8)], we have, with

$$f(x) = e^x - 3x; \qquad f'(x) = e^x - 3; \qquad \tfrac{1}{2}f''(x) = \tfrac{1}{2}e^x$$

and starting at $x = 0.4$,

x	0.4	0.594	0.618	0.619
$f(x)$	0.292	0.029	0.001	0.0001
$f'(x)$	-1.508	-1.189	-1.145	
h	0.194	0.024	0.001	

By Newton's second-order method [Eq. (1.2.10)], we obtain, similarly,

x	0.4	0.614	0.619
$f(x)$	0.292	0.006	0.0001
$f'(x)$	-1.508	-1.152	
$\frac{1}{2}f''(x)$	0.746	0.924	
$1/h$	4.669	191.2	
h	0.214	0.005	

Another method for the determination of the real roots of a transcendental equation, *which does not converge in all cases*, consists in expanding the functions appearing in the equation into power series (whenever possible) and in solving the algebraic equations obtained by cutting the series off after 2, 3, ..., n terms.

For example, the expansion of the left-hand member of Eq. (a) gives:

$$f(x) = e^x - 3x = \left(1 + x + \frac{x^2}{2} + \frac{x^3}{6} + \frac{x^4}{24} + \dots\right) - 3x$$

$$= 1 - 2x + \frac{x^2}{2} + \frac{x^3}{6} + \frac{x^4}{24} + \dots,$$

and the successive algebraic equations with their lower root are

$$1 - 2x = 0 \qquad\qquad x_1 = 0.5$$

$$x^2 - 4x + 2 = 0 \qquad\qquad x_1 = 0.586$$

$$x^3 + 3x^2 - 12x + 6 = 0 \qquad\qquad x_1 = 0.613$$

$$x^4 + 4x^3 + 12x^2 - 48x + 24 = 0 \qquad x_1 = 0.618.$$

This method may become advantageous when the first few roots of a transcendental equation must be determined.

To find the complex roots of a transcendental equation $f(z) = 0$, substitute $z = x + iy$ for the unknown and set equal to zero the real and the imaginary parts of $f(z)$. This leads to the solution of two simultaneous nonlinear equations, which may be carried out by the method of Sec. 1.17.

For example, the complex roots of Eq. (a) are obtained by changing x into z:

$$f(z) = e^z - 3z = e^{x+iy} - 3(x + iy) = e^x(\cos y + i \sin y)$$

$$- 3x - 3yi = 0$$

and solving the two nonlinear equations:

$$e^x \cos y - 3x = 0; \qquad e^x \sin y - 3y = 0. \qquad\qquad \text{(b)}$$

1.7 *Determinantal Solution of Linear Simultaneous Algebraic Equations*

The solution of systems of simultaneous linear equations is among the most important and most frequently encountered problems of numerical mathematics. A large number of methods has been proposed to perform the task, and various special computers (of the digital and the analogue type) are now available to solve such equations.

The roots x_j $(j = 1,2,\ldots,n)$ of the system

$$a_{11}x_1 + a_{12}x_2 + \ldots + a_{1j}x_j + \ldots + a_{1n}x_n = c_1$$
$$a_{21}x_1 + a_{22}x_2 + \ldots + a_{2j}x_j + \ldots + a_{2n}x_n = c_2 \tag{1.7.1}$$
$$\ldots\ldots\ldots\ldots\ldots\ldots\ldots\ldots\ldots\ldots\ldots\ldots\ldots\ldots\ldots$$
$$a_{n1}x_1 + a_{n2}x_2 + \ldots + a_{nj}x_j + \ldots + a_{nn}x_n = c_n$$

are formally given by the ratio of determinants:

$$x_j = \frac{D_j}{D}, \tag{1.7.2}$$

where

$$D = \begin{vmatrix} a_{11} & a_{12} & \ldots & a_{1j} & \ldots & a_{1n} \\ a_{21} & a_{22} & \ldots & a_{2j} & \ldots & a_{2n} \\ \cdots\cdots\cdots\cdots\cdots\cdots\cdots\cdots \\ a_{n1} & a_{n2} & \ldots & a_{nj} & \ldots & a_{nn} \end{vmatrix} \tag{1.7.3}$$

is the determinant of the coefficients, and

$$D_j = \begin{vmatrix} a_{11} & a_{12} & \ldots & c_1 & \ldots & a_{1n} \\ a_{21} & a_{22} & \ldots & c_2 & \ldots & a_{2n} \\ \cdots\cdots\cdots\cdots\cdots\cdots\cdots\cdots \\ a_{n1} & a_{n2} & \ldots & c_n & \ldots & a_{nn} \end{vmatrix}. \tag{1.7.4}$$

The most efficient method of evaluating a numerical (or literal) determinant is, in general, by *pivotal condensation* (Chio's method), according to the following scheme,* in which each element is evaluated by means of a second-order determinant:

$$D = \frac{1}{a_{11}^{n-2}} \begin{vmatrix} \begin{vmatrix} a_{11} & a_{12} \\ a_{21} & a_{22} \end{vmatrix} & \begin{vmatrix} a_{11} & a_{13} \\ a_{21} & a_{23} \end{vmatrix} & \cdots & \begin{vmatrix} a_{11} & a_{1n} \\ a_{21} & a_{2n} \end{vmatrix} \\ \begin{vmatrix} a_{11} & a_{12} \\ a_{31} & a_{32} \end{vmatrix} & \begin{vmatrix} a_{11} & a_{13} \\ a_{31} & a_{33} \end{vmatrix} & \cdots & \begin{vmatrix} a_{11} & a_{1n} \\ a_{31} & a_{3n} \end{vmatrix} \\ \cdots\cdots\cdots\cdots\cdots\cdots\cdots\cdots \\ \begin{vmatrix} a_{11} & a_{12} \\ a_{n1} & a_{n2} \end{vmatrix} & \begin{vmatrix} a_{11} & a_{13} \\ a_{n1} & a_{n3} \end{vmatrix} & \cdots & \begin{vmatrix} a_{11} & a_{1n} \\ a_{n1} & a_{nn} \end{vmatrix} \end{vmatrix} \tag{1.7.5}$$

* See, for example, *Engineering Problems*, pp. 121 ff.

For example,

$$\begin{vmatrix} 2 & 1 & 2 & 1 \\ 1 & 1 & 1 & 2 \\ 2 & 1 & 1 & 1 \\ 1 & 2 & 1 & 2 \end{vmatrix} = \frac{1}{2^{4-2}} \begin{vmatrix} 1 & & 0 & 3 \\ 0 & & -2 & 0 \\ 3 & & 0 & 3 \end{vmatrix}$$

$$= \frac{1}{4} \cdot \frac{1}{1^{3-2}} \begin{vmatrix} -2 & 0 \\ 0 & -6 \end{vmatrix} = \frac{1}{4} \cdot \frac{1}{1} \cdot 12 = 3.$$

The solution by determinants becomes cumbersome as soon as n is larger than 4 or 5. Numerous other procedures have therefore been devised to achieve the same results with greater efficiency.

The four methods presented here are all well adapted to use on either calculator or slide rule and have the following properties:

1. *Gauss's scheme* is a perfectly general systematic procedure for the elimination of the unknowns, particularly adapted to slide rule use and easily remembered.

2. *Cholesky's scheme* is a perfectly general systematic procedure for the elimination of the unknowns, well adapted to machine calculations.

3. The *Gauss-Seidel iteration method* is a process of successive approximations applicable to certain types of equations and well adapted to machine computations.

4. *Relaxation* is a method of successive approximations applicable to a large variety of equations and well adapted to slide rule use.

All these methods will be illustrated by means of examples in the following sections.

1.8 Gauss's Scheme*

Gauss's elimination scheme is applied in Table 1.5 to the following system:†

Eqs.	x_1	x_2	x_3	x_4	c
I	2	2	4	-2	10
II	1	3	2	1	17
III	3	1	3	1	18
IV	1	3	4	2	27

(1.8.1)

---

* Gauss's scheme is also known in the United States under the name of Doolittle's method.

† This example, entirely solvable by integers, is taken from Sec. 4.3 of *Engineering Problems,* and was suggested by Dr. V. P. Jensen, to whom the authors are indebted.

in which, for example, Eq. (I) reads

$$2x_1 + 2x_2 + 4x_3 - 2x_4 = 10.^*$$

Table 1.5 is self-explanatory, except for the numbers r and the column S. The numbers r are ratios of coefficients obtained as follows: r_2 is the ratio of the encircled coefficient 1 of x_1 in row 2 to the boxed coefficient 2 of x_1 in row 1; r_3 is the ratio of the encircled coefficient 3 of x_1 in row 5 to the boxed coefficient 2 of x_1 in row 1; r'_3 is the ratio of the encircled coefficient -2 of x_2 in row 7 to the boxed coefficient 2 of x_2 in row 4, etc. The column S is used as a check: it contains the sum of all the coefficients and the constant of each row and is operated upon as any other number of the same row.   Once the number S of a given row has been obtained by the operations indicated in the explanation column, it must check with the sum of all numbers of that row.   The use of a sum check column is imperative as soon as the number of the unknowns is higher than 4. The roots are obtained from the equations appearing in the rows of the scheme labeled n^2 (1,4,9,16), which contain, respectively, 4, 3, 2, 1 unknowns, by back substitution starting from the last equation. Thus†

Row 16:	$5x_4 = 20$	$x_4 = 4$
Row 9:	$-3x_3 + 6x_4 = 15$	$x_3 = 3$
Row 4:	$2x_2 + 0x_3 + 2x_4 = 12$	$x_2 = 2$
Row 1:	$2x_1 + 2x_2 + 4x_3 - 2x_4 = 10$	$x_1 = 1$

In the solution by Gauss's scheme of two or more systems having the same coefficients of the unknowns but different values of the constants c, only the columns c and S of the scheme must be evaluated for each system, since the other columns of the scheme remain unchanged. It is possible to use this important property of the scheme to evaluate additional figures in the roots with little additional labor. To this purpose one evaluates the left-hand members c' of the equations for the obtained values of the roots and computes the differences e between the constants c and c'. Using the *errors e* as new constants, one evaluates the new values of the unknowns x', which, added to the old values of the unknowns, give improved values $x + x'$ of the roots of the original system.‡

---

* The constants c are always written at the right-hand members of the equations.
† These operations can also be performed as indicated in the lower part of Table 1 5.
‡ See, for example, *Engineering Problems*, pp. 129 ff.

Table 1.5
Gauss's Scheme

Rows	r	x_1	x_2	x_3	x_4	c	S	Explanations
(1)		2	2	4	-2	10	16	(I)
2	$r_2 = 1/2$	1	3	2	1	17	24	(II)
3		-1	-1	-2	1	-5	-8	$-r_2 \times (1)$
(4)		0	2	0	2	12	16	(2) + (3)
5	$r_3 = 3/2$	3	1	3	1	18	26	(III)
6		-3	-3	-6	3	-15	-24	$-r_3 \times (1)$
7	$r'_3 = -2/2$	0	-2	-3	4	3	2	(5) + (6)
8			2	0	2	12	16	$-r'_3 \times (4)$
(9)			0	-3	6	15	18	(7) + (8)
10	$r_4 = 1/2$	1	3	4	2	27	37	(IV)
11		-1	-1	-2	1	-5	-8	$-r_4 \times (1)$
12	$r'_4 = 2/2$	0	2	2	3	22	29	(10) + (11)
13			-2	0	-2	-12	-16	$-r'_4 \times (4)$
14	$r''_4 = 2/-3$		0	2	1	10	13	(12) + (13)
15				-2	4	10	12	$-r''_4 \times (9)$
(16)				0	5	20	25	(14) + (15)
17	Const. c_i	10	12	15	20			
18	$-x_4 a_{i4}$	8	-8	-24	20	$x_4 = 20/5 = 4$		
19	$-x_3 a_{i3}$	-12	0	-9		$x_3 = (-9)/(-3) = 3$		
20	$-x_2 a_{i2}$	-4	4			$x_2 = 4/2 = 2$		
21	$(i = 1,4,9,16)$	2				$x_1 = 2/2 = 1$		

For example, assuming that an evaluation of the roots of the following system (a) to two significant figures gives $x_1 = 1.60$, $x_2 = 1.50$,

Eqs.	x_1	x_2	x_3	c
I	1	2	1	6.00
II	2	1	1	6.11
III	1	1	2	5.73

(a)

$x_3 = 1.30$, we compute

$$e_1 = 6.00 - (1.60 + 2 \cdot 1.50 + 1.30) = 0.10$$

$$e_2 = 6.11 - (2 \cdot 1.60 + 1.50 + 1.30) = 0.11$$

$$e_3 = 5.73 - (1.60 + 1.50 + 2 \cdot 1.30) = 0.03$$

and solve the system of so-called *error equations:*

Eqs.	x_1'	x_2'	x_3'	e
I	1	2	1	0.10
II	2	1	1	0.11
III	1	1	2	0.03

obtaining $x_1' = 0.05$, $x_2' = 0.04$, $x_3' = -0.03$. The improved roots

$$x_1 = 1.60 + 0.05 = 1.65$$

$$x_2 = 1.50 + 0.04 = 1.54$$

$$x_3 = 1.30 - 0.03 = 1.27$$

are, in this case, the correct roots of the original system (a).

1.9 Matrices

A rectangular array of numbers with m rows and n columns is called an m by n *matrix*, and is indicated by a capital letter. The array

$$A = \begin{bmatrix} 2 & 1 & 3 \\ 3 & 2 & 1 \end{bmatrix}$$

is a 2 by 3 matrix. The element of A located at the ith row and the jth column is indicated by a_{ij}. An n by n matrix is called a *square matrix*. The elements a_{ii} constitute the *main diagonal* of a square matrix. The determinant of the elements of a square matrix A is called the determinant of A and is indicated by $|A|$. A square matrix with zeros below its main diagonal is called an *upper triangular matrix;* a square matrix with zeros above its main diagonal is called a *lower triangular matrix,* and will be indicated by L. A square matrix with ones on and zeros below the main diagonal is called a *unit upper triangular matrix,* and will be indicated by T.

An m by 1 matrix is called a *column.* A *zero matrix* has all its elements equal to zero. The *identity matrix* I is a square matrix with ones on its main diagonal and zeros everywhere else.

Two matrices A and B are equal if and only if each a_{ij} equals the corresponding b_{ij}.

A matrix C is the *sum* of two matrices A and B if $c_{ij} = a_{ij} + b_{ij}$.

A matrix C is called the *product AB* (or the result of *premultiplying B by A*) if

$$c_{ij} = \sum_{k=1}^{n} a_{ik}b_{kj}, \tag{1.9.1}$$

where n is the number of columns of A and of rows of B.

The product AB is hence obtained by "rows into columns" multiplication and, in general, is different from the product BA (when this product exists). The product AB exists only if the number of columns of A equals the number of rows of B. For example, given:

$$A = \begin{bmatrix} 2 & 1 \\ 1 & 3 \end{bmatrix}; \qquad B = \begin{bmatrix} 2 & 1 & 1 \\ 1 & 2 & 1 \end{bmatrix},$$

the product AB equals

$$AB = \begin{bmatrix} 2 & 1 \\ 1 & 3 \end{bmatrix} \begin{bmatrix} 2 & 1 & 1 \\ 1 & 2 & 1 \end{bmatrix}$$

$$= \begin{bmatrix} (2 \cdot 2 + 1 \cdot 1) & (2 \cdot 1 + 1 \cdot 2) & (2 \cdot 1 + 1 \cdot 1) \\ (1 \cdot 2 + 3 \cdot 1) & (1 \cdot 1 + 3 \cdot 2) & (1 \cdot 1 + 3 \cdot 1) \end{bmatrix}$$

$$= \begin{bmatrix} 5 & 4 & 3 \\ 5 & 7 & 4 \end{bmatrix} = C.$$

The determinant of the product of two square matrices is equal to the product of the determinants of the matrices. For example, with

$$A = \begin{bmatrix} 2 & 1 \\ 1 & 2 \end{bmatrix}; \qquad B = \begin{bmatrix} 1 & 3 \\ 2 & 1 \end{bmatrix}; \qquad C = AB = \begin{bmatrix} 4 & 7 \\ 5 & 5 \end{bmatrix};$$

$$|A| = 3; \qquad |B| = -5,$$

the determinant of C equals

$$|C| = |A|\,|B| = (3)(-5) = -15.^{*}$$

---

* For a complete treatment of the algebra of matrices see, for instance, A. C. Aitken, *Determinants and Matrices,* Oliver and Boyd, London, 1939, or any book on advanced algebra.

Remembering the rule for matric multiplication, a system of, say, three simultaneous equations

$$a_{11}x_1 + a_{12}x_2 + a_{13}x_3 = c_1$$

$$a_{21}x_1 + a_{22}x_2 + a_{23}x_3 = c_2$$

$$a_{31}x_1 + a_{32}x_2 + a_{33}x_3 = c_3$$

may be written in matric form as

$$\begin{bmatrix} a_{11} & a_{12} & a_{13} \\ a_{21} & a_{22} & a_{23} \\ a_{31} & a_{32} & a_{33} \end{bmatrix} \begin{bmatrix} x_1 \\ x_2 \\ x_3 \end{bmatrix} = \begin{bmatrix} c_1 \\ c_2 \\ c_3 \end{bmatrix}$$

or simply as $$AX = C.$$

The matrix $A = [a_{ij}]$ is called the *matrix of the system*, the columns $X = [x_i]$ and $C = [c_i]$ the *column of the unknowns* and *of the constants*, respectively.

The fundamental step in any method of solution of simultaneous equations by elimination consists in reducing the system to unit upper triangular form:

$$\begin{bmatrix} 1 & t_{12} & t_{13} \\ 0 & 1 & t_{23} \\ 0 & 0 & 1 \end{bmatrix} \begin{bmatrix} x_1 \\ x_2 \\ x_3 \end{bmatrix} = \begin{bmatrix} k_1 \\ k_2 \\ k_3 \end{bmatrix},$$

or $$TX = K,$$

since the system

$$x_1 + t_{12}x_2 + t_{13}x_3 = k_1$$

$$x_2 + t_{23}x_3 = k_2$$

$$x_3 = k_3$$

can be immediately solved by back substitution.

*1.10 Cholesky's Scheme**

Cholesky's method is conveniently presented in matric form since it consists essentially in determining an auxiliary matrix L of the lower

---

* Cholesky's method was used by A. L. Cholesky in France before 1916 in connection with symmetrical systems, was given in matric form in Poland by Th. Banachiewicz in 1938, rediscovered and adapted to machine computations in the United States by P. D. Crout in 1941, studied again in England by A. M. Turing in 1948 and in Germany by A. Zurmühl in 1949.

triangular type capable of reducing the original system $AX - C = 0$ to the unit triangular form $TX - K = 0$.

To this purpose let us assume that the system to be solved has been reduced to the unit triangular form $TX - K = 0$ and that pre-multiplication of this equation by a lower triangular matrix L will return it to its original form:

$$L(TX - K) = AX - C = 0.$$

This implies the two matric equations

$$LT = A; \qquad LK = C.$$

Remembering the rule for matric multiplication, these matric equations allow the determination of L, T, and K in a very simple manner.* In fact, writing these equations out in explicit form and adding the column C to A and the column K to T for compactness, these equations become for the case of a three-equation system

$$\begin{array}{cc} [A] & [C] \\ \begin{bmatrix} a_{11} & a_{12} & a_{13} & c_1 \\ a_{21} & a_{22} & a_{23} & c_2 \\ a_{31} & a_{32} & a_{33} & c_3 \end{bmatrix} \end{array} = \begin{array}{c} [L] \\ \begin{bmatrix} l_{11} & 0 & 0 \\ l_{21} & l_{22} & 0 \\ l_{31} & l_{32} & l_{33} \end{bmatrix} \end{array} \begin{array}{cc} [T] & [K] \\ \begin{bmatrix} 1 & t_{12} & t_{13} & k_1 \\ 0 & 1 & t_{23} & k_2 \\ 0 & 0 & 1 & k_3 \end{bmatrix} \end{array},$$

from which the following equations are obtained for the elements of L, T, and K:

$$a_{i1} = l_{i1} \times 1 + l_{i2} \times 0 + l_{i3} \times 0 = l_{i1}, \tag{a}$$

that is, the first column of L is identical with the first column of A.

$$a_{1j} = l_{11}t_{1j} + 0 \times t_{2j} + 0 \times t_{3j} = l_{11}t_{1j} = a_{11}t_{1j}, \tag{b}$$

that is, the first row of T equals the first row of A divided by a_{11}.

$$\begin{aligned} a_{22} &= l_{21}t_{12} + l_{22} \times 1 & \therefore \quad l_{22} &= a_{22} - l_{21}t_{12} \\ a_{23} &= l_{21}t_{13} + l_{22}t_{23} & \therefore \quad t_{23} &= (a_{23} - l_{21}t_{13})/l_{22} \\ a_{32} &= l_{31}t_{12} + l_{32} \times 1 & \therefore \quad l_{32} &= a_{32} - l_{31}t_{12} \\ c_2 &= l_{21}k_1 + l_{22}k_2 & \therefore \quad k_2 &= (c_2 - l_{21}k_1)/l_{22} \end{aligned} \tag{c}$$

and so forth.

In this manner the elements of L, T, and K are obtained successively in terms of previously determined elements, *proceeding horizontally from l_{22} on.*

---

* The procedure used to obtain L, T, and K shows that these three matrices are uniquely determined once A and C are known.

The general formulas for the computations are

$$l_{ij} = a_{ij} - \sum_{r=1}^{j-1} l_{ir}t_{rj}; \qquad l_{i1} = a_{i1} \tag{1.10.1}$$

$$t_{ij} = \frac{1}{l_{ii}}[a_{ij} - \sum_{r=1}^{i-1} l_{ir}t_{rj}]; \qquad t_{1j} = \frac{a_{1j}}{a_{11}} \tag{1.10.2}$$

where for simplicity $a_{i,n+1} = c_i$ and $t_{i,n+1} = k_i$, and $n + 1$ indicates the last column of the *augmented* matrices $A + C$ and $T + K$.*

It is seen from Eqs. (1.10.1) and (1.10.2) that, if A is *symmetrical* $(a_{ij} = a_{ji})$,

$$l_{ij} = t_{ji} \times l_{ii} \qquad (i,j = 1,2,\ldots,n-1; i \neq j), \tag{1.10.3}$$

and hence the elements of L below the main diagonal are obtained as an intermediate step in the computation of the t_{ij}.

The operations in Eqs. (1.10.1) and (1.10.2) can be performed on a calculating machine without writing any of the intermediate steps; that is, *each element l_{ij}, t_{ij} is obtained in a single machine operation*. This makes Cholesky's method the simplest and fastest among known elimination methods. Counting only multiplications, divisions,† and recording of numbers, the Gauss's elimination process applied to a system of n equations requires $\frac{1}{3}n^3 +$ (a number of the order of n^2) operations, while Cholesky's method requires $n^2 +$ (a number of the order of n) operations. For example, for the case of $n = 10$ equations, Gauss's scheme requires approximately $(10^3/3) + 10^2 = 433$ operations versus only $10^2 + 10 = 110$ operations required by Cholesky's.

The time involved in solving a system of n equations by Cholesky's method on a desk calculator is of the order of $0.001n^4$ hours. Thus a system of 10 equations can easily be solved in approximately 10 hours. The number of figures lost in the computations varies from system to system, but statistically is of the order of $0.3n$. Thus a system of 10 equations should be solved carrying 3 more significant figures than those required in the roots.

In Table 1.6 the system (1.8.1) is solved by Cholesky's method as follows. Write the first column of L, which equals the first column of A [2,1,3,1], and the first row of the augmented matrix $T + K$, which equals the first row of the augmented matrix $A + C$ divided by $a_{11} = 2$ and hence equals [1,1,2,−1,5]. Compute l_{22} by equating a_{22} to the row-

---

* It may be noticed here that, since $A = LT$, $|A| = |L||T|$ and hence, if $|A|$ is different from zero, both $|L|$ and $|T|$ must be different from zero. But the determinant of a triangular matrix equals the product of its main diagonal elements. Hence $l_{ii} \neq 0$ and the divisions indicated in Eqs. (1.10.2) are always possible.

† A division is counted as two multiplications in this count.

Table 1.6
Cholesky's Scheme

i \ j	1	2	3	4	5	6	1	2	3	4	1	2	3	4	5	6
	A				**C**		**L**				**T**				**K**	
	x_1	x_2	x_3	x_4	c	S					x_1	x_2	x_3	x_4	k	S
1	2	2	4	−2	10	16	2	0	0	0	1	1	2	−1	5	8
2	1	3	2	1	17	24	1	2	0	0	0	1	0	1	6	8
3	3	1	3	1	18	26	3	−2	−3	0	0	0	1	−2	−5	−6
4	1	3	4	2	27	37	1	2	2	5	0	0	0	1	4	5
5	7	9	13	2	72	S	7	2	−1	5						

into-column product of the second row of L by the second column of T:

$$3 = 1 \cdot 1 + l_{22} \cdot 1 + 0 \cdot 0 + 0 \cdot 0 \quad \therefore \quad l_{22} = 2,$$

or directly by using Eq. (1.10.1). Compute t_{23}, the first unknown element of the second row of T, by equating a_{23} to the product of the second row of L by the third column of T:

$$a_{23} = 2 = 1 \cdot 2 + 2 \cdot t_{23} + 0 \cdot 1 + 0 \cdot 0 \quad \therefore \quad t_{23} = 0,$$

or directly by Eq. (1.10.2).

Compute t_{24} by the same procedure:

$$a_{24} = 1 = 1 \cdot (-1) + 2 \cdot t_{24} + 0 \cdot t_{34} + 0 \cdot t_{44} \quad \therefore \quad t_{24} = 1,$$

and evaluate next $t_{25} = k_2$:

$$a_{25} = c_2 = 17 = 1 \cdot 5 + 2 \cdot t_{25} + 0 \cdot t_{35} + 0 \cdot t_{45} \quad \therefore \quad t_{25} = k_2 = 6.$$

All the other elements of L and T are similarly computed. Check columns S may be carried in the augmented matrices $A + C$ and $T + K$, as well

Table 1.7
Cholesky's Condensed Scheme

i \ j	1	2	3	4	5	6	1	2	3	4	5	6
	A				**C**		**L** and **T**				**K**	
	x_1	x_2	x_3	x_4	c	S	x_1	x_2	x_3	x_4	k	S
1	2	2	4	−2	10	16	2	1	2	−1	5	8
2	1	3	2	1	17	24	1	2	0	1	6	8
3	3	1	3	1	18	26	3	−2	−3	−2	−5	−6
4	1	3	4	2	27	37	1	2	2	5	4	5
5	7	9	13	2	72	S'	7	2	−1	5		

as check rows S' in the matrices A and L. These columns (and rows) are operated upon as the columns (and rows) of the corresponding matrices, and must check with the sums of the elements in the same column (or row).

Additional columns C and K may be used in the solution of a set of systems having the same matrix of coefficients and different columns of constants.

As soon as the method is clearly understood, the two triangular matrices L and T may be written as a single square matrix, since the main diagonal elements of T are all unity. This gives the condensed scheme of Table 1.7.

The values of the x_i are obtained from the triangular system $TX = K$ by back substitution, as follows:

$$\text{Row 4} \qquad x_4 = 4$$

$$\text{Row 3} \qquad x_3 - 2 \cdot 4 = -5 \qquad \therefore \quad x_3 = 3$$

$$\text{Row 2} \qquad x_2 + 0x_3 + x_4 = 6 \qquad \therefore \quad x_2 = 2$$

$$\text{Row 1} \qquad x_1 + x_2 + 2x_3 - x_4 = 5 \quad \therefore \quad x_1 = 1.$$

Table 1.8
Cholesky's Scheme for Symmetrical Matrices

$i \diagdown {}^j$	A			C	S	L			T			K	S
	1	2	3	4	5	1	2	3	1	2	3	4	5
1	2	2	4	8	16	2	0	0	1	1	2	4	8
2	2	1	2	5	10	2	−1	0	0	1	2	3	6
3	4	2	3	9	18	4	−2	−1	0	0	1	1	2
4	8	5	9	22	S'	8	−3	−1					

(1) $l_{22} = 1 - 2 = -1;$

(2) $t_{23} = (2 - 2 \cdot 2)/(-1) = -2/-1 = l_{32}/-1 = 2;$

(3) $t_{24} = (5 - 2 \cdot 4)/(-1) = l_{42}/-1 = 3;$

$(3a)$ $t_{25} = (10 - 2 \cdot 8)/(-1) = 6;$

(4) $l_{32} = -2;$

$(4a)$ $l_{42} = -3;$

(5) $l_{33} = 3 - 4 \cdot 2 + 2 \cdot 2 = -1;$

(6) $t_{34} = (9 - 4 \cdot 4 + 2 \cdot 3)/(-1) = l_{43}/-1 = 1;$

$(6a)$ $t_{35} = (18 - 4 \cdot 8 + 2 \cdot 6)/(-1) = 2.$

$x_3 = 1; \qquad x_2 = 3 - 2 \cdot 1 = 1; \qquad x_1 = 4 - 2 \cdot 1 - 1 \cdot 1 = 1.$

Table 1.8 illustrates the solution of a symmetrical system of three equations, which is simplified by the use of Eq. (1.10.3).

1.11 The Inverse of a Matrix

A square matrix of order n with ones along the main diagonal and zeros elsewhere is called an *identity matrix* and is indicated by I:

$$I = \begin{bmatrix} 1 & 0 & 0 \\ 0 & 1 & 0 \\ 0 & 0 & 1 \end{bmatrix}. \tag{1.11.1}$$

A matrix is said to be the *inverse* A^{-1} of a matrix A if

$$AA^{-1} = A^{-1}A = I. \tag{1.11.2}$$

Indicating by b_{ij} the elements of A^{-1}, it is seen from Eq. (1.11.2) that the b_{ij} are the roots of n systems of n equations each with identical coefficients a_{ij} and constants c_i equal to

$$1,0,0,0,\ldots; \quad 0,1,0,0,\ldots; \quad 0,0,1,0,\ldots; \quad \ldots. \tag{1.11.3}$$

For a system of three equations, for example, Eq. (1.11.2) becomes

$$\begin{bmatrix} a_{11} & a_{12} & a_{13} \\ a_{21} & a_{22} & a_{23} \\ a_{31} & a_{32} & a_{33} \end{bmatrix} \begin{bmatrix} b_{11} & b_{12} & b_{13} \\ b_{21} & b_{22} & b_{23} \\ b_{31} & b_{32} & b_{33} \end{bmatrix} = \begin{bmatrix} 1 & 0 & 0 \\ 0 & 1 & 0 \\ 0 & 0 & 1 \end{bmatrix}$$

and gives rise to the three systems of three equations each:

$$a_{11}b_{11} + a_{12}b_{21} + a_{13}b_{31} = 1,$$
$$a_{21}b_{11} + a_{22}b_{21} + a_{23}b_{31} = 0,$$
$$a_{31}b_{11} + a_{32}b_{21} + a_{33}b_{31} = 0;$$

$$a_{11}b_{12} + a_{12}b_{22} + a_{13}b_{32} = 0,$$
$$a_{21}b_{12} + a_{22}b_{22} + a_{23}b_{32} = 1,$$
$$a_{31}b_{12} + a_{32}b_{22} + a_{33}b_{32} = 0;$$

$$a_{11}b_{13} + a_{12}b_{23} + a_{13}b_{33} = 0,$$
$$a_{21}b_{13} + a_{22}b_{23} + a_{23}b_{33} = 0,$$
$$a_{31}b_{13} + a_{32}b_{23} + a_{33}b_{33} = 1.$$

The evaluation of the b_{ij} may, therefore, be easily performed by elimination, using n sets of constants of the type given in Eq. (1.11.3).

The following scheme gives the inversion by elimination of a 3 by 3 matrix. The first nine rows of the scheme reduce the matrix A to triangular form, and the remaining three eliminate the unknowns x_3 and x_2 from equations (4), (7) and (9) so as to obtain in equations (12), (11) and (9) the values of the b_{1j}, b_{2j}, b_{3j}, respectively. Notice that the solution is started with a unit matrix b_{ij} and ends with a unit matrix a_{ij}.

	\[A\]			\[A^{-1}\]			Expl.	
	a_{1j}	a_{2j}	a_{3j}	b_{1j}	b_{2j}	b_{3j}		
1	2	1	1	1	0	0		
2	1	3	1	0	1	0		
3	1	1	4	0	0	1		
4	1	1/2	1/2	1/2	0	0	(1/2)(1)	
5	0	5/2	1/2	$-1/2$	1	0	(2) $-$ (4)	
6	0	1/2	7/2	$-1/2$	0	1	(3) $-$ (4)	
7	0	1	1/5	$-1/5$	2/5	0	(2/5)(5)	
8	0	0	17/5	$-2/5$	$-1/5$	1	$-(1/2)(7) + (6)$	j
9	0	0	1	$-2/17$	$-1/17$	5/17	(5/17)(8)	3
10	1	1/2	0	19/34	1/34	$-5/34$	$-(1/2)(9) + (4)$	
11	0	1	0	$-3/17$	7/17	$-1/17$	$-(1/5)(9) + (7)$	2
12	1	0	0	11/17	$-3/17$	$-2/17$	$-(1/2)(11) + (10)$	1

$$A^{-1} = \begin{bmatrix} \frac{11}{17} & -\frac{3}{17} & -\frac{2}{17} \\ -\frac{3}{17} & \frac{7}{17} & -\frac{1}{17} \\ -\frac{2}{17} & -\frac{1}{17} & \frac{5}{17} \end{bmatrix}$$

The knowledge of A^{-1} is essential whenever a system of n equations must be solved for a number of sets of constants $m \gg n$, since the roots x_j corresponding to a set of constants c_i are given by

$$x_i = c_1 b_{i1} + c_2 b_{i2} + \ldots + c_n b_{in}. \qquad (1.11.4)$$

Thus the root x_2 of the system

$$AX = C; \qquad C = \begin{bmatrix} 3 \\ -2 \\ -6 \end{bmatrix}$$

where A is the matrix used in the previous example, is given by

$$x_2 = 3(-\tfrac{3}{17}) - 2(\tfrac{7}{17}) - 6(-\tfrac{1}{17}) = -\tfrac{17}{17} = -1$$

1.12 The Gauss-Seidel Iteration Method

A system of simultaneous linear equations is called *diagonal* when in each equation the coefficient of a *different* unknown is greater in absolute value than the sum of the absolute values of the other coefficients. The large coefficient is usually located in the main diagonal position a_{ii}. Many of the systems stemming from physical problems are of the diagonal type.

Diagonal systems have the fundamental property of being solvable by methods of successive approximations, among which the *Gauss-Seidel iterative process* presents great advantages of simplicity. To apply Gauss's method, solve each equation of the system for the unknown with the largest coefficient:

$$
\begin{aligned}
x_1 &= b_{12}x_2 + b_{13}x_3 + \ldots + b_{1n}x_n + k_1 \\
x_2 &= b_{21}x_1 + b_{23}x_3 + \ldots + b_{2n}x_n + k_2 \\
&\cdots\cdots\cdots\cdots\cdots\cdots\cdots\cdots\cdots\cdots \\
x_n &= b_{n1}x_1 + b_{n2}x_2 + \ldots + b_{n,n-1}x_{n-1} + k_n
\end{aligned}
\tag{1.12.1}
$$

and substitute in the right-hand members of Eqs. (1.12.1) any initial values $x_j^{(0)}$ for the unknowns, thus obtaining new values $x_j^{(1)}$ in the left-hand members. Substitute the new values $x_j^{(1)}$ in the right-hand members of the equations, obtaining improved values $x_j^{(2)}$ and continue the process until $x_j^{(m)}$ is equal to $x_j^{(m+1)}$ within the required accuracy. The $x_j^{(m)}$ are the roots of the system.

In Gauss's method each approximation of a root is obtained by means of a single machine operation, and errors do not impair the convergence of the process, since they are equivalent to a new set of starting values; the method, if convergent, converges, *whatever* the starting values. If the last available approximation of the unknowns is used in the right-hand members of Eqs. (1.12.1), as suggested by Seidel, the rapidity of convergence of the method is greatly increased. Any guess which may accelerate the convergence is permissible at any stage of the process.

As an example of application of the Gauss-Seidel iteration method, consider the system

Eqs.	x_1	x_2	x_3	c
I	10	1	1	12
II	2	10	1	13
III	2	2	10	14

(a)

which, when "ready for iteration" in the form (1.12.1), becomes

$$
x_1 = 1.2 - 0.1x_2 - 0.1x_3;
$$

$$
x_2 = 1.3 - 0.2x_1 - 0.1x_3;
$$

$$
x_3 = 1.4 - 0.2x_1 - 0.2x_2.
$$

Starting with $x_2 = x_3 = 0$, the first equation gives $x_1 = 1.2$. With $x_1 = 1.2$ and $x_3 = 0$, the second equation gives $x_2 = 1.3 - 0.2 \cdot 1.2 = 1.06$, and with $x_1 = 1.2$ and $x_2 = 1.06$, the third equation gives $x_3 = 1.40 - 0.2 \cdot 1.2 - 0.2 \cdot 1.06 = 0.95$. Returning to the first equation with $x_2 = 1.06$ and $x_3 = 0.95$, we obtain $x_1 = 0.99$, and repeating the process, we have the results of Table 1.9.

Table 1.9

n	1	2	3	4
x_1	1.20	0.99	1.00	1.00
x_2	1.06	1.00	1.00	
x_3	0.95	1.00	1.00	

When the computations are carried out on a slide rule, they are conveniently organized as in Table 1.10, in which equations (a) are written vertically.

Table 1.10

	I	II	III
x_1	1	-0.2	-0.2
x_2	-0.1	1	-0.2
x_3	-0.1	-0.1	1
c	1.20	1.30	1.40
	(1.20)	-0.24	-0.24
	-0.11	(1.06)	-0.24
	-0.10	-0.10	(0.95)
	(0.99)	-0.20	-0.20
	-0.10	(1.00)	-0.20
	-0.10	-0.10	(1.00)
	(1.00)	-0.20	-0.20
	-0.10	(1.00)	-0.20
	-0.10	-0.10	(1.00)
	(1.00)		

The operations involved in the solution by iteration are clearly representable in matrix form. The solution by Gauss's iteration, for example, does state that

$$x_1^{(i+1)} = k_1 - b_{12}x_2^{(i)} - b_{13}x_3^{(i)} - \ldots - b_{1n}x_n^{(i)}$$
$$x_2^{(i+1)} = k_2 - b_{21}x_1^{(i)} - b_{23}x_3^{(i)} - \ldots - b_{2n}x_n^{(i)}$$
$$\ldots\ldots\ldots\ldots\ldots\ldots\ldots\ldots\ldots\ldots\ldots\ldots\ldots\ldots$$
$$x_n^{(i+1)} = k_n - b_{n1}x_1^{(i)} - b_{n2}x_2^{(i)} - \ldots - b_{n,n-1}x_{n-1}^{(i)}$$

or, in matrix form, that

$$X^{(i+1)} = K + BX^{(i)}$$

where

$$B = \begin{bmatrix} 0 & -b_{12} & -b_{13} \ldots & -b_{1n} \\ -b_{21} & 0 & -b_{22} \ldots & -b_{2n} \\ \hdotsfor{4} \\ -b_{n1} & -b_{n2} \ldots & -b_{n,n-1} & 0 \end{bmatrix}$$

1.13 Solution of Linear Equations by Relaxation

Relaxation is a method for the solution of linear algebraic equations by successive approximations in which the mathematical skill and the physical intuition of the computer may be used in an infinite variety of ways to accelerate the convergence of the process. Relaxation owes its name and its deserved popularity to the labors of Southwell and his school.*

Consider a system "ready for relaxation" with the main diagonal coefficients equal to -1 and the constants k *at the left-hand members of the equations:*

$$-x_1 + b_{12}x_2 + b_{13}x_3 + \ldots + b_{1n}x_n + k_1 = 0$$

$$b_{21}x_1 - x_2 + b_{23}x_3 + \ldots + b_{2n}x_n + k_2 = 0$$

$$\ldots \ldots \ldots \ldots \ldots \ldots \ldots \ldots \ldots \ldots \ldots \ldots$$

$$b_{n1}x_1 + b_{n2}x_2 + b_{n3}x_3 + \ldots - x_n + k_n = 0$$

(1.13.1)

and indicate by R_i (*residuals*) the value of the left-hand member of the ith equation for an assumed set of starting values $x_j^{(0)}$:

$$-x_1^{(0)} + b_{12}x_2^{(0)} + b_{13}x_3^{(0)} + \ldots + b_{1n}x_n^{(0)} + k_1 = R_1$$

$$b_{21}x_1^{(0)} - x_2^{(0)} + b_{23}x_3^{(0)} + \ldots + b_{2n}x_n^{(0)} + k_2 = R_2$$

$$\ldots \ldots \ldots \ldots \ldots \ldots \ldots \ldots \ldots \ldots \ldots \ldots$$

$$b_{n1}x_1^{(0)} + b_{n2}x_2^{(0)} + b_{n3}x_3^{(0)} + \ldots - x_n^{(0)} + k_n = R_n.$$

(1.13.2)

The relaxation procedure consists in changing the starting values of the unknowns, *one or more at a time*, until all the R_i become negligible. For this purpose note that, if a given $x_j^{(0)}$, say $x_k^{(0)}$, is changed by an amount δx_k, then R_k changes by $-\delta x_k$, while the other R_i change by

* See R. V. Southwell, *Relaxation Methods in Theoretical Physics*, Oxford University Press, London, 1946; R. V. Southwell, *Relaxation Methods in Engineering Science*, Oxford University Press, London, 1940; also D. N. de G. Allen, *Relaxation Methods*, McGraw-Hill Book Company, Inc., New York, 1954.

$b_{ik}\delta x_k$. Hence, to reduce a given R_i, say R_k, to zero, we change $x_k^{(0)}$ by $\delta x_k = R_k$. In so doing, the other R_i will also change and must be reduced to zero one by one by suitable changes δx_i. It is convenient to eliminate the largest residual appearing in the system at any stage in the process.

This procedure is conveniently carried out in tabular form by writing the initial value of each unknown $x_j^{(0)}$ and its successive changes δx_j in a column and the residuals in another column (usually to the right of the x_j column); thus the relaxation table has two columns for each unknown. When the residuals have vanished to the degree of accuracy required, the sum of $x_j^{(0)}$ and of all the changes δx_j gives the value of the unknown x_j.

Consider, for example, the system

Eqs.	x_1	x_2	x_3	c
I	10	-2	-2	6
II	-1	10	-2	7
III	-1	-1	10	8

(a)

which, when ready for relaxation [Eqs. (1.13.1)], becomes

Eqs.	x_1	x_2	x_3	k
I	-1	0.2	0.2	0.6
II	0.1	-1	0.2	0.7
III	0.1	0.1	-1	0.8

(b)

Using the starting values $x_1^{(0)} = x_2^{(0)} = x_3^{(0)} = 0$, the corresponding residuals are

$$R_1 = 0.60; \qquad R_2 = 0.70; \qquad R_3 = 0.80.$$

The initial values $x_j^{(0)}$ and the residuals appear, respectively, in the columns x_j and R_i in the first row of Table 1.11. The largest residual $R_3 = 0.80$ is first reduced to zero by a change $\delta x_3 = 0.80$, which introduces a change $b_{23}\delta x_3 = 0.2 \cdot 0.80 = 0.16$ in R_2 and a change $b_{13}\delta x_3 = 0.2 \cdot 0.80 = 0.16$ in R_1. The new residuals are now $R_1 = 0.60 + 0.16 = 0.76$, $R_2 = 0.70 + 0.16 = 0.86$, and $R_3 = 0.80 - 0.80 = 0$. The largest residual $R_2 = 0.86$ is now wiped out by means of a change $\delta x_2 = 0.86$, introducing changes $\delta R_3 = b_{32}\delta x_2 = 0.1 \cdot 0.86 = 0.09$ and $\delta R_1 = b_{12}\delta x_2 = 0.2 \cdot 0.86 = 0.17$. The residuals at this stage are $R_1 = 0.76 + 0.17 = 0.93$, $R_2 = 0$, and $R_3 = 0 + 0.09 = 0.09$. We now wipe out R_1 by means of a change $\delta x_1 = 0.93$, introducing new changes $\delta R_2 = b_{21}\delta x_1 = 0.1 \cdot 0.93 = 0.09$, $\delta R_3 = b_{31}\delta x_1 = 0.1 \cdot 0.93 = 0.09$. The process is repeated until the residuals are reduced to one unit in the last significant

Table 1.11

x_1	R_1	x_2	R_2	x_3	R_3
0	0.60	0	0.70	0	0.80
	0.16		0.16	0.80	−0.80
	0.76	0.86	0.86		0
	0.17		−0.86		0.09
0.93	0.93		0		0.09
	−0.93		0.09		0.09
	0		0.09	0.18	0.18
	0.04		0.04		−0.18
	0.04	0.13	0.13		0
	0.03		−0.13		0.01
0.07	0.07		0		0.01
	−0.07		0.01		0.01
	0		0.01	0.02	0.02
	0		0		−0.02
	0	0.01	0.01		0
	0		−0.01		0
1.00	0	1.00	0	1.00	0

figure, and the value of x_j is the sum of all the figures in the x_j column:

$$x_1 = 0.93 + 0.07 = 1.00;$$
$$x_2 = 0.86 + 0.13 + 0.01 = 1.00;$$
$$x_3 = 0.80 + 0.18 + 0.02 = 1.00.$$

The results can be (*and should be*) checked by substitution in the original equations.

In practice, the changes in the residuals are added directly to the residuals without writing them down, and the scheme takes the more compact form of Table 1.12, in which all numbers are multiplied by 100 to avoid the use of the decimal point.

Table 1.12

x_1	R_1	x_2	R_2	x_3	R_3
0	60	0	70	0	80
	76	86	86	80	9
93	93		9	18	18
	4	13	13		1
7	7	1	1	2	2
100		100		100	

In order to show additional characteristic features of the relaxation technique, we shall solve the following system (c), which is ready for relaxation and represents a physical problem dealt with in Chapter IV (see p. 162 ff.):

v_1	v_2	v_3	k	
-1	0.3951	0	0.2695	(c)
0.3556	-1	0.3556	0.4763	
0	0.3232	-1	1.0717	

In a first approximation, the coefficients b_{ij} may be rounded off to one or two figures, since the errors thus introduced may always be wiped out by relaxation of the more accurate residuals computed by means of the complete coefficients. Thus, to obtain a solution with 1 per cent accuracy, we round off the coefficients and the constants of (c) to two figures, using the relaxation table

v_1	v_2	v_3	k	B	
-1	0.40	0	0.27	-0.60	(d)
0.36	-1	0.36	0.48	-0.28	
0	0.32	-1	1.07	-0.68	

The assumed starting values are

$$v_1^{(0)} = 0.25; \qquad v_2^{(0)} = 0.50; \qquad v_3^{(0)} = 0.75.$$

Table 1.13

v_1	R_1	v_2	R_2	v_3	R_3
25	22	50	34	75	48
42	42	51	51	48	16
8	8	21	15	16	7
2	2	5	21	7	2
1	1	2	3	2	1
78			5	1	
			1	149	
			2		
		129			

The residuals corresponding to the $v_j^{(0)}$ are

$$R_1 = -0.25 + 0.40 \cdot 0.50 + 0.27 = 0.22;$$

$$R_2 = 0.36 \cdot 0.25 - 0.50 + 0.36 \cdot 0.75 + 0.48 = 0.34;$$

$$R_3 = 0.32 \cdot 0.50 - 0.75 + 1.07 = 0.48.$$

Table 1.13 gives the solution of the system by relaxation of the largest residual at each step.

Table 1.14 shows how two additional figures in the v_j may be obtained by computing the residuals corresponding to the above values by means of the complete coefficients of Eqs. (c), and by relaxing them by means of the rounded coefficients of Eqs. (d). The largest residual is wiped out at every stage. Both residuals and unknowns are multiplied by 10^4 to avoid the decimal point.

Table 1.14

v_1	R_1	v_2	R_2	v_3	R_3
7800	−8	12900	−65	14900	−14
−34	−34	−65	−12	−35	−35
−9	−9	−24	−24	−8	−8
−2	2	−6	3	−2	−2
−1	1	−2	−6	1	−1
7754			−1	14854	
			−2		
		12803			

In the previous examples, relaxation was applied mechanically, always reducing to zero the largest residual, but the method becomes particularly advantageous if no such rule is used. In *block relaxation*, for example, all (or a group of) the variables are changed by the same amount δ whenever convenient, changing the residual R_i by

$$\delta R_i = \left(-1 + \sum_{\substack{j=1 \\ j \neq i}}^{n} b_{ij}\right)\delta = B_i\delta, \qquad (1.13.3)$$

while in *underrelaxation* and *overrelaxation* the changes in the variables are taken small or large enough to obtain new residuals with a sign equal or opposite, respectively, to that of the previous residuals. In Table 1.15

the system of Eqs. (c), in which

$$B_1 = -1 + 0.40 = -0.60,$$

$$B_2 = 0.36 - 1.00 + 0.36 = -0.28,$$

$$B_3 = 0.32 - 1 = -0.68,$$

is first solved with an accuracy of 1 per cent by means of an initial block change of $+0.60$ and successive overrelaxation, while two more figures in the roots are then obtained by simple relaxation. The last two lines contain the residuals computed by means of the complete coefficients of Eqs. (c) and the final values.

Table 1.15

v_1	R_1	v_2	R_2	v_3	R_3	Explanations
25	22	50	34	75	48	$v_j^{(0)}$ and $R_i^{(0)}$ of Eqs. (d)
60	−14	60	17	60	7	Block change $\delta = 60$
−7	−6	20	−3	15	13	Overrelaxation
	1		2	−2	−2	
78			−1	148		Roots to 1 per cent
		130				
7800	31	13000	−200	14800	119	Residuals of Eqs. (c)
−49	−49	−200	20	55	55	Simple relaxation
1	1	2	2	1	1	
7752	1	12802	0	14856	1	Roots to 0.01 per cent and check of residuals
1				−1		Simple relaxation
7753		12802		14855		Final values of roots

One of the most efficient ways of using block relaxation is to reduce to zero the *total residual*, i.e., the sum of all the R_i. For example, in Table 1.16 the solution of the system of equations (e) is started by an initial block change obtained as minus the ratio of the total residual $-(4 + 18 + 45)$ $= -67$ to the *total relaxation coefficient* $-6 - 7 - 8 = -21$; i.e., a $\delta x = -67/-21 \approx 3$. The corresponding δR_i are

$$\delta R_1 = 3(-6) = -18; \quad \delta R_2 = 3(-7) = -21; \quad \delta R_3 = 3(-8) = -24.$$

The new set of residuals ($R_1 = -14$, $R_2 = -3$, $R_3 = 21$) has alternating signs, a feature that usually accelerates convergence. The rest of the solution is obtained by relaxation of the largest residual.

x_1	x_2	x_3	k	B	
-10	2	2	4	-6	(e)
1	-10	2	18	-7	
1	1	-10	45	-8	
			67	-21	

Table 1.16

x_1	R_1	x_2	R_2	x_3	R_3
0	~~4~~	0	~~18~~	0	~~45~~
3	~~−14~~	3	~~−8~~	3	~~21~~
	−10		~~1~~	2	~~1~~
−1	0		0		0
2		3		5	

The skill acquired by solving a number of systems and a certain amount of physical intuition related to the problem at hand will usually suggest changes which will lead to the correct roots in a few cycles. It is important to go through the process by choosing suitable values of δx rather than by trying to wipe out exactly the residuals. Beginners are inclined to decide on reducing to zero a given R_i and to choose the δx_i that will produce this result. It is instead more expedient to choose the value of δx_i in round figures and to compute the corresponding δR_i.

1.14 Sets of Infinite Equations

In the solution of many technical problems a need arises for the evaluation of the roots of a set with an infinite number of linear equations. These usually stem from methods of successive approximations and lead to roots of x_j decreasing in absolute value with increasing j. To obtain an insight into the trend of the values of the unknowns one may use the following elementary procedure. Consider the first n equations of the system and triangularize it by elimination. Solve then consecutively the first equation for x_1, the first and second equations for x_1 and x_2, the first, second, and third for x_1, x_2, x_3, etc., ignoring the remaining unknowns. One thus obtains n approximations for x_1, $n - 1$ for x_2, $n - 2$ for x_3, etc., and one may gauge the influence of the remaining unknowns on the first few.

This procedure is applied in the following scheme to the system

$$-x_{j-1} + (j + 1)x_j - x_{j+1} = 10; \qquad j = 1, 2, 3, \ldots \quad (x_0 = 0), \qquad \text{(a)}$$

considering its first six equations.

x_1	x_2	x_3	x_4	x_5	x_6	C	Row	Expl.
2	−1					10	1	I
−1	3	−1				10	2	II
	−1	4	−1			10	3	III
		−1	5	−1		10	4	IV
			−1	6	−1	10	5	V
				−1	7	10	6	VI
2	−1					10	7	(1)
	5	−2				30	8	2(2) + (7)
		18	−5			80	9	5(3) + (8)
			85	−18		260	10	18(4) + (9)
				492	−85	1110	11	85(5) + (10)
					3359	5030	12	492(6) + (11)
5.00							13	
8.00	6.00						14	
8.89	7.78	4.44					15	
9.06	8.12	5.29	3.06				16	
9.09	8.17	5.43	3.54	2.26			17	
9.09	8.18	5.44	3.59	2.52	1.50		18	

1.15 Consistency of Equations

An m by n matrix is said to be of *rank r* if the largest nonzero determinant (*minor*) which can be extracted from the matrix is of order r. For instance, the 2 by 3 matrix

$$A = \begin{bmatrix} 1 & 0 & 2 \\ 2 & 0 & 4 \end{bmatrix}$$

is of rank 1, since all the second-order minors of A

$$\begin{vmatrix} 1 & 0 \\ 2 & 0 \end{vmatrix}; \qquad \begin{vmatrix} 1 & 2 \\ 2 & 4 \end{vmatrix}; \qquad \begin{vmatrix} 0 & 2 \\ 0 & 4 \end{vmatrix}$$

are equal to zero, but not all its elements (minors of order 1) are zero.

The fundamental theorem on the consistency of linear equations will be here stated without proof:

A system of m equations in n unknowns is consistent, i.e., has a solution, if and only if the matrix A of its coefficients, and the *augmented matrix B,* obtained by adding to A the column C of its constants, have the same rank.

For instance, the system

$$x_1 + 2x_2 + 3x_3 = 10$$
$$2x_1 + 4x_2 + 6x_3 = 20$$

(a)

is consistent, since both

$$A = \begin{bmatrix} 1 & 2 & 3 \\ 2 & 4 & 6 \end{bmatrix} \quad \text{and} \quad B = \begin{bmatrix} 1 & 2 & 3 & 10 \\ 2 & 4 & 6 & 20 \end{bmatrix}$$

are of rank 1. The same system with a column of constants

$$C = \begin{bmatrix} 10 \\ 15 \end{bmatrix}$$

would be inconsistent, since the augmented matrix

$$B = \begin{bmatrix} 1 & 2 & 3 & 10 \\ 2 & 4 & 6 & 15 \end{bmatrix}$$

has rank 2, as shown, for example, by the minor

$$\begin{vmatrix} 3 & 10 \\ 6 & 15 \end{vmatrix} = -15 \neq 0.$$

When the number of the unknowns n is larger than the rank r, r unknowns may be expressed in terms of the remaining $n - r$. For instance, in the case of Eqs. (a),

$$x_1 = 10 - 2x_2 - 3x_3$$

satisfies both equations identically, whatever the values of x_2 and x_3. Hence this system has actually a double infinity of solutions.

Similarly, the system

$$x_1 + 2x_2 = 10$$
$$x_1 + 3x_2 = 15$$
$$2x_1 + 5x_2 = 25$$

(b)

has matrices

$$A = \begin{bmatrix} 1 & 2 \\ 1 & 3 \\ 2 & 5 \end{bmatrix}; \quad B = \begin{bmatrix} 1 & 2 & 10 \\ 1 & 3 & 15 \\ 2 & 5 & 25 \end{bmatrix}$$

of rank 2 and roots (obtained by simultaneous solution of any two equations of the system)

$$x_1 = 0; \quad x_2 = 5,$$

which satisfy all three equations. The solution is unique, since $n = r = 2$.

1.16 Homogeneous Equations

A system of n linear equations in n unknowns with constants c_i all equal to zero, i.e., a *homogeneous system*, has always a solution, since its augmented matrix is necessarily of the same rank as the matrix of its coefficients. This solution is called the *zero solution* or the *trivial solution* and consists of x_j all equal to zero.

A nontrivial solution exists if and only if the rank of the coefficient matrix r is less than n. For example, the system

$$x_1 + 2x_2 + x_3 = 0$$
$$2x_1 + x_2 - x_3 = 0 \qquad \text{(a)}$$
$$3x_1 + 3x_2 \qquad\quad = 0$$

has a coefficient matrix of rank 2 and roots

$$x_1 = x_3; \qquad x_2 = -x_3; \qquad x_3 = \text{arbitrary};$$

that is,

$$\frac{x_1}{x_3} = 1; \qquad \frac{x_2}{x_3} = -1.$$

In many problems involving vibrations and instability the coefficients of a homogeneous system of linear equations depend on a parameter λ, and the nontrivial solutions are found by determining the values of λ, called its *characteristic values*, which make the rank of the coefficient matrix equal to $n - 1$. For example, given

$$(2 - \lambda)x_1 + x_2 = 0$$
$$x_1 + (2 - \lambda)x_2 = 0, \qquad \text{(b)}$$

the values of λ making the determinant of the coefficients equal to zero are determined by the equation

$$\begin{vmatrix} 2 - \lambda & 1 \\ 1 & 2 - \lambda \end{vmatrix} = (2 - \lambda)^2 - 1 = 0,$$

from which

$$\lambda_1 = 3; \qquad \lambda_2 = 1.$$

The corresponding systems of equations are

$$\begin{array}{cc} \lambda = 3 & \lambda = 1 \\ -x_1 + x_2 = 0 & x_1 + x_2 = 0 \\ x_1 - x_2 = 0 & x_1 + x_2 = 0 \end{array}$$

and their roots (*characteristic vectors*) are

$$x_1 = x_2; \qquad x_1 = -x_2.$$

The necessary and sufficient condition for the iterational procedures of solution of linear equations can now be stated in terms of the parameter λ. The iterational processes converge whenever the characteristic values of the iteration matrix $\boldsymbol{B}$ are less than 1 in absolute value.

The solution of system (b) for the *largest* characteristic value and the corresponding characteristic vector can be obtained by iteration starting with a guess of the characteristic vector. For example, writing system as (b)

$$\begin{bmatrix} 2 & 1 \\ 1 & 2 \end{bmatrix} \begin{bmatrix} x_1 \\ x_2 \end{bmatrix} = \lambda \begin{bmatrix} x_1 \\ x_2 \end{bmatrix}$$

and assuming $x_1 = 2$, $x_2 = 1$, the successive iterations give

$$\begin{bmatrix} 2 & 1 \\ 1 & 2 \end{bmatrix} \begin{bmatrix} 2 \\ 1 \end{bmatrix} = \begin{bmatrix} 5 \\ 4 \end{bmatrix} = 4 \begin{bmatrix} \frac{5}{4} \\ 1 \end{bmatrix}$$

$$\begin{bmatrix} 2 & 1 \\ 1 & 2 \end{bmatrix} \begin{bmatrix} \frac{5}{4} \\ 1 \end{bmatrix} = \begin{bmatrix} \frac{14}{4} \\ \frac{13}{4} \end{bmatrix} = \frac{13}{4} \begin{bmatrix} \frac{14}{13} \\ 1 \end{bmatrix}$$

$$\begin{bmatrix} 2 & 1 \\ 1 & 2 \end{bmatrix} \begin{bmatrix} \frac{14}{13} \\ 1 \end{bmatrix} = \begin{bmatrix} \frac{41}{13} \\ \frac{40}{13} \end{bmatrix} = \frac{40}{13} \begin{bmatrix} \frac{41}{40} \\ 1 \end{bmatrix}$$

$$\begin{bmatrix} 2 & 1 \\ 1 & 2 \end{bmatrix} \begin{bmatrix} \frac{41}{40} \\ 1 \end{bmatrix} = \begin{bmatrix} \frac{122}{40} \\ \frac{121}{40} \end{bmatrix} = \frac{121}{40} \begin{bmatrix} \frac{122}{121} \\ 1 \end{bmatrix}.$$

The characteristic vectors are defined within a constant, and it is customary to have one of its elements equal to 1.

The last approximation gives

$$\lambda = \tfrac{121}{40} = 3.025; \qquad x_1 = \tfrac{122}{121} = 1.008; \qquad x_2 = 1.$$

1.17 Simultaneous Nonlinear Equations

There are no general procedures for the solution of simultaneous nonlinear equations. Initial values of the real unknowns are usually located by trial and error or by graphical means. The solution may then be continued by Newton's method of tangents, *provided the initial values be sufficiently close to the roots.*

Given, for example, the two nonlinear equations

$$f(x,y) = 0; \qquad \phi(x,y) = 0, \tag{1.17.1}$$

and knowing the initial approximations x_0, y_0 of x, y, the functions f and

ϕ are expanded into Taylor series about x_0, y_0 up to their linear terms:

$$f(x,y) = f_0 + f_{x,0}h + f_{y,0}k + \ldots = 0$$

$$\phi(x,y) = \phi_0 + \phi_{x,0}h + \phi_{y,0}k + \ldots = 0$$

(a)

where

$$f_{x,0} = \frac{\partial f}{\partial x}\bigg]_{\substack{x=x_0 \\ y=y_0}} ; \quad \ldots ;$$

(b)

and

$$h = x - x_0; \qquad k = y - y_0.$$

Solving the two linear equations (a) for h, k,

$$h = - \frac{f_0\phi_{y,0} - \phi_0 f_{y,0}}{f_{x,0}\phi_{y,0} - \phi_{x,0}f_{y,0}}$$

$$k = - \frac{f_{x,0}\phi_0 - \phi_{x,0}f_0}{f_{x,0}\phi_{y,0} - \phi_{x,0}f_{y,0}}$$

(1.17.2)

Eqs. (b) give the values of the first approximations:

$$x_1 = x_0 + h; \qquad y_1 = y_0 + k.$$

(1.17.3)

The extension to more than two equations is immediate.

For example, given

$$f(x,y) = x^2 - y^2 - 1 = 0; \qquad \phi(x,y) = x + y^3 + 2 = 0;$$

$$f_x = 2x, \qquad f_y = -2y; \qquad \phi_x = 1, \quad \phi_y = 3y^2,$$

and starting with $x_0 = -1$, $y_0 = -0.5$, we obtain, with two-decimal accuracy,

n	0	1	2	3	4
x	-1.00	-1.43	-1.34	-1.33	-1.33
y	-0.50	-1.10	-0.92	-0.88	-0.88
f	-0.25	-0.17	-0.051	-0.0055	
f_x	-2.00	-2.86	-2.64	-2.66	
f_y	1.00	2.20	1.84	1.76	
ϕ	0.88	-0.76	-0.12	-0.0115	
ϕ_x	1.00	1.00	1.00	1.00	
ϕ_y	0.75	3.63	2.55	2.32	
h	-0.43	0.09	0.01	0	
k	-0.60	0.18	0.04	0.0046	

1.18 Linear Programming

Linear programming is a mathematical technique for the solution of important technical, financial, and organizational problems in which a number of variables must be chosen so as to make a linear function of these variables maximum or minimum, while satisfying certain linear equations and/or inequalities, usually referred to as *constraints*. Here is a typical linear programming problem.

A manufacturer may produce two items in his factory. Item A requires 1 hour of furnace baking and 3 hours of finishing; item B requires 2 hours of baking and 4 hours of finishing. The manufacturer makes a profit of \$1 on each item A and of \$3 on each item B. He may put as many as 10 workers on the finishing job to work a regular 8-hour shift and has one furnace which, to economize fuel, should work 24 hours a day.

How many items A and how many items B should be manufactured per day to obtain a maximum profit?

Indicating by x_1 and x_2 the number of items A and B giving the maximum profit, the finishing operation is so limited by the number of man-hours available for this job (10 workers doing 8 hours each) that

$$3x_1 + 4x_2 \leq 80. \tag{a}$$

On the other hand, the requirement of 24 hours a day of baking implies that

$$x_1 + 2x_2 = 24. \tag{b}$$

Calling p_1 the unit profit on A and p_2 the unit profit on B, the profit per day is given by the linear function of x_1 and x_2:

$$P = p_1 x_1 + p_2 x_2 = x_1 + 3x_2. \tag{c}$$

We may try to obtain a solution of this problem by using all the available manpower in the finishing operation, i.e., by solving the two equations:

$$3x_1 + 4x_2 = 80$$

$$x_1 + 2x_2 = 24.$$

The values of x_1 and x_2 thus obtained are $x_1 = 32$, $x_2 = -4$. Since it is impossible to manufacture a *negative* number of items B, this solution is meaningless: the manufacturer cannot use 80 man-hours on finishing. The problem to be solved, then, consists in finding *non-negative* values of the unknowns:

$$x_1 \geq 0; \qquad x_2 \geq 0 \tag{d}$$

satisfying the inequality (a) and the equation (b) such that P, as given by Eq. (c), be a maximum.

The *simplex method** is an elementary step-by-step process for the

---

* For a complete explanation of the method, see S. I. Gass, "Linear Programming, Methods and Applications," McGraw-Hill Book Company, Inc., New York, 1958.

solution of linear programming problems. It is based on the following theorem:

If n variables x must satisfy $m \leq n$ constraints, the maximum of the linear combination P is obtained with not more than m variables having nonzero values.

In the initial trial solution m of the n variables are given nonzero values; the linear combination P is then increased by dropping one of the variables included in the initial solution and including one of the other variables originally equal to zero. The process is stopped when P becomes maximum, as shown by the calculations.

In the solution by the simplex method all inequalities are first transformed into equalities by the introduction of *slack variables* with zero profit (since they do not represent physical quantities), and *artificial variables* are added to all equations, with large *negative* profit $-L$ so that P cannot become maximum unless the artificial variables are equal to zero (as they must be for the equations to be satisfied). Thus, a slack variable x_3 is introduced in Eq. (a) and an artificial variable x_4 in Eq. (b), while the profit P becomes

$$P = p_1 x_1 + p_2 x_2 + 0 \cdot x_3 - L x_4 \qquad (c')$$

Table 1.17

i \ j	x_1	x_2	x_3	x_4	C	x_i	p_i
3	3	4	1	0	80	x_3	0
4	1	2	0	1	24	x_4	$-L$
						$-24\,L = P$	

The new equations (a), (b) with the slack variable x_3 and artificial variable x_4 appear in rows 3, 4 of Table 1.17. The initial solution is one with zero values of x_1, x_2 and nonzero values of x_3, x_4. Since x_3, x_4 appear in a unit matrix (and this is the reason for the introduction of artificial variables to the equations), the initial solution is $x_3 = 80$, $x_4 = 24$. The corresponding profit is obtained by writing the values of $p_3 = 0$ and $p_4 = -L$ in a column next to these variables and by computing $P = \sum_i p_i x_i = -24L$.

This large negative profit is increased by dropping x_3 or x_4 and introducing x_1 or x_2. If, for example, x_2 takes the place of x_4 and is given a value r, the new set of variables becomes

$$\begin{aligned}
x_1' &= x_1 + \Delta x_1 = x_1 = 0; \\
x_2' &= x_2 + \Delta x_2 = r; \\
x_3' &= x_3 + \Delta x_3 = 80 + \Delta x_3; \\
x_4' &= x_4 + \Delta x_4 = x_4 - x_4 = 24 - 24 = 0.
\end{aligned} \qquad (e)$$

Introducing these values in Eqs. (3), (4) of Table 1.17, we find that these equations are satisfied if

$$4r + \Delta x_3 = 0$$

$$2r = 24$$

from which

$$x_1' = 0; \qquad x_2' = r = 12; \qquad x_3' = 80 - 4r = 32; \qquad x_4' = 0;$$

$$P = 3x_2 + 0 \cdot x_3 = 36.$$

On the other hand, if x_2 had taken the place of x_3, we would have obtained

$$4r = 80; \qquad 2r + \Delta x_4 = 0;$$

$$x_1' = 0; \qquad x_2' = r = 20; \qquad x_3' = 0; \qquad x_4' = 24 - 2r = -16,$$

an unacceptable solution since all x_i must be ≥ 0.

It is obvious that substitution rules are needed as soon as the number of variables is high, in order to avoid innumerable trials. These are easily determined as follows.

Consider the equations of Table 1.18 and indicate by x_j the variable that will take the place of the variable x_i of the initial solution. When

Table 1.18

$-p_j$	$-p_1$	$-p_2$	$-p_3$	$-p_4$		
$\diagdown$ $\begin{smallmatrix} & j \\ i & \end{smallmatrix}$	x_1	x_2	x_3	x_4	$C = x_i$	p_i
3	a_{31}	a_{32}	$a_{33} = 1$	$a_{34} = 0$	x_3	p_3
4	a_{41}	a_{42}	$a_{43} = 0$	$a_{44} = 1$	x_4	p_4
	Δ_1	Δ_2	Δ_3	Δ_4	P	

$x_j = r$ substitutes x_i in the ith equation, the change in the lefthand member is $a_{ij}r - a_{ii}x_i = a_{ij}r - x_i$ and must be equal to zero. Hence

$$x_j' = r = \frac{x_i}{a_{ij}}. \tag{1.18.1}$$

In order to obtain positive values for all the variables x_j', *for a given j, i must be so chosen to give the smallest positive value of r.* Thus, for $j = 2$, $i = 4$ gives $r = \frac{24}{2} = 12$, $i = 3$ gives $r = \frac{80}{4} = 20$, and $i = 4$ must be chosen.

In order to select j, we compute the changes in all the variables due to the introduction of $x_j' = r$ in the new solution to take the place of the old variable x_i:

$$\Delta x_j = r,$$

$$\Delta x_i = -x_i = -a_{ij}r,$$

$$\Delta x_k = -a_{kj}r,$$

where x_k is one of the changing variables (like x_3 in Table 1.17) and $\Delta x_k + a_{kj}x_j' = 0$ in order to satisfy equation (k) in Table 1.18.

The corresponding change in P is given by

$$\Delta P = p_j r - p_i a_{ij} r - \sum_k p_k a_{kj} r$$

or, letting the sum include all the changing x_j' and calling the running subscript i,

$$\Delta P = -r[\sum_i p_i a_{ij} - p_j]. \tag{1.18.2}$$

The x_j will be so chosen as to make ΔP a large *positive* change. This is easily achieved by chosing the j for which

$$\Delta_j = \sum_i p_i a_{ij} - p_j \tag{1.18.3}$$

is the largest *negative* number.* The Δ_j are computed by adding the $-p_j$ above the x_j in Table 1.18. It may be noticed that the Δ_j of the unit matrix variables are all equal to zero. The corresponding table for the present problem, Table 1.19, shows that the largest negative Δ_j is $\Delta_2 = -2L - 3$, so that $j = 2$, while the smallest $r = x_i/a_{i2}$ is $x_4/a_{42} = 12$. Thus x_2 must substitute x_4.

Table 1.19

$-p_i$	-1	-3	0	L			
i $\diagdown$ j	x_1	x_2	x_3	x_4	C	x_i	p_i
3	3	4	1	0	80	x_3	0
4	1	2	0	1	24	x_4	$-L$
Δ_j	$-L-1$	$-2L-3$	0	0	$-24L$	P	

To obtain the new values x_j' of the variables, Eqs. (3) and (4) of Table 1.19 are linearly combined to obtain a unit matrix in the new nonzero variables x_2, x_3, as shown in Table 1.20.

---

* The choice of j here suggested does not guarantee the *largest* increase in P, since a smaller Δ_j with a greater r may give a larger ΔP.

Table 1.20

$-p_j$	-1	-3	0	L				
$\diagdown \; j$ i	x_1'	x_2'	x_3'	x_4'	C	x_i	p_i	Expl.
3	1	0	1	-2	32	x_3	0	$(3) - 2(4)$
2	1/2	1	0	1/2	12	x_2	3	$(1/2)(4)$
Δ_j	$(3/2) - 1$	0	0	$(3/2) + L$	36	P'		

The new values of the variables are $x_2' = 12$ and $x_3' = 32$; the new value of P is $P' = 36$, and since all the Δ_j are positive, any new substitution of variables would decrease P. The optimum solution is $x_1 = 0$, $x_2 = 12$, $P = 36$.

The following linear programing problem is solved in Table 1.21:

$$x_1 + 2x_2 - 3x_3 = 10; \qquad x_2 + x_3 \leq 20; \qquad -x_2 + 2x_3 \leq 15;$$

$$x_1 \geq 0; \qquad x_2 \geq 0; \qquad x_3 \geq 0; \qquad P = x_1 - x_2 + 4x_3 = \text{max.}$$

Notice that no artificial variable was added to the equation, since x_1 already appears with coefficients in unit vector form.

Table 1.21

$-p_j$	-1	$+1$	-4	0	0					
$\diagdown \; j$ i	x_1	x_2	x_3	x_4	x_5	C	x_i	p_i	Expl.	
1	1	2	-3	0	0	10	x_1	1		$j = 3$
4	0	1	1	1	0	20	x_4	0		$i = 5$
5	0	-1	2	0	1	15	x_5	0		$r = 15/2$
Δ_j	0	3	-7	0	0	10	P			
$1'$	1	1/2	0	0	3/2	65/2	x_1'	1	$(1) + (3/2)(5)$	$j = 2$
$4'$	0	3/2	0	1	$-1/2$	25/2	x_4'	0	$(4) - (1/2)(5)$	$i = 4$
$3'$	0	$-1/2$	1	0	1/2	15/2	x_3'	4	$(1/2)(5)$	$r = 25/3$
Δ_j	0	$-1/2$	0	0	7/2	125/2	P'			
$1''$	1	0	0	$-1/3$	5/3	85/3	x_1''	1	$(2/3)(4)$	
$2''$	0	1	0	2/3	$-1/3$	25/3	x_2''	-1	$(1') - (1/2)(2'')$	
$3''$	0	0	1	1/3	1/3	35/3	x_3''	4	$(3') + (1/2)(2'')$	
Δ_j	0	0	0	1/3	10/3	200/3	P''			

The optimum solution $x_1 = \frac{85}{3}$, $x_2 = \frac{25}{3}$, $x_3 = \frac{35}{3}$, $P = \frac{200}{3}$ is obtained with a nonzero value of x_2, although x_2 has a negative unit profit $p_2 = -1$.

The simplex method may be extended to more general problems as follows:

(a) Problems involving the minimization of a linear function f of the x_j are solved by maximizing the function:

$$\phi(x_j) = -f(x_j)$$

(b) Restraints of the type

$$a_{i1}x_1 + a_{i2}x_2 + \ldots + a_{in}x_n \geq c_i$$

are reduced to the type considered above by writing

$$-a_{i1}x_1 - a_{i2}x_2 - \ldots - a_{in}x_n \leq -c_i$$

(c) Restraints of the type

$$x_j \geq a_j$$

are reduced to "positive variable" restraint by means of the new variables:

$$y_j = x_j - a_j \geq 0$$

(d) Restraints of the type

$$x_j \leq b_j$$

are reduced to "positive variable" restraint by means of the new variables:

$$y_j = b_j - x_j \geq 0$$

(e) Restraints of the type

$$a_j \leq x_j \leq b_j$$

are reduced to the restraints

$$1 \geq y_j \geq 0$$

by the new variables

$$y_j = \frac{b_j - x_j}{b_j - a_j}$$

and then the added restraints:

$$1 - y_j \geq 0$$

are considered in the calculations.

(f) Since all restraints may be equations, the simplex method is also a process for the solution of linear simultaneous equations.

(g) A linear programming problem may have no solution. This is usually shown by the impossibility of obtaining a positive profit.

PROBLEMS

1.1 Evaluate the roots of the following equations by Newton's method of tangents and synthetic substitution to the number of figures specified.

(a) $x^3 + 1.2x^2 - 4x - 4.8 = 0$ (two figures).
(b) $x^3 - 0.87x^2 - 15.651x + 23.701 = 0$ (three figures).
(c) $x^3 + 6.6x^2 - 29.05x + 22.64 = 0$ (three figures).

Ans.   (a) $x_1 = 2$; $x_2 = -2$; $x_3 = -1.2$.   (c) $x_1 = 2.10$; $x_2 = -9.80$; $x_3 = 1.10$.

1.2 Evaluate the roots of the following equations to three significant figures by Newton's second-order method and synthetic substitution, and the quadratic formula, when necessary.

(a) $x^3 + 2.9x^2 + 14.89x + 6.85 = 0$.
(b) $x^3 - 2.4x^2 - 1.4x - 6.8 = 0$.
(c) $x^4 + 6.4x^3 + 24.04x^2 + 36.96x + 18.72 = 0$.
(d) $x^4 - 2x^3 + 1.99x^2 - 2x + 0.99 = 0$.
(e) $x^4 - x^3 - 0.44x^2 - 13.88x + 2.8 = 0$.

Ans.   (b) $x_1 = 3.40$; $x_{2,3} = -0.500 \pm 1.323i$.   (d) $x_1 = 1.100$; $x_2 = 0.900$; $x_{3,4} = \pm i$.

1.3 Evaluate to four significant figures the roots of the following equations. Evaluate the largest root by synthetic substitution and linear interpolation.

(a) $x^3 - 4.65x^2 - 49.92x - 76.67 = 0$.
(b) $x^3 + 6.8x^2 - 62.49x + 63.468 = 0$.
(c) $x^3 - 13.6x^2 - 57.4x - 228.8 = 0$.
(d) $x^3 - 10.2x^2 - 51.8x - 71.00 = 0$.

Ans.   (a) $x_1 = 10.25$; $x_2 = -3.40$; $x_3 = -2.20$.   (c) $x_1 = 17.6$; $x_{2,3} = -2.00 \pm 3.00i$.

1.4 Evaluate to three significant figures the four roots of the following equations, two of which are almost equal.

(a) $x^4 - 0.41x^3 + 1.632x^2 - 9.146x + 7.260 = 0$.
(b) $x^4 - 5.81x^3 + 7.64x^2 + 7.2x - 14.47 = 0$.

Ans.   (a) $x_1 = 1.21$; $x_2 = 1.20$; $x_{3,4} = -1.00 \pm 2.00i$.

1.5 Evaluate the quadratic factors of the following quartic equations, using Brown's method.

(a) $x^4 - 4x^3 - 7x^2 + 34x - 24 = 0$.
(b) $x^4 - 3x^3 + x^2 - 7x - 30 = 0$.

Ans.   (a) $(x^2 + 2x - 3)(x^2 - 6x + 8)$; $x_i = 2, 1, -3, 4$.

1.6 Evaluate the roots of the following equations to three significant figures using (a) Graeffe's method and (b) Friedmann's method to determine their complex roots.

(a) $x^4 - 14x^3 + 69.09x^2 + 182.56x + 109 = 0.$
(b) $x^5 - 20.2x^4 + 132.18x^3 - 60.592x^2 - 72.693x - 14.525 = 0.$
(c) $x^4 + 18x^3 + 245x^2 + 496x + 1040 = 0.$
(d) $x^4 - 6.4x^3 + 40.04x^2 - 100.96x + 226.72 = 0.$

Ans. (a) $x_{1,2} = -1.00 \pm 0.30i$; $x_{3,4} = 8.00 \pm 6.00i.$
        (c) $x_{1,2} = -8 \pm 12i$; $x_{3,4} = -1 \pm 2i.$

1.7 Evaluate the real roots of the following equation to three significant figures by Newton's method of tangents.

$$\cos x = x^2.$$

Ans. $x_{1,2} = \pm 0.824.$

1.8 Evaluate the two smallest positive roots of the following equations to three significant figures (a) by Newton's method of tangents; (b) by Newton's second-order method.

(a) $\tan x = \tanh x.$ (b) $\cos x \cosh x + 1 = 0.$
(c) $\cos x \cosh x = 1.$ (d) $\tan x = x.$
(e) $\tan x = -x.$ (f) $\tan x = 2x.$
(g) $x \tan x = 1.$ (h) $x \tan x = 2.$

Ans. (a) $x_1 = 3.93$; $x_2 = 7.07.$ (c) $x_1 = 4.73$; $x_2 = 7.85.$ (e) $x_1 = 2.03$;
        $x_2 = 4.91.$ (g) $x_1 = 0.860$; $x_2 = 3.43.$

1.9 Evaluate the lowest positive root of the following equation to three significant figures by expanding the function into a power series.

$$x \tan x = 1.$$

Ans. $x_1 = 0.860.$

1.10 Evaluate the positive root of the following equation to three significant figures by expanding the function into a power series.

$$\cos x = x^2.$$

1.11 Evaluate the first two zeros of the Bessel function of the first kind of order one to three significant figures by Newton's method. *Hint:* Use a table of Bessel functions and remember that

$$J_1'(x) = -\frac{1}{x} J_1(x) + J_0(x).$$

Ans. $x_1 = 3.83$; $x_2 = 7.02.$

1.12 Evaluate the complex roots of the following transcendental equations.

(a) $\cosh z = 4.$ (b) $\sin z = 2.$ (c) $e^{2z} + z = 2,$

Ans. (b) $z_n = \dfrac{(2n - 1)\pi}{2} + 1.32i,$ $n = 1, 3, 5, \ldots .$

1.13 Evaluate to three significant figures the roots of the following systems of equations by determinants.

(a)

x_1	x_2	x_3	c
2	4	−2	14
1	3	−4	16
−1	2	3	1

(b)

x_1	x_2	x_3	x_4	c
3.0	−4.0	2.4	2.0	−21.3
−3.0	1.0	4.2	−3.0	−15.4
2.0	1.5	1.0	6.2	1.7
4.0	−1.0	−3.4	3.0	10.3

(c)

x_1	x_2	x_3	c
3.0	−1.3	4.0	3.9
−2.0	4.5	3.2	10.4
1.4	2.0	−3.0	7.7

Ans.   (b) $x_1 = -1.5$; $x_2 = 2.0$; $x_3 = -4.5$; $x_4 = 1.0$.

1.14 Evaluate to three significant figures the roots of the following systems of equations by Gauss's scheme.

(a)

x_1	x_2	x_3	c
3.5	2.8	6.2	9.87
2.7	8.0	3.0	−6.17
−4.0	−3.6	−2.8	5.65

(b)

x_1	x_2	x_3	c
2.1	−4.5	−2.0	19.07
3.0	2.5	4.3	3.21
−6.0	3.5	2.5	−18.25

(c)

x_1	x_2	x_3	x_4	c
2.0	−4	−3.25	1	4.84
3.0	−3	−4.30	8	8.89
1.0	−5	3.30	−20	−14.01
2.5	−4	2.00	−3	−20.29

(d)

x_1	x_2	x_3	x_4	x_5	c
3	−2	5.3	−2.1	1.0	28.3
1	4	−6.0	4.5	−6.0	−36.2
3	6	−7.3	−9.0	3.4	24.5
−2	−3	1.0	−4.0	6.0	16.2
1	−4	6.5	1.0	−3.0	4.3

Ans.   (b) $x_1 = 1.34$; $x_2 = -4.76$; $x_3 = 2.58$.   (d) $x_1 = 2.06$; $x_2 = 3.22$; $x_3 = 4.03$; $x_4 = -2.01$; $x_5 = 3.00$.

1.15 Obtain a first approximation of the roots of the following systems of equations by Gauss's scheme, using a slide rule. Compute the corresponding errors longhand or on a calculator, and obtain additional significant figures by solving the error equations by slide rule.

(a)

x_1	x_2	x_3	c
3.5	2.8	6.2	9.8999
2.7	8.0	3.0	−6.1744
−4.0	−3.6	−2.8	5.6512

(b)

x_1	x_2	x_3	x_4	c
2.0	−4.0	−3.25	1.0	4.8392
3.0	−3.0	−4.30	8.0	8.8581
1.0	−5.0	3.30	−20.0	−13.9212
2.5	−4.0	2.00	−3.0	−20.2815

Ans.   (a) $x_1 = -3.0347$; $x_2 = -1.1904$; $x_3 = 3.8475$.

1.16 Perform the following matric operations.

(a) $\begin{bmatrix} 2 & 3 & 4 \\ 1 & 4 & 1 \\ 2 & 1 & 4 \end{bmatrix} + \begin{bmatrix} 1 & 2 & 0 \\ 3 & 7 & 2 \\ 1 & 8 & 5 \end{bmatrix}$ (b) $\begin{bmatrix} 2 & 1 \\ 3 & 3 \\ 4 & -1 \\ 5 & 2 \end{bmatrix} + \begin{bmatrix} 3 & 0 \\ 1 & 1 \\ 4 & 1 \\ 3 & 2 \end{bmatrix}$

(c) $\begin{bmatrix} 2 & 1 \\ 3 & 2 \\ 2 & 3 \end{bmatrix} \begin{bmatrix} 3 & 1 & 1 \\ 1 & 3 & 1 \end{bmatrix} + \begin{bmatrix} 6 & 1 & 2 \\ 2 & 4 & 3 \\ 3 & 0 & 1 \end{bmatrix}$

(d) $\begin{bmatrix} 3 & 2 & 2 \\ 4 & -3 & 0 \\ 5 & 0 & 5 \end{bmatrix} \begin{bmatrix} 1 & 3 & 0 \\ -1 & 0 & 1 \\ 2 & 5 & 2 \end{bmatrix}$ (e) $\begin{bmatrix} 2 & 0 & -3 \\ 4 & 1 & 1 \\ -2 & 0 & 4 \end{bmatrix} \begin{bmatrix} 1 & 1 & 2 \\ 0 & -1 & 3 \\ 4 & 0 & 0 \end{bmatrix}$

(f) $\begin{bmatrix} 1 & 2 & 0 & 3 \\ -1 & -1 & 5 & 4 \\ 2 & 0 & 2 & 1 \\ 0 & 1 & 2 & 1 \end{bmatrix} \begin{bmatrix} 1 & 2 & 3 & 0 \\ 1 & 0 & 3 & 2 \\ 2 & 3 & 0 & 1 \\ 5 & 1 & -1 & 0 \end{bmatrix}$ (g) $\begin{bmatrix} 2 & 1 \\ 3 & 2 \\ 1 & 2 \end{bmatrix} \begin{bmatrix} 3 & 1 & 1 \\ 1 & 3 & 1 \end{bmatrix}$

(h) $\begin{bmatrix} 2 & 1 \\ 1 & 3 \end{bmatrix} \begin{bmatrix} 2 & 1 & 1 \\ 1 & 2 & 1 \end{bmatrix}$ (i) $\begin{bmatrix} 0 & 2 & 3 \\ -2 & 1 & 1 \\ 3 & -4 & 6 \\ 1 & 0 & 0 \end{bmatrix} \begin{bmatrix} 3 & -1 \\ 2 & 4 \\ -1 & 0 \end{bmatrix}$

Ans.   (a) $\begin{bmatrix} 3 & 5 & 4 \\ 4 & 11 & 3 \\ 3 & 9 & 9 \end{bmatrix}$ (d) $\begin{bmatrix} 5 & 19 & 6 \\ 7 & 12 & -3 \\ 15 & 40 & 10 \end{bmatrix}$

(f) $\begin{bmatrix} 18 & 5 & 6 & 4 \\ 28 & 17 & -10 & 3 \\ 11 & 11 & 5 & 2 \\ 10 & 7 & 2 & 4 \end{bmatrix}$ (h) $\begin{bmatrix} 5 & 4 & 3 \\ 5 & 7 & 4 \end{bmatrix}$

1.17 Evaluate to three significant figures the roots of the following systems of equations by Cholesky's method.

(a)

x_1	x_2	x_3	c
2.5	−3.0	4.6	− 1.05
−3.5	2.6	1.5	−14.46
−6.5	−3.5	7.3	−17.735

(b)

x_1	x_2	x_3	c
−3.60	2.40	1.50	−1.359
1.40	−1.30	2.65	−3.725
4.26	−3.00	2.85	−3.623

(c) System of Problem 1.14(c).
(d) System of Problem 1.14(d).

x_1	x_2	x_3	x_4	x_5	c
2	−1	4	−3	1	11
−1	1	2	1	3	14
4	2	3	3	−1	4
−3	1	3	2	4	16
1	3	−1	4	4	18

(e)

Ans. (a) $x_1 = 1.24$; $x_2 = -2.45$; $x_3 = -2.50$. (c) $x_1 = 2.34$; $x_2 = 4.51$; $x_3 = -6.00$; $x_4 = -1.30$. (e) $x_1 = 1.00$; $x_2 = 2.00$; $x_3 = 1.00$; $x_4 = -1.00$; $x_5 = 4.00$.

1.18 Evaluate the inverse of the following matrices.

(a) $\begin{bmatrix} 2 & 4 & 3 \\ 1 & 3 & 4 \\ -1 & 3 & 6 \end{bmatrix}$
(b) $\begin{bmatrix} 3 & 2 & 1 \\ 6 & -2 & 3 \\ 1 & 4 & 3 \end{bmatrix}$
(c) $\begin{bmatrix} 1 & 3 & 7 & 5 \\ 2 & 4 & -1 & 3 \\ 3 & -2 & 6 & 2 \\ 1 & 3 & -1 & 4 \end{bmatrix}$

Ans. (b) $\begin{bmatrix} \dfrac{9}{29} & \dfrac{1}{29} & \dfrac{-4}{29} \\[2mm] \dfrac{15}{58} & \dfrac{-4}{29} & \dfrac{3}{58} \\[2mm] \dfrac{-13}{29} & \dfrac{5}{29} & \dfrac{9}{29} \end{bmatrix}$

1.19 Evaluate to three significant figures the roots of the following system of equations by iteration.

(a)

x_1	x_2	x_3	c
−6	1	1	−1133
1	−6	1	−3200
1	1	−6	−4200

(b)

x_1	x_2	x_3	c
−1	0.4	0.5	−1.41
0	−1	0.3	2.81
0.2	0.3	−1	−4.48

(c)

x_1	x_2	x_3	x_4	c
10	8	6	0	16.4
0	10	8	4	−3.8
2	0	10	2	36.9
1	0	6	10	30.9

(d)

x_1	x_2	x_3	x_4	x_5	c
10	1	1	1	1	15
2	10	2	1	1	17
2	1	10	1	2	18
1	2	2	10	2	19
1	1	1	2	10	25

(e)

x_1	x_2	x_3	x_4	x_5	c
8.0	−2.4	−1.6	2.0	0	12.00
0	10.0	0	−4.0	−2.3	21.06
0	3.2	8.0	1.6	2.4	−23.28
−3.2	0	4.8	10.0	2.1	−14.06
−1.6	0	1.6	2.4	8.0	−22.32

(f)

x_1	x_2	x_3	x_4	x_5	c
4.00	0.80	0	1.20	0	5.60
0	8.00	1.60	1.60	2.40	−13.472
2.40	0.80	8.00	0	1.60	30.16
0	1.80	0	6.00	0.60	6.54
2.20	0	2.30	1.50	10.00	−15.631

Ans. (a) $x_1 = 467$; $x_2 = 762$; $x_3 = 905$. (c) $x_1 = 2.40$; $x_2 = −3.20$; $x_3 = 3.00$; $x_4 = 1.05$. (e) $x_1 = 1.20$; $x_2 = 2.00$; $x_3 = −3.25$; $x_4 = 1.00$; $x_5 = −2.20$.

1.20 Evaluate to three significant figures the roots of the following system of equations by relaxation.

(a) System of Problem 1.19(b).

(b)

x_1	x_2	x_3	c
-6	2	4	0
1	1	-5	-350
1	-6	2	-700

(c) System of Problem 1.19(c).
(d) System of Problem 1.19(e).
(e) System of Problem 1.19(f).

Ans.   (b) $x_1 = 155$; $x_2 = 189$; $x_3 = 139$.   (e) $x_1 = 1.20$; $x_2 = -2.00$; $x_3 = 4.23$; $x_4 = 2.00$; $x_5 = -3.10$.

1.21 Solve by relaxation to three significant figures the following systems of equations. Obtain first a rough approximation of the roots by means of coefficients and constants rounded off as indicated.

(a)

x_1	x_2	x_3	c
-1	0.875	0.121	1.132
0.444	-1	0.222	-1.266
0.092	0.545	-1	-2.256

(round off to one decimal figure)

(b)

x_1	x_2	x_3	c
10.22	1.25	3.12	21.047
1.25	10.45	4.15	62.440
3.12	4.15	10.62	109.726

(round off to two significant figures)

Ans.   (a) $x_1 = 2.10$; $x_2 = 3.12$; $x_3 = 4.15$.

1.22 Evaluate x_1 and x_2 to three significant figures in the following infinite sets of equations, using successive approximations.

(a) $-2x_{j-1} + (2j + 4)x_j - jx_{j+1} = 6$ $(x_0 = 0)$.
(b) $-x_{j-1} + (j + 3)x_j - 2x_{j+1} = 12$ $(x_0 = 0)$.

Ans.   (a) $x_1 = 1.22$; $x_2 = 1.34$.

1.23 Determine the rank of the following matrices.

(a) $\begin{bmatrix} 2 & 0 & 2 & 6 \\ 2 & 1 & 0 & -2 \\ -1 & -1 & 1 & 5 \end{bmatrix}$

(b) $\begin{bmatrix} 2 & 0 & 4 \\ 1 & -3 & 6 \end{bmatrix}$

(c) $\begin{bmatrix} 2 & -3 & 8 \\ 3 & 6 & -9 \\ 4 & 1 & -2 \end{bmatrix}$ (d) $\begin{bmatrix} 1 & 2 & -3 \\ 10 & -3 & 4 \\ 4 & 1 & -2 \end{bmatrix}$

Ans.   (a) $r = 2$.   (c) $r = 3$.

1.24 Investigate the following systems of equations for consistency, and find the solutions whenever the systems are consistent.

(a) $-4x_1 + 3x_2 + 2x_3 = 6;$
$\quad 5x_1 - 14x_2 + 10x_3 = -8;$
$\quad 4x_1 - 15x_2 - 6x_3 = 14.$

(b) $2x_1 + 2x_2 + 3x_3 = 5;$
$\quad 2x_1 - x_2 + 3x_3 = 6;$
$\quad -3x_1 + 9x_2 + 3x_3 = 15.$

(c) $4x - 2y + 6z = 8;$
$\quad x + y - 3z = -1;$
$\quad 15x - 3y + 9z = 21.$

(d) $4x_1 + 3x_2 + 4x_3 + 5x_4 = 3;$
$\quad 2x_1 + 4x_2 + 3x_3 - x_4 = 4;$
$\quad 3x_1 - 4x_2 + 3x_3 - 5x_4 = 1.$

(e) $x_1 + 4x_2 + 3x_3 = 5;$
$\quad 2x_1 - 5x_2 + 4x_3 = 10.$

Ans.   (a) Consistent; $x_1 = -3.03;\ x_2 = -1.30;\ x_3 = -1.10.$
$\quad\quad$ (c) Consistent; $x = 1;\ y = 3z - 2;\ z = $ arb.

1.25 Investigate the following systems of homogeneous equations and obtain nonzero solutions where they exist.

(a) $x + y + 4z = 0;$
$\quad 2x - y - z = 0;$
$\quad 6x + 4y + 18z = 0.$

(b) $4x - 2y + z = 0;$
$\quad 2x - y + 3z = 0;$
$\quad 6x - 3y - 6z = 0;$
$\quad 6x - 3y + 4z = 0.$

(c) $2x + 2y + 2z + 2t = 0;$
$\quad 2x + 6y + 4z + 4t = 0;$
$\quad 7x + 9y + 8z + 8t = 0;$
$\quad 5x + 3y + 4z + 4t = 0.$

(d) $2x - y + 3z = 0;$
$\quad 4x + 8y - 4z = 0;$
$\quad 3x + 4y + 2z = 0.$

Ans.   (b) $x = $ arb.; $y = 2x;\ z = 0.$
$\quad\quad$ (d) $x = y = z = 0.$

1.26 (a) Evaluate the smallest characteristic value of the parameter λ and the corresponding characteristic vectors. (b) Evaluate by iteration the largest characteristic value of the parameter λ and the corresponding characteristic vectors.

(a) $(4 - \lambda)x_1 + x_2 = 0;$
$x_1 + (3 - \lambda)x_2 = 0.$

(b) $(3 - 2\lambda)x_1 + x_2 = 0;$
$2x_1 + (5 - \lambda)x_2 = 0.$

(c) $(20 - 2\lambda)x_1 - 16x_2 + 8x_3 + (2\lambda - 16)x_4 = 0;$
$-8x_1 + (22 - 2\lambda)x_2 + (2\lambda - 16)x_3 + 4x_4 = 0;$
$2x_1 + (\lambda - 8)x_2 + (22 - 2\lambda)x_3 - 8x_4 = 0;$
$(\lambda - 8)x_1 + 4x_2 - 16x_3 + (20 - 2\lambda)x_4 = 0.$

(d) $(\lambda - 2)x_1 + x_2 + 3x_3 = 0;$
$x_1 + (\lambda - 1)x_2 - 5x_3 = 0;$
$3x_1 - 5x_2 + (2\lambda - 3)x_3 = 0.$

Ans.   (a) $\lambda_{\min.} = 2.38;$ $x_2/x_1 = -1.62.$ (b) $\lambda_{\max.} = 5.27;$ $x_2/x_1 = 7.54.$
(c) $\lambda_{\min.} = 63.814.$ (d) $\lambda_{\max.} = 6.03;$ $x_1/x_3 = -1.04,$ $x_2/x_3 = 1.20.$

1.27 Determine to three significant figures the root of the following pairs of simultaneous nonlinear equations, starting at the given point.

(a) $x^2 - 2y^2 + 4.82 = 0;$ $x_0 = 1.30;$ $y_0 = 1.70;$
$2x + 4y^2 - 16.74 = 0.$

(b) $x^3 + 3y^2 - 20.92 = 0;$ $x_0 = 1.30;$ $y_0 = -2.00;$
$x^2 + 2y + 1.958 = 0.$

(c) $x^3 + 4z^2 + 14.30 = 0;$ $x_0 = -2.50; z_0 = 2.00;$
$-x^2 + 6z - 3.44 = 0.$

Ans.   (b) $x = 1.65; y = -2.34.$

1.28 Maximize the profit P in the following linear programming problems.

(a) $x_1 + 2x_2 - x_3 = 10;$
$x_2 + x_3 \leq 20;$
$-x_2 + 2x_3 = 15;$
$P = x_1 - x_2 + 4x_3.$

(b) $x_1 + 2x_2 - x_3 = 20;$
$x_2 + 2x_3 \leq 30;$
$-x_2 + 4x_3 \leq 10;$
$P = x_1 - 3x_2 + 4x_3.$

(c) $x_1 + 4x_2 + 2x_3 - x_4 = 0;$
$2x_1 + 3x_2 - 4x_4 \leq 5;$
$3x_1 + 2x_2 + 5x_3 \leq 10;$
$4x_2 + 2x_3 - 2x_4 \leq 8;$
$P = x_1 + 4x_2 + 3x_3 - x_4.$

Ans.   (b) $x_1 = 22.5; x_2 = 0; x_3 = 2.50; P = 32.5.$

II

Finite Differences and Their Applications

2.1 Introduction

Whenever a technical problem leads to a differential equation which cannot be integrated in closed form, approximate methods of solution must be employed. These may be based, for example, on series expansions, or may be purely numerical methods leading to the evaluation of the unknown integral at specified points of its interval of definition by simple arithmetical means. Initial value and boundary value problems, involving either ordinary or partial differential equations, may be solved by such methods. These numerical solutions do not usually allow the determination of general physical laws but do often indicate the dependence of the desired variables on the various parameters of the problem, particularly if the equations are written in nondimensional form.

Numerical methods for the solution of differential equations have become particularly popular in recent years because modern technical problems lead to complicated equations seldom solvable in finite terms and because calculating machines and electronic computers have become widely available. The numerical approach also has the advantage of allowing the actual work to be carried out by operators without a knowledge of higher mathematics or of physics, with a resulting economy of effort on the part of highly trained personnel.

The numerical solution of differential equations consists essentially in obtaining the numerical values of the unknown integral at some *pivotal points*, spaced along the x-axis for ordinary differential equations, and in the x,y-plane for two-dimensional partial differential equations. To obtain the *pivotal values* of the integral f, the derivatives of f appearing in the differential equation are approximated either by the derivatives of nth degree parabolas passing through a certain number of pivotal points, or by Taylor expansions of the unknown function f, as shown in the following sections.

2.2 Differentiation Formulas by Interpolating Parabolas

The simplest method of obtaining approximate expressions for the derivatives of a function $y(x)$, which is known graphically or by means of a table at some pivotal points i, consists in substituting for the function y a parabola passing through a certain number of pivotal points, and in taking the derivatives of the parabola as approximate values of the derivatives of y.

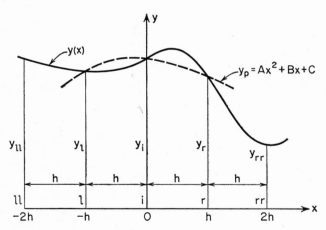

Fig. 2.1.   Interpolating parabola.

For example, to evaluate the second derivative y'' of y, when y is known at three consecutive pivotal points l, i, r, evenly spaced by h on the x-axis, call the corresponding pivotal values y_l, y_i, y_r (Fig. 2.1)* and

---

* The subscript i indicates the pivotal point at which we evaluate the derivative, while the subscripts l and r indicate the pivotal points to the left and right of i, respectively (Fig. 2.1).

pass a quadratic parabola

$$y_p = Ax^2 + Bx + C \tag{a}$$

through these points. Choosing, without loss of generality and for simplicity, the abscissa of the ith point as the origin, we obtain

$$y(-h) = y_l = Ah^2 - Bh + C$$

$$y(0) = y_i = C$$

$$y(h) = y_r = Ah^2 + Bh + C,$$

from which $\qquad y_l - 2y_i + y_r = 2Ah^2.$

Since the second derivative of the parabola (a) equals $2A$, the second derivative y_i'' of y at i, is approximated by

$$y_i'' = \frac{1}{h^2}(y_l - 2y_i + y_r). \tag{2.2.1}$$

Analogous expressions for higher-order derivatives may be obtained by means of higher-degree interpolating parabolas, which may be made to pass through pivotal points symmetrically or unsymmetrically located with respect to the point i. Thus passing a cubic parabola

$$y_p = Ax^3 + Bx^2 + Cx + D \tag{b}$$

through l, i, r, and the point rr to the right of r (Fig. 2.1), and choosing again i to be the origin, we obtain

$$y(-h) = y_l = -Ah^3 + Bh^2 - Ch + D;$$

$$y(0) = y_i = D;$$

$$y(h) = y_r = Ah^3 + Bh^2 + Ch + D;$$

$$y(2h) = y_{rr} = 8Ah^3 + 4Bh^2 + 2Ch + D.$$

Eliminating B, C, and D among these equations we obtain the value $6A$ of the third derivative of the parabola (b) and hence the following unsymmetrical approximation for y_i''':

$$y_i''' = \frac{1}{h^3}(-y_l + 3y_i - 3y_r + y_{rr}). \tag{2.2.2}$$

A list of such formulas for evenly spaced points is available, under the name of *Bickley's formulas*, in Southwell's *Relaxation Methods in Theoretical Physics*.*

* R. V. Southwell, *Relaxation Methods in Theoretical Physics*, Oxford University Press, London, 1946.

Similar formulas can be obtained when the pivotal points are *not evenly spaced.* For example, the second derivative at i of a function known at three points spaced by h and αh, respectively (Fig. 2.2), is obtained by means of a quadratic parabola through these three points:

$$y(-h) = y_l = Ah^2 - Bh + C;$$

$$y(0) = y_i = C;$$

$$y(\alpha h) = y_r = \alpha^2 Ah^2 + \alpha Bh + C.$$

Eliminating the constants B and C, the derivative $2A$ of the parabola in terms of y_l, y_i, and y_r gives

$$y_i'' = \frac{1}{h^2}\,\frac{2}{\alpha(\alpha+1)}\,[\alpha y_l - (1+\alpha)y_i + y_r], \qquad (2.2.3)$$

which is identical with Eq. (2.2.1) for $\alpha = 1$.

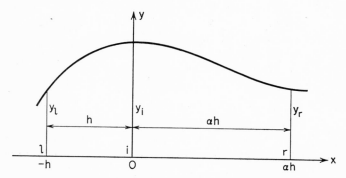

Fig. 2.2.   Unequal spacing of pivotal points.

2.3 Differentiation Formulas by Taylor Series Expansions

It is obvious that, while a certain error is inherent in formulas of the type of Eqs. (2.2.1), (2.2.2), and (2.2.3), this error will vanish as the spacing h is made smaller and smaller. In order to find out how the error depends on h, it is convenient to derive again these formulas by Taylor series expansions.

The Taylor series of $y(x + h)$ about x is given by*

$$y(x+h) = y(x) + hy'(x) + \frac{h^2}{2!}\,y''(x) + \frac{h^3}{3!}\,y'''(x) + \ldots$$

$$= \sum_{n=0}^{\infty} \frac{h^n}{n!}\,y^{(n)}(x), \qquad (2.3.1)$$

where $y^{(n)}$ stands for $d^n y/dx^n$, $y^{(0)}(x) = y(x)$, and $0! = 1$.

* See, for example, *Engineering Problems*, pp. 167 ff.

Applying Eq. (2.3.1) with the symbols of Fig. 2.2, we obtain the expansions at $x + \alpha h$ and at $x - h$:

$$y_r = y_i + \alpha h y'_i + \frac{\alpha^2 h^2}{2} y''_i + \frac{\alpha^3 h^3}{6} y'''_i + \frac{\alpha^4 h^4}{24} y_i^{iv} + \cdots$$

$$y_l = y_i - h y'_i + \frac{h^2}{2} y''_i - \frac{h^3}{6} y'''_i + \frac{h^4}{24} y_i^{iv} - \cdots. \qquad (2.3.2)$$

An approximate expression for y'_i is immediately obtained by subtraction:

$$y_r - y_l = (\alpha + 1) h y'_i + (\alpha^2 - 1) \frac{h^2}{2} y''_i + (\alpha^3 + 1) \frac{h^3}{6} y'''_i + \cdots.$$

from which

$$y'_i = \frac{1}{(\alpha + 1)h} (y_r - y_l) + (1 - \alpha) \frac{h}{2} y''_i - \frac{1 + \alpha^3}{1 + \alpha} \frac{h^2}{6} y'''_i + \cdots.$$

This result indicates that the approximate expression for the first derivative:

$$y'_i = \frac{1}{(\alpha + 1)h} (y_r - y_l) \qquad (2.3.3)$$

has an error

$$(1 - \alpha) \frac{h}{2} y''_i - \frac{1 + \alpha^3}{1 + \alpha} \frac{h^2}{6} y'''_i + \cdots,$$

which approaches zero as fast as h if $\alpha \neq 1$, and as fast as h^2 if $\alpha = 1$, that is, if the pivotal points are evenly spaced.

Eliminating y''_i between the two Eqs. (2.3.2), we obtain similarly an expression for y'_i:

$$y'_i = \frac{1}{\alpha(\alpha + 1)h} [y_r - (1 - \alpha^2)y_i - \alpha^2 y_l], \qquad (2.3.4)$$

whose error approaches zero as fast as h^2 whatever α, and which becomes identical with Eq. (2.3.3) for $\alpha = 1$.

Eliminating y'_i between the two Eqs. (2.3.2), we obtain an expression for y''_i:

$$y''_i = \frac{1}{h^2} \frac{2}{\alpha(\alpha + 1)} [\alpha y_l - (1 + \alpha)y_i + y_r] + (1 - \alpha) \frac{h}{3} y'''_i$$
$$- \frac{1 + \alpha^3}{1 + \alpha} \frac{h^2}{12} y_i^{iv} + \cdots, \qquad (2.3.5)$$

which shows that the expression (2.2.3) for y''_i has an error approaching zero as fast as h for $\alpha \neq 1$, and as fast as h^2 for $\alpha = 1$.

A variety of formulas may be obtained by this technique, and their error can be evaluated without difficulty. For example, the reader may want to prove that the approximate value of y_i''

$$y_i'' = \frac{1}{\alpha(\alpha + 1)(\alpha + 2)h^2} [\alpha(\alpha^2 - 1)y_{ll} - 2(\alpha^3 - 4\alpha)y_l$$
$$+ (\alpha^3 - 7\alpha - 6)y_i + 6y_r], \quad (2.3.6)$$

obtained by equal spacing h between ll and l, and i and l, and spacing αh between i and r (Fig. 2.3*a*), has an error approaching zero as h^2. The corresponding formula for the points of Fig. 2.3*b* is given by

$$y_i'' = \frac{1}{\alpha'(\alpha' + 1)(\alpha' + 2)h^2} [6y_l + (\alpha'^3 - 7\alpha' - 6)y_i$$
$$- 2(\alpha'^3 - 4\alpha')y_r + \alpha'(\alpha'^2 - 1)y_{rr}] \quad (2.3.7)$$

and has also an error approaching zero as h^2.

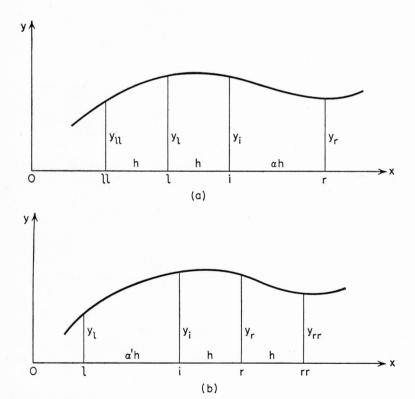

Fig. 2.3.   Unequal spacing of pivotal points.

Whenever the pivotal points are *evenly spaced*, the Taylor series technique can be applied symbolically in conjunction with the concept of *difference*, which plays a most important role in all numerical computations. In this manner a large variety of practical approximations for the derivatives and the corresponding errors may be economically obtained, as shown in the following sections.

2.4 Backward Differences

Given the values

$$y_0, y_1, y_2, \ldots, y_u, y_l, y_i, y_r, y_{rr}, \ldots, y_{n-2}, y_{n-1}, y_n$$

of a function $y(x)$ at the pivotal points of its interval of definition, evenly spaced by h, we call the *first backward difference of y at i* the difference

$$\nabla y_i \equiv y_i - y_l.^* \tag{2.4.1}$$

The *second backward difference of y at i* is defined as the difference of the first difference and is therefore given by

$$\nabla(\nabla y_i) \equiv \nabla^2 y_i = (y_i - y_l) - (y_l - y_u)$$

$$= y_i - 2y_l + y_u. \tag{2.4.2}$$

Similarly, the nth backward difference is the difference of the $(n-1)$th difference:

$$\nabla^n y_i \equiv \nabla(\nabla^{n-1} y_i).$$

It is easy to verify that the coefficients of the pivotal values in the nth difference are the coefficients of the binomial expansion of $(a - b)^n$. Thus, for example,

$$\nabla^3 y_i = y_i - 3y_{i-1} + 3y_{i-2} - y_{i-3}; \tag{2.4.3}$$

$$\nabla^4 y_i = y_i - 4y_{i-1} + 6y_{i-2} - 4y_{i-3} + y_{i-4}. \tag{2.4.4}$$

The successive backward differences of a function are tabulated as shown in Table 2.1.

It is well known[†] that the differential operator $D \equiv d/dx$ can be used symbolically as if it were a number, inasmuch as it satisfies formally the fundamental laws of algebra. The difference operator ∇ may also

---

[*] The inverted capital Greek delta is used for backward differences, the normal capital delta for forward differences, and the lower-case delta for central differences.

[†] See any book on differential equations, or E. Stephens, *The Elementary Theory of Operational Mathematics*, McGraw-Hill Book Company, Inc., New York, 1937.

Table 2.1
Backward Differences

i	y_i	∇y_i	$\nabla^2 y_i$	$\nabla^3 y_i$	$\nabla^4 y_i$	$\nabla^5 y_i$
0	y_0					
1	y_1	∇y_1				
2	y_2	∇y_2	$\nabla^2 y_2$			
3	y_3	∇y_3	$\nabla^2 y_3$	$\nabla^3 y_3$		
4	y_4	∇y_4	$\nabla^2 y_4$	$\nabla^3 y_4$	$\nabla^4 y_4$	
5	y_5	∇y_5	$\nabla^2 y_5$	$\nabla^3 y_5$	$\nabla^4 y_5$	$\nabla^5 y_5$

be used symbolically as a number (or variable), since it satisfies formally the laws of algebra, as shown by the following identities:

$$\nabla(y_i + y_j) = \nabla y_i + \nabla y_j = \nabla y_j + \nabla y_i;$$

$$\nabla(cy_i) = c\nabla y_i;$$

$$\nabla^m(\nabla^n y_i) = \nabla^{m+n} y_i.$$

Making use of these properties, it is possible to express the differences of a function y in terms of its successive derivatives and, conversely, its derivatives in terms of its successive differences. The derivation of these expressions by symbolical methods is by far the most efficient.

Consider for this purpose the Taylor expansion of $y(x + h)$ about x:

$$y(x + h) = y(x) + \frac{h}{1!} y'(x) + \frac{h^2}{2!} y''(x) + \frac{h^3}{3!} y'''(x) + \dots, \tag{a}$$

which, using the powers of the symbol D to indicate the derivatives of y, becomes

$$y(x + h) = y(x) + \frac{h}{1!} Dy(x) + \frac{h^2}{2!} D^2 y(x) + \frac{h^3}{3!} D^3 y(x) + \dots$$

$$= \left(1 + \frac{h}{1!} D + \frac{h^2}{2!} D^2 + \frac{h^3}{3!} D^3 + \dots\right) y(x). \tag{b}$$

By means of the series expansion for $e^{\pm x}$,

$$e^{\pm x} = 1 \pm \frac{x}{1!} + \frac{x^2}{2!} \pm \frac{x^3}{3!} + \dots,$$

the differential operator on the right-hand side of Eq. (b) may be written symbolically as

$$1 + \frac{hD}{1!} + \frac{h^2 D^2}{2!} + \frac{h^3 D^3}{3!} + \dots = e^{hD}, \tag{2.4.5}$$

and hence $y(x + h)$ may also be written *symbolically* as

$$y(x + h) = e^{hD}y(x). \tag{2.4.6}$$

Setting $x = x_i$ and indicating as before $y(x_i + h)$ by y_r and $y(x_i)$ by y_i, Eq. (2.4.6) becomes

$$y_r = e^{hD}y_i. \tag{2.4.7}$$

Similarly, changing h into $-h$ in Eq. (2.4.6),

$$y(x - h) = e^{-hD}y(x) \tag{2.4.8}$$

and letting, as before, $y(x) = y_i$, and $y_l = y(x_i - h)$, we obtain

$$y_l = e^{-hD}y_i. \tag{2.4.9}$$

The first backward difference ∇y_i [Eq. (2.4.1)] may now be written by means of Eq. (2.4.9) as

$$\nabla y_i = y_i - y_l = [1 - e^{-hD}]y_i \tag{2.4.10}$$

or, by Eq. (2.4.5), as

$$\nabla y_i = \left[\frac{hD}{1!} - \frac{h^2D^2}{2!} + \frac{h^3D^3}{3!} - \frac{h^4D^4}{4!} + \cdots \right] y_i$$

$$= \left[1 - \frac{hD}{2} + \frac{h^2D^2}{6} - \frac{h^3D^3}{24} + \cdots \right] hDy_i. \tag{2.4.11}$$

Equation (2.4.11) gives the expansion of ∇y_i into an infinite series of *all* the derivatives of y at i.

If Eq. (2.4.10) is written in purely operational form, by dropping y_i on both sides of the equation,

$$\nabla = 1 - e^{-hD}, \tag{2.4.12}$$

its "powers" may be used to evaluate the series expansions for the successive differences of a function. Thus, squaring Eq. (2.4.12), and making use of Eq. (2.4.5), we obtain the expansion for the second difference ∇^2 in the form

$$\nabla^2 = (1 - e^{-hD})^2 = (1 + e^{-2hD} - 2e^{-hD})$$

$$= 1 + \left(1 - \frac{2hD}{1!} + \frac{4h^2D^2}{2!} - \frac{8h^3D^3}{3!} + \frac{16h^4D^4}{4!} - \cdots \right)$$

$$-2\left(1 - \frac{hD}{1!} + \frac{h^2D^2}{2!} - \frac{h^3D^3}{3!} + \frac{h^4D^4}{4!} - \cdots \right),$$

or

$$\nabla^2 = h^2D^2 - h^3D^3 + \tfrac{7}{12}h^4D^4 - \cdots. \tag{2.4.13}$$

Similarly, cubing Eq. (2.4.12) or multiplying Eq. (2.4.12) by Eq. (2.4.13), we obtain

$$\nabla^3 = h^3D^3 - \tfrac{3}{2}h^4D^4 + \tfrac{5}{4}h^5D^5 - \ldots, \qquad (2.4.14)$$

while the higher powers of Eq. (2.4.12) will similarly give the expansion of $\nabla^n y_i$ in terms of the derivatives of y at i.

Conversely, to obtain expressions for the derivatives of y in terms of its differences, solve Eq. (2.4.12) for e^{-hD}:

$$e^{-hD} = 1 - \nabla, \qquad (2.4.15)$$

and take the natural logarithms of both sides of this equation, obtaining

$$\ln e^{-hD} = -hD = \ln(1 - \nabla) = -\left(\nabla + \frac{\nabla^2}{2} + \frac{\nabla^3}{3} + \frac{\nabla^4}{4} + \cdots\right).^*$$

Hence the expansion of the first derivative D into an infinite series of differences becomes

$$hD = \nabla + \frac{\nabla^2}{2} + \frac{\nabla^3}{3} + \frac{\nabla^4}{4} + \cdots. \qquad (2.4.16)$$

Taking successive powers of Eq. (2.4.16), we obtain the following expressions for the higher derivatives in terms of differences:

$$h^2D^2 = \nabla^2 + \nabla^3 + \tfrac{11}{12}\nabla^4 + \tfrac{5}{6}\nabla^5 + \cdots;$$

$$h^3D^3 = \nabla^3 + \tfrac{3}{2}\nabla^4 + \tfrac{7}{4}\nabla^5 + \cdots;$$

$$h^4D^4 = \nabla^4 + 2\nabla^5 + \tfrac{17}{6}\nabla^6 + \cdots; \qquad (2.4.17)$$

$$h^5D^5 = \nabla^5 + \tfrac{5}{2}\nabla^6 + \tfrac{25}{6}\nabla^7 + \cdots.$$

The difference expansions (2.4.11), (2.4.12), (2.4.13), (2.4.14), (2.4.16), and (2.4.17) allow the simple derivation of *unilateral differentiation formulas* and of their errors.

For example, solving Eqs. (2.4.11), (2.4.13), and (2.4.14) for D, D^2, and D^3, respectively, we obtain

$$D = \frac{\nabla}{h} + \frac{hD^2}{2} - \frac{h^2D^3}{6} + \frac{h^3D^4}{24} - \cdots,$$

$$D^2 = \frac{\nabla^2}{h^2} + hD^3 - \frac{7h^2D^4}{12} + \cdots, \qquad (2.4.18)$$

$$D^3 = \frac{\nabla^3}{h^3} + \frac{3hD^4}{2} - \frac{h^2D^5}{4} + \cdots,$$

---

* The series expansion of $\ln(1 \pm x)$ equals

$$\ln(1 \pm x) = \pm x - \frac{x^2}{2} \pm \frac{x^3}{3} - \frac{x^4}{4} \pm \frac{x^5}{5} - \cdots$$

from which, taking into account the first term of the series only,

$$Dy_i = \frac{1}{h}(y_i - y_l) + 0(h),$$

$$D^2y_i = \frac{1}{h^2}(y_i - 2y_l + y_{ll}) + 0(h), \tag{2.4.19}$$

$$D^3y_i = \frac{1}{h^3}(y_i - 3y_l + 3y_{ll} - y_{lll}) + 0(h),$$

where the symbol $0(h)$ stands for an error "of the order of h" and is the sum of the terms neglected in Eqs. (2.4.18).

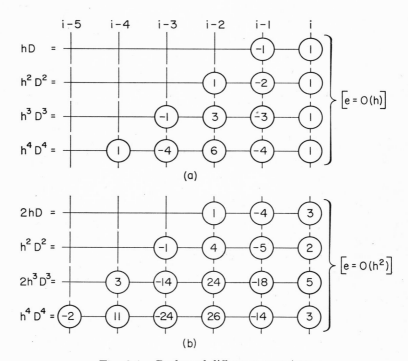

Fig. 2.4.   Backward difference operators.

It can similarly be proved that the approximation of the nth derivative by the first term of its backward difference expansion has an error of the order of h.

To obtain formulas with errors of order h^2, the first two terms of the derivative expansions into differences must be taken into account.

Thus, eliminating h^2D^2 between Eqs. (2.4.11) and (2.4.13), we obtain

$$\nabla + \frac{\nabla^2}{2} = hD - \tfrac{1}{3}h^3D^3 + \dots$$

or, by Eqs. (2.4.1) and (2.4.2),

$$Dy_i = \frac{1}{2h}\,(3y_i - 4y_l + y_{ll}) + 0(h^2). \qquad (2.4.20)$$

Similarly, adding Eqs. (2.4.13) and (2.4.14), we have

$$\nabla^2 + \nabla^3 = h^2D^2 - \tfrac{11}{12}h^4D^4 + \dots$$

or, by Eqs. (2.4.2) and (2.4.3),

$$D^2y_i = \frac{1}{h^2}\,(2y_i - 5y_l + 4y_{ll} - y_{lll}) + 0(h^2). \qquad (2.4.21)$$

In general, if the first m terms of the derivative expansions into backward differences are taken into account, the corresponding formulas have errors of order h^m.

The most commonly encountered derivative expressions in terms of backward differences are given in the "mathematical molecules" of Fig. 2.4 with the corresponding order of error in the derivatives.

2.5 Forward Differences

Just as backward differences are defined by points all to the left of i, *forward differences* are defined by points all to the right of i.

The first forward difference of y at i is defined as

$$\Delta y_i \equiv y_r - y_i \qquad (2.5.1)$$

and can be written symbolically by means of Eq. (2.4.7) as

$$\Delta = e^{hD} - 1. \qquad (2.5.2)$$

The successive forward differences

$$\Delta^2 y_i = y_{rr} - 2y_r + y_i,$$

$$\Delta^3 y_i = y_{rrr} - 3y_{rr} + 3y_r - y_i, \qquad (2.5.3)$$

. . . .

have pivotal coefficients equal to the binomial coefficients of $(a - b)^n$ and are tabulated as in Table 2.2.

Table 2.2
Forward Differences

i	y_i	Δy_i	$\Delta^2 y_i$	$\Delta^3 y_i$	$\Delta^4 y_i$	$\Delta^5 y_i$
0	y_0	Δy_0	$\Delta^2 y_0$	$\Delta^3 y_0$	$\Delta^4 y_0$	$\Delta^5 y_0$
1	y_1	Δy_1	$\Delta^2 y_1$	$\Delta^3 y_1$	$\Delta^4 y_1$	
2	y_2	Δy_2	$\Delta^2 y_2$	$\Delta^3 y_2$		
3	y_3	Δy_3	$\Delta^2 y_3$			
4	y_4	Δy_4				
5	y_5					

In order to expand the derivatives of a function in terms of its forward differences, solve Eq. (2.5.2) for e^{hD} and take logs on both sides*:

$$hD = \ln (1 + \Delta) = \Delta - \frac{\Delta^2}{2} + \frac{\Delta^3}{3} - \frac{\Delta^4}{4} + \dots \qquad (2.5.4)$$

Taking the powers of this equation, we obtain

$$h^2 D^2 = \Delta^2 - \Delta^3 + \tfrac{11}{12}\Delta^4 - \tfrac{5}{6}\Delta^5 + \dots;$$

$$h^3 D^3 = \Delta^3 - \tfrac{3}{2}\Delta^4 + \tfrac{7}{4}\Delta^5 - \dots;$$

$$h^4 D^4 = \Delta^4 - 2\Delta^5 + \tfrac{17}{6}\Delta^6 - \dots; \qquad (2.5.5)$$

$$h^5 D^5 = \Delta^5 - \tfrac{5}{2}\Delta^6 + \tfrac{25}{6}\Delta^7 - \dots.$$

Conversely, expanding Eq. (2.5.2), we obtain

$$\Delta = hD + \frac{h^2 D^2}{2!} + \frac{h^3 D^3}{3!} + \frac{h^4 D^4}{4!} + \dots, \qquad (2.5.6)$$

from which, taking powers of Δ,

$$\Delta^2 = h^2 D^2 + h^3 D^3 + \tfrac{7}{12}h^4 D^4 + \dots;$$

$$\Delta^3 = h^3 D^3 + \tfrac{3}{2}h^4 D^4 + \tfrac{5}{4}h^5 D^5 + \dots; \qquad (2.5.7)$$

. . . .

It may be proved that the error in the expansion of derivatives in terms of forward differences [Eqs. (2.5.4) and (2.5.5)] in which m terms are taken into account is of order h^m.

The "mathematical molecules" of Fig. 2.5 give the most commonly

* See footnote on page 73.

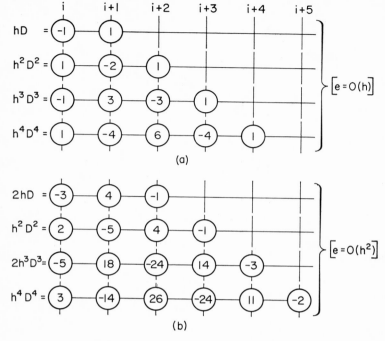

Fig. 2.5.   Forward difference operators.

needed expressions for the derivatives in terms of forward differences and the corresponding errors in the derivatives.

2.6 *Gregory-Newton Interpolation Formulas*

Two important interpolation formulas, often used in engineering problems, are easily obtained by means of the forward and backward differences of a function.

Let us assume that the values of a Taylor-expandable function $y(x)$ be known at the pivotal points of its interval of definition, which are evenly spaced by h, and let us call a the abscissa of one of these points. Let the abscissa of the point at which we wish to evaluate the function be $a \pm xh$, where x is any real number. Expanding $y(a \pm xh)$ in a Taylor series about a, we obtain

$$y(a \pm xh) = y(a) \pm xhy'(a) + \frac{x^2h^2}{2} y'(a) \pm \frac{x^3h^3}{6} y'''(a) + \dots . \quad (a)$$

The *Gregory-Newton forward interpolation formula* is obtained by substituting in the expansion of $y(a + xh)$ for the derivatives of y at a

their expansions in terms of forward differences, given by Eqs. (2.5.4) and (2.5.5). Substituting in the expansion of $y(a - xh)$ for the derivatives of y at a their expansions in terms of backward differences, given by Eqs. (2.4.16) and (2.4.17), we obtain the *Gregory-Newton backward interpolation formula*. These substitutions, which the reader may want to check directly, are easily performed by symbolical methods.

Since, by Eq. (2.5.2),

$$e^{hD} = 1 + \Delta \tag{b}$$

and, by Eq. (2.4.6), with a in place of x and xh in place of h,

$$y(a + xh) = e^{xhD}y(a) = (e^{hD})^x y(a),$$

the expansion of Eq. (a) may be written symbolically:

$$y(a + xh) = (1 + \Delta)^x y(a).$$

The binomial expansion of $(1 + \Delta)^x$ in this equation gives the *forward interpolation formula:*

$$y(a + xh) = \left[1 + x\Delta + \frac{x(x-1)}{2!}\Delta^2 \right.$$
$$\left. + \frac{x(x-1)(x-2)}{3!}\Delta^3 + \dots \right] y(a). \tag{2.6.1}$$

Similarly, since by Eq. (2.4.12),

$$e^{-hD} = 1 - \nabla \tag{c}$$

and, by Eq. (2.4.8), in which a is substituted for x and xh for h,

$$y(a - xh) = e^{-xhD}y(a) = (e^{-hD})^x y(a),$$

the expansion of $y(a - xh)$ of Eq. (a) is written symbolically as

$$y(a - xh) = (1 - \nabla)^x y(a).$$

The binomial expansion of $(1 - \nabla)^x$ in this equation gives the *backward interpolation formula:*

$$y(a - xh) = \left[1 - x\nabla + \frac{x(x-1)}{2!}\nabla^2 \right.$$
$$\left. - \frac{x(x-1)(x-2)}{3!}\nabla^3 + \dots \right] y(a). \tag{2.6.2}$$

For example, given the values of $y = \sin\theta$ for $\theta = 10°(1°)13°,$* the

* The symbol $\theta = a(h)b$ stands for "values of θ from a to b in steps of h."

Table 2.3

i	θ_i^0	y_i	Δy_i	$\Delta^2 y_i$	$\Delta^3 y_i$
0	10	0.17365	0.01716	−0.00006	0
1	11	0.19081	0.01710	−0.00006	
2	12	0.20791	0.01704		
3	13	0.22495			

value of sin θ at 10°20′ is obtained as shown in Table 2.3 by forward differences, with $a = 10°$ and $xh = (20') = \frac{1}{3}°$:

$$\sin 10°20' = 0.17365 + \frac{\frac{1}{3}}{1}(0.01716) + \frac{(\frac{1}{3})(-\frac{2}{3})}{2}(-0.00006)$$

$$+ \frac{(\frac{1}{3})(-\frac{2}{3})(-\frac{5}{3})}{6}(0) = 0.17938.$$

The same value is obtained by backward differences with $a = 13°$ and xh ($= 2°40'$) $= \frac{8}{3}°$, as shown in Table 2.4:

$$\sin 10°20' = 0.22495 - \frac{\frac{8}{3}}{1}(0.01704) + \frac{(\frac{8}{3})(\frac{5}{3})}{2}(-0.00006)$$

$$- \frac{(\frac{8}{3})(\frac{5}{3})(\frac{2}{3})}{6}(0) = 0.17938.$$

The true value of sin 10°20′ is 0.17937.

Table 2.4

i	θ_i^0	y_i	∇y_i	$\nabla^2 y_i$	$\nabla^3 y_i$
0	10	0.17365			
1	11	0.19081	0.01716		
2	12	0.20791	0.01710	−0.00006	
3	13	0.22495	0.01704	−0.00006	0

The Gregory-Newton formulas may also be used to *extrapolate* beyond the interval in which y is known. For example, by means of Table 2.3 the value of sin 13°30′ is computed, letting in Eq. (2.6.1) $a = 10°$, $xh = (3°30') = 3.5°$:

$$\sin 13°30' = 0.17365 + (3.5)(0.01716) + \frac{(3.5)(2.5)}{2}(-0.00006)$$

$$= 0.23345.$$

This result is correct to the last figure computed.

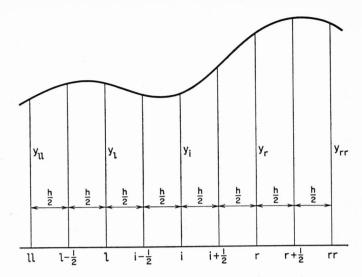

Fig. 2.6. Pivotal points for central differences.

2.7 Central Differences

Backward and forward differences were shown in Secs. 2.4 and 2.5 to lead to unilateral expressions for the derivatives of a function y, which in their simplest form have errors of order h.

Central differences, involving pivotal points symmetrically located with respect to i, are more accurate than backward or forward differences and are particularly useful in the solution of boundary value problems.

Let the function $y(x)$ be known at the evenly spaced pivotal points i and, for the time being, at the middle points of the intervals defined by the pivotal points (Fig. 2.6). The *first central difference of $y(x)$ at i* is defined by

$$\delta y_i \equiv y\left(x_i + \frac{h}{2}\right) - y\left(x_i - \frac{h}{2}\right)$$

$$= y_{i+\frac{1}{2}} - y_{i-\frac{1}{2}}. \tag{2.7.1}$$

The second central difference at i is the difference of the first difference:

$$\delta^2 y_i \equiv \delta(\delta y_i) = [y_{(i+\frac{1}{2})+\frac{1}{2}} - y_{(i-\frac{1}{2})+\frac{1}{2}}] - [y_{(i+\frac{1}{2})-\frac{1}{2}} - y_{(i-\frac{1}{2})-\frac{1}{2}}]$$

$$= y_r - 2y_i + y_l. \tag{2.7.2}$$

The nth central difference is defined by

$$\delta^n y_i \equiv \delta(\delta^{n-1} y_i),$$

which leads to

$$\delta^3 y_i = y_{r+\frac{1}{2}} - 3y_{i+\frac{1}{2}} + 3y_{i-\frac{1}{2}} - y_{l-\frac{1}{2}}; \tag{2.7.3}$$

$$\delta^4 y_i = y_{rr} - 4y_r + 6y_i - 4y_l + y_{ll}. \tag{2.7.4}$$

The coefficients of the pivotal values in the nth central difference are equal to the coefficients of the binomial expansion of $(a - b)^n$. Central differences are tabulated as shown in Table 2.5.

Table 2.5
Central Differences

i	y_i	δy_i	$\delta^2 y_i$	$\delta^3 y_i$	$\delta^4 y_i$	$\mu\delta y_i$	$\mu\delta^3 y_i$
0	y_0						
1	y_1	$\delta y_{\frac{1}{2}}$	$\delta^2 y_1$			$\mu\delta y_1$	
2	y_2	$\delta y_{\frac{3}{2}}$	$\delta^2 y_2$	$\delta^3 y_{\frac{3}{2}}$	$\delta^4 y_2$	$\mu\delta y_2$	$\mu\delta^3 y_2$
3	y_3	$\delta y_{\frac{5}{2}}$	$\delta^2 y_3$	$\delta^3 y_{\frac{5}{2}}$	$\delta^4 y_3$	$\mu\delta y_3$	$\mu\delta^3 y_3$
4	y_4	$\delta y_{\frac{7}{2}}$	$\delta^2 y_4$	$\delta^3 y_{\frac{7}{2}}$		$\mu\delta y_4$	
5	y_5	$\delta y_{\frac{9}{2}}$					

The tabulation of central differences offers one of the simplest ways of checking a table of computed values of a function. As shown in Table 2.6, if the ith value of a function is affected by an error ϵ, so that $y_i + \epsilon$ appears in the table rather than y_i, the error spreads through the successive differences with the coefficients of the binomial expansion of $(a - b)^n$. If a function is rather smooth, i.e., if its successive derivatives decrease in value, their nth difference will approach zero with increasing n, and hence $\delta^n(y_i + \epsilon)$ will become practically equal to $\delta^n\epsilon$. Thus, as soon as the ratios of the $\delta^n y_i$ are approximately equal to the ratios of the binomial coefficients, we can evaluate ϵ and hence the corrected value of y_i.

Table 2.6
Diffusion of Error in Central Difference Table

i	ϵ	$\delta\epsilon$	$\delta^2\epsilon$	$\delta^3\epsilon$	$\delta^4\epsilon$	$\delta^5\epsilon$	$\delta^6\epsilon$	$\delta^7\epsilon$	$\delta^8\epsilon$
$i-3$							ϵ		
$i-2$					ϵ	ϵ	-6ϵ	-7ϵ	28ϵ
$i-1$			ϵ	ϵ	-4ϵ	-5ϵ	15ϵ	21ϵ	-56ϵ
i	ϵ	ϵ	-2ϵ	-3ϵ	6ϵ	10ϵ	-20ϵ	-35ϵ	70ϵ
$i+1$		$-\epsilon$	ϵ	3ϵ	-4ϵ	-10ϵ	15ϵ	35ϵ	-56ϵ
$i+2$				$-\epsilon$	ϵ	5ϵ	-6ϵ	-21ϵ	28ϵ
$i+3$						$-\epsilon$	ϵ	7ϵ	

Table 2.7

i	x_i	y_i	δy_i	$\delta^2 y_i$	$\delta^3 y_i$	$\delta^4 y_i$	$\delta^5 y_i$	$\delta^6 y_i$	$\delta^7 y_i$
1	0	1.00000							
			0.10517						
2	0.1	1.10517		0.01106					
			0.11623		0.00117				
3	0.2	1.22140		0.01223		0.08010			
			0.12846		0.08127		−0.39993		
4	0.3	1.34986		0.09350		−0.31983		1.19988	
			0.22196		−0.23856		0.79995		−2.79978
5	0.4	1.57182		−0.14506		0.48012		−1.59990	
			0.07690		0.24156		−0.79995		
6	0.5	1.64872		0.09650		−0.31983			
			0.17340		−0.07827				
7	0.6	1.82212		0.01823					
			0.19163						
8	0.7	2.01375							

For example, from Table 2.7, containing the first seven central differences of $y = e^x$ for $x = 0(.1)0.7$, we notice that the $\delta^3 y_i$ about $i = 5$ have values roughly proportional to $1, -3, +3, -1$. Hence,

$$\epsilon + 3\epsilon + 3\epsilon + \epsilon = 8\epsilon = 0.08127 + 0.23856 + 0.24156 + 0.07827$$
$$= 0.63966;$$

$$\epsilon_5^{(3)} = 0.07996.$$

Similarly the $\delta^4 y_i$ give (noticing that $\delta^4 y_5$ cannot be evaluated for lack of pivotal values):

$$\epsilon + 4\epsilon + 6\epsilon + 4\epsilon + 0 = 15\epsilon = 0.08010 + 0.31983 + 0.48012 + 0.31983$$
$$= 1.19988;$$

$$\epsilon_5^{(4)} = 0.07999.$$

The values of ϵ obtainable by fifth, sixth, and seventh differences are given by

$$\epsilon_5^{(5)} = \epsilon_5^{(6)} = \epsilon_5^{(7)} = 0.07999,$$

and the corrected value of y_5 is

$$y_5 = 1.57182 - 0.07999 = 1.49183.$$

It is important to notice that, since more than one value y_i may be affected by errors and since the errors spread, the higher-order differences may be affected by a combination of errors and become less reliable than the lower-order differences for the evaluation of one error.

In order to eliminate the values of y at the intermediate points $\ldots, l - \frac{1}{2}, i \pm \frac{1}{2}, r + \frac{1}{2}, \ldots$ appearing in the expressions for the odd central differences, new averaged odd differences at i are defined as the average of the odd central differences at $i + \frac{1}{2}$, and $i - \frac{1}{2}$. Thus the *first averaged difference* at i is expressed by

$$\tfrac{1}{2}(\delta y_{i+\frac{1}{2}} + \delta y_{i-\frac{1}{2}}) = \tfrac{1}{2}[(y_r - y_i) + (y_i - y_l)] = \tfrac{1}{2}(y_r - y_l). \tag{a}$$

This averaging process is geometrically equivalent to taking as slope at i the slope of the chord $P_r P_l$ rather than the slope of the chords $P_l P_i$ or $P_i P_r$ (Fig. 2.7). The averaging operation used in obtaining Eq. (a) is

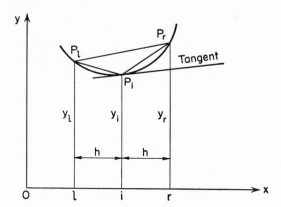

Fig. 2.7.   Averaged central difference.

usually symbolized by an operator μ, called the *averager* and defined by

$$\mu y_i \equiv \tfrac{1}{2}(y_{i+\frac{1}{2}} + y_{i-\frac{1}{2}}). \tag{2.7.5}$$

By means of the averager, the first averaged difference is written as

$$\mu \delta y_i = \tfrac{1}{2}[\delta y_{i+\frac{1}{2}} + \delta y_{i-\frac{1}{2}}] = \tfrac{1}{2}(y_r - y_l). \tag{2.7.6}$$

The operators μ and δ are connected by a simple relation. In fact, squaring the μ operator,

$$\mu^2 y_i = \mu[\tfrac{1}{2}(y_{i+\frac{1}{2}} + y_{i-\frac{1}{2}})] = \tfrac{1}{2}[\tfrac{1}{2}(y_r + y_i) + \tfrac{1}{2}(y_i + y_l)]$$
$$= \tfrac{1}{4}(y_r + 2y_i + y_l),$$

and operating with $(1 + \delta^2/4)$ on y_i, we see, by Eq. (2.7.2), that

$$\left(1 + \frac{\delta^2}{4}\right) y_i = y_i + \frac{1}{4}(y_r - 2y_i + y_l)$$

$$= \frac{1}{4}(y_r + 2y_i + y_l) = \mu^2 y_i.$$

Hence, we may write in symbolical form

$$\mu^2 = 1 + \frac{\delta^2}{4}. \tag{2.7.7}$$

Equations (2.7.2), (2.7.6), and (2.7.7) allow the expansion of the derivatives of y in terms of its central differences, and the inverse expansions of differences in terms of derivatives, by symbolical methods.

By means of Eqs. (2.4.7) and (2.4.9), Eq. (2.7.6) becomes

$$\mu\delta y_i = \frac{1}{2}\,(y_r - y_l) = \frac{1}{2}\,e^{hD}y_i - \frac{1}{2}\,e^{-hD}y_i$$

$$= \frac{e^{hD} - e^{-hD}}{2}\,y_i = \sinh\,(hD)y_i$$

or, in purely symbolical form,

$$\mu\delta = \sinh\,(hD). \tag{2.7.8}$$

Remembering the Taylor expansion for the hyperbolic sine,

$$\sinh x = x + \frac{x^3}{3!} + \frac{x^5}{5!} + \cdots,$$

the expansion of the first averaged central difference in terms of derivatives becomes:

$$\mu\delta = hD + \frac{h^3 D^3}{6} + \frac{h^5 D^5}{120} + \cdots. \tag{2.7.9}$$

Similarly by Eq. (2.7.2) and Eqs. (2.4.7) and (2.4.9), the second central difference becomes

$$\delta^2 y_i = e^{hD}y_i - 2y_i + e^{-hD}y_i = 2\left(\frac{e^{hD} + e^{-hD}}{2} - 1\right)y_i$$

$$= 2[\cosh\,(hD) - 1]y_i.$$

Remembering the Taylor expansion for $\cosh x$,

$$\cosh x = 1 + \frac{x^2}{2!} + \frac{x^4}{4!} + \cdots,$$

the second central difference may be written in symbolical form as

$$\delta^2 = h^2 D^2 + \frac{h^4 D^4}{12} + \frac{h^6 D^6}{360} + \cdots. \tag{2.7.10}$$

The same result may be obtained by expanding into series the first *unaveraged* central difference [Eq. (2.7.1)]:

$$\delta y_i = y_{i+\frac{1}{2}} - y_{i-\frac{1}{2}} = (e^{hD/2} - e^{-hD/2})y_i$$

$$= 2\sinh\left(\frac{hD}{2}\right)y_i = \left(hD + \frac{h^3 D^3}{2^2 \cdot 3!} + \frac{h^5 D^5}{2^4 \cdot 5!} + \cdots\right)y_i,$$

from which, in general,

$$\delta^n = 2^n \sinh^n\left(\frac{hD}{2}\right) \tag{2.7.11}$$

and in particular, for $n = 2$, we obtain Eq. (2.7.10).

The product of Eqs. (2.7.9) and (2.7.10) gives the third averaged difference expansion:

$$\mu\delta^3 = h^3 D^3 + \frac{h^5 D^5}{4} + \frac{h^7 D^7}{40} + \cdots, \qquad (2.7.12)$$

and the square of Eq. (2.7.10) the expansion of the fourth central difference:

$$\delta^4 = h^4 D^4 + \frac{h^6 D^6}{6} + \frac{h^8 D^8}{80} + \cdots. \qquad (2.7.13)$$

Conversely, to obtain the expansion of the first derivative in terms of central differences, we solve Eq. (2.7.8) for hD:

$$hD = \sinh^{-1}(\mu\delta).$$

Remembering the Taylor series for $\sinh^{-1} x$,

$$\sinh^{-1} x = x - \frac{x^3}{6} + \frac{3x^5}{40} - \cdots,$$

we obtain

$$hD = \mu\delta - \frac{\mu^3\delta^3}{6} + \frac{3\mu^5\delta^5}{40} - \cdots,$$

and using Eq. (2.7.7) to eliminate even powers of μ, the expansion for hD finally becomes

$$hD = \mu\left(\delta - \frac{\delta^3}{6} + \frac{\delta^5}{30} - \cdots\right). \qquad (2.7.14)$$

Taking powers of hD and using again Eq. (2.7.7) to eliminate even powers of μ, we obtain similarly

$$h^2 D^2 = \delta^2 - \frac{\delta^4}{12} + \frac{\delta^6}{90} - \cdots;$$

$$h^3 D^3 = \mu\left(\delta^3 - \frac{\delta^5}{4} + \frac{7\delta^7}{120} - \cdots\right); \qquad (2.7.15)$$

$$h^4 D^4 = \delta^4 - \frac{\delta^6}{6} + \frac{7\delta^8}{240} - \cdots.$$

Using the first term of these expansions, the derivatives of y may be approximated by the following central difference expansions, whose errors ϵ are given in terms of differences:

$$2hDy_i = (y_r - y_l) + 2\epsilon_1$$

$$\left[\epsilon_1 = \mu\left(-\frac{\delta^3}{6} + \frac{\delta^5}{30} - \cdots\right)y_i\right];$$

$$h^2D^2y_i = y_r - 2y_i + y_l + \epsilon_2$$

$$\left[\epsilon_2 = \left(-\frac{\delta^4}{12} + \frac{\delta^6}{90} - \cdots\right)y_i\right]; \qquad [\epsilon = 0(h^2)]$$

$$2h^3D^3y_i = (y_{rr} - 2y_r + 2y_l - y_{ll}) + 2\epsilon_3 \qquad (2.7.16)$$

$$\left[\epsilon_3 = \mu\left(-\frac{\delta^5}{4} + \frac{7\delta^7}{120} - \cdots\right)y_i\right];$$

$$h^4D^4y_i = y_{rr} - 4y_r + 6y_i - 4y_l + y_{ll} + \epsilon_4;$$

$$\left[\epsilon_4 = \left(-\frac{\delta^6}{6} + \frac{7\delta^8}{240} - \cdots\right)y_i\right].$$

A comparison of these equations with the expansions of Eqs. (2.7.9) to (2.7.13) proves that the error in the corresponding derivatives is of order h^2 and hence that averaged central difference expressions are more accurate than either forward or backward unilateral expressions. It may

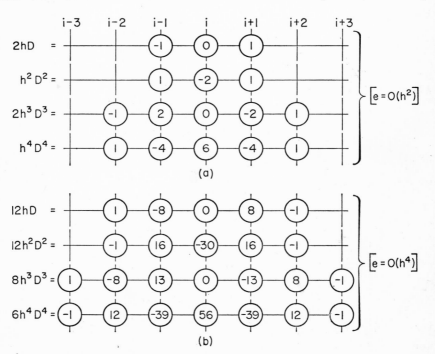

Fig. 2.8. Central difference operators.

similarly be proved that by taking into account the first two terms of the expansions (2.7.14) and (2.7.15) the error in the corresponding derivatives is of order h^4, and that considering m terms one obtains errors of order h^{2m}.

The "molecules" of Fig. 2.8 give the most commonly used central difference expressions for derivatives with errors of order h^2 and h^4.

2.8 Sterling's Interpolation Formula

An interpolation formula based on averaged central differences can be obtained from the Taylor expansion, Eq. (a) of Sec. 2.6, by expressing the derivatives of y at $x = a$ in terms of their central difference expansions of Sec. 2.7. Thus,

$$y(a + xh) = \left[1 + \frac{x}{1!} hD + \frac{x^2}{2!} h^2D^2 + \frac{x^3}{3!} h^3D^3 + \ldots \right] y(a)$$

$$= \left[1 + x\mu \left(\delta - \frac{\delta^3}{6} + \frac{\delta^5}{30} - \ldots \right) + \frac{x^2}{2!} \left(\delta^2 - \frac{\delta^4}{12} + \ldots \right) \right.$$

$$\left. + \frac{x^3}{3!} \mu \left(\delta^3 - \frac{\delta^5}{4} + \ldots \right) + \frac{x^4}{4!} (\delta^4 - \ldots) + \frac{x^5}{5!} (\delta^5 - \ldots) + \ldots \right] y(a)$$

$$= \left\{ 1 + x\mu\delta + \frac{x^2}{2!} \delta^2 + \frac{x(x^2 - 1)}{3!} \mu\delta^3 + \frac{x^2(x^2 - 1)}{4!} \delta^4 \right.$$

$$+ \frac{x(x^2 - 1)(x^2 - 4)}{5!} \mu\delta^5 + \ldots + \frac{1}{(2k - 1)!} x(x^2 - 1)(x^2 - 4)\ldots$$

$$[x^2 - (k - 1)^2]\mu\delta^{2k-1} + \frac{1}{2k!} x^2(x^2 - 1)(x^2 - 4)\ldots$$

$$\left. [x^2 - (k - 1)^2]\delta^{2k} + \ldots \right\} y(a). \quad (2.8.1)$$

Equation (2.8.1) is known as *Sterling's interpolation formula.*

For example, by means of Table 2.8, in which $y = \tan \theta$ is tabulated for $\theta = 0(5°)30°$, the value of $\tan 16°$ ($a = 15°$, $h = 5°$, $x = 0.2$) is

Table 2.8

θ	$y = \tan \theta$	$\mu\delta y$	δ^2	$\mu\delta^3$	δ^4
0	0.0000				
5	0.0875	0.0882	0.0013		
10	0.1763	0.0902	0.0028	0.0016	
15	0.2679	0.0938	0.0045	0.0017	0.0004
20	0.3640	0.0992	0.0062	0.0022	
25	0.4663	0.1067	0.0088		
30	0.5774				

obtained as

$$\tan 16° = 0.2679 + 0.2 \times 0.0938 + \frac{\overline{0.2}^2}{2!} 0.0045 + \frac{0.2(\overline{0.2}^2 - 1)}{3!} 0.0017$$

$$+ \frac{\overline{0.2}^2(\overline{0.2}^2 - 1)}{4!} \times 0.0004 = 0.2867.$$

2.9 Lagrange's Interpolation for Unevenly Spaced Points

When the pivotal points are not evenly spaced, it is easier to build interpolation formulas by passing an nth-degree polynomial through $n + 1$ pivotal points.

Given the points

$$(x_0, y_0); \quad (x_1, y_1); \quad (x_2, y_2); \quad \ldots; \quad (x_n, y_n), \tag{2.9.1}$$

the polynomial

$$P_k(x) \equiv C_k p_k(x)$$
$$= C_k(x - x_0)(x - x_1) \ldots (x - x_{k-1})(x - x_{k+1}) \ldots (x - x_n)$$

equals zero at all the x_i except at $x = x_k$.

If P_k is to be equal to 1 at $x = x_k$,

$$C_k = \frac{1}{[(x_k - x_0)(x_k - x_1) \ldots (x_k - x_{k-1})(x_k - x_{k+1}) \ldots (x_k - x_n)]}. \tag{2.9.2}$$

The linear combination of nth-degree polynomials,

$$P(x) = \sum_{k=0}^{n} y_k P_k(x) \tag{2.9.3}$$

goes through the $(n + 1)$ points of Eq. (2.9.1), since

$$P_k(x_i) = \begin{cases} 0 & i \neq k \\ 1 & i = k. \end{cases}$$

Equation (2.9.3) is known as *Lagrange's interpolation formula.*

For example, given the points

$$(1,2); \quad (3,5); \quad (7,12); \quad (13,20),$$

$$C_0 = \frac{1}{(1 - 3)(1 - 7)(1 - 13)} = -\frac{1}{144};$$

$$C_1 = \frac{1}{(3 - 1)(3 - 7)(3 - 13)} = +\frac{1}{80};$$

$$C_2 = \frac{1}{(7 - 1)(7 - 3)(7 - 13)} = -\frac{1}{144};$$

$$C_3 = \frac{1}{(13 - 1)(13 - 3)(13 - 7)} = +\frac{1}{720}.$$

To find the value of $P(x)$ at $x = 4$, we compute the $p_k(4)$:

$$p_0(4) = (4 - 3)(4 - 7)(4 - 13) = 27,$$

$$p_1(4) = (4 - 1)(4 - 7)(4 - 13) = 81,$$

$$p_2(4) = (4 - 1)(4 - 3)(4 - 13) = -27,$$

$$p_3(4) = (4 - 1)(4 - 3)(4 - 7) = -9,$$

by means of which

$$P(4) = -\tfrac{27}{144}(2) + \tfrac{81}{80}(5) + \tfrac{27}{144}(12) - \tfrac{9}{720}(20) = 6.6875.$$

2.10 Integration Formulas by Interpolating Parabolas

Whenever a function cannot be integrated in finite terms or the evaluation of its integral is too cumbersome, integration may be conveniently performed by numerical methods.

A variety of integration formulas can be obtained by interpolating parabolas through a number of pivotal points of the integrand and using the area under the parabolas as an approximation to the area under the integrand.

Given the pivotal values of $f(x)$:

$$\ldots, \quad f_{i-2}, \quad f_{i-1}, \quad f_i, \quad f_{i+1}, \quad f_{i+2}, \quad \ldots, \tag{a}$$

evenly spaced by h, and taking (without loss of generality) the origin at $x = x_i$, the straight line

$$f(x) = Ax + B$$

will go through $(0, f_i)$ and (h, f_{i+1}) provided

$$A = \frac{f_{i+1} - f_i}{h}; \qquad B = f_i.$$

The approximating first-order parabola is thus

$$f(x) = \frac{f_{i+1} - f_i}{h} x + f_i \tag{b}$$

and the area under $f(x)$ between 0 and h is approximated by

$$A_1 = \int_0^h f(x)\, dx \doteq \frac{f_{i+1} - f_i}{h}\left(\frac{h^2}{2}\right) + f_i h = \frac{h}{2}(f_i + f_{i+1}). \tag{2.10.1}$$

This is known as the *trapezoidal rule formula*, since it approximates the area under one strip by the area of a trapezoid (Fig. 2.9).

A quadratic parabola

$$f(x) = Ax^2 + Bx + C \tag{c}$$

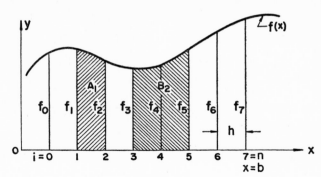

Figure 2.9

goes through the points $(-h, f_{i-1})$, $(0, f_i)$, (h, f_{i+1}) if

$$A = \frac{f_{i+1} - 2f_i + f_{i-1}}{2h^2}; \qquad B = \frac{f_{i+1} - f_{i-1}}{2h}; \qquad C = f_i. \qquad (d)$$

The area under this parabola between $-h$ and $+h$ gives

$$B_2 = \int_{-h}^{h} f(x) \, dx \doteq \frac{2h^3}{3} A + 2hC = \frac{h}{3} [f_{i+1} + 4f_i + f_{i-1}]. \qquad (2.10.2)$$

This is *Simpson's $\frac{1}{3}$ rule formula* for the area under two strips of width h.

Similarly, the area under four strips of parabola (c), (d), between $-2h$ and $+2h$ becomes

$$B_4 = \int_{-2h}^{2h} f(x) \, dx \doteq \frac{4h}{3} [2f_{i+1} - f_i + 2f_{i-1}]. \qquad (2.10.3)$$

A cubic parabola

$$f(x) = Ax^3 + Bx^2 + Cx + D \qquad (e)$$

has an area over three strips of width h:

$$C_3 = \int_{-3h/2}^{3h/2} f(x) \, dx = \tfrac{9}{4} Bh^3 + 3Dh \qquad (f)$$

and an area over one strip:

$$C_1 = \int_{-h/2}^{h/2} f(x) \, dx = \tfrac{1}{12} Bh^3 + Dh. \qquad (g)$$

The coefficients B and D of the parabola (e) passing through the points f_0, f_1, f_2, f_3 are

$$B = \frac{1}{4h^2} (f_0 - f_1 - f_2 + f_3);$$

$$D = \frac{1}{16} (-f_0 + 9f_1 + 9f_2 - f_3). \qquad (h)$$

Thus,

$$C_1 = \int_{-h/2}^{h/2} f(x)\,dx \doteq \frac{h}{24}\left(-f_0 + 13f_1 + 13f_2 - f_3\right); \quad (2.10.4)$$

$$C_3 = \int_{-3h/2}^{3h/2} f(x)\,dx \doteq \frac{3h}{8}\left(f_0 + 3f_1 + 3f_2 + f_3\right). \quad (2.10.5)$$

Equation (2.10.5) is known as *Simpson's $\frac{3}{8}$ rule* for the area under three strips of width h and is conveniently used in connection with Simpson's $\frac{1}{3}$ rule to cover an odd number of strips.

Any number of integration formulas may be obtained by this technique, and any such formulas may be combined to obtain new formulas.

2.11 Integration Formulas by Taylor Series

In order to evaluate the error inherent in the integration formulas derived in Sec. 2.10, it is necessary to obtain them by means of a Taylor expansion, just as was done for differentiation formulas.

By means of the successive derivatives of the integral,

$$y(x) = \int_a^x f(z)\,dz; \tag{a}$$

$$y' = f(x); \quad y'' = f'(x); \quad \ldots; \quad y^{(n)} = f^{(n-1)}(x); \quad \ldots,$$

the Taylor expansion of $y(x \pm h)$ about x becomes

$$y(x \pm h) = y(x) \pm \frac{h}{1!}f(x) + \frac{h^2}{2!}f'(x) \pm \frac{h^3}{3!}f''(x) + \ldots. \tag{b}$$

The areas under one and two strips of $f(x)$ are thus

$$I_1 = \int_x^{x+h} f(z)\,dz = y(x + h) - y(x)$$

$$= h\left[f(x) + \frac{1}{2!}hf'(x) + \frac{1}{3!}h^2 f''(x) + \ldots\right]; \quad (2.11.1)$$

$$I_2 = \int_{x-h}^{x+h} f(z)\,dz = y(x + h) - y(x - h)$$

$$= h[2f(x) + \tfrac{1}{3}h^2 f''(x) + \tfrac{1}{60}h^4 f^{iv}(x) + \ldots]. \quad (2.11.2)$$

To obtain the error in the trapezoidal rule, we substitute hf_i' in terms of the first forward difference from Eq. (2.5.6):

$$A_1 = h\{f_i + [\tfrac{1}{2}(f_{i+1} - f_i) - \tfrac{1}{4}h^2 f_i'' - \tfrac{1}{6}h^3 f_i''' - \ldots] + \tfrac{1}{6}h^2 f_i'' + \ldots\}$$

$$= \frac{h}{2}(f_{i+1} + f_i) - \frac{h^3}{12}f_i''' - \frac{h^4}{24}f_i^{iv} + \ldots. \tag{2.11.3}$$

It is thus seen that the error in Eq. (2.10.1) is of order h^3.

Similarly, substituting in Eq. (2.11.2) for $h^2 f''(x)$ its central difference expansion of Eq. (2.7.10):

$$B_2 = h\{2f_i + \tfrac{1}{3}[f_{i+1} - 2f_i + f_{i-1} - \tfrac{1}{12}h^4 f_i^{iv} - \dots] + \tfrac{1}{60}h^4 f_i^{iv} + \dots\}$$

$$= \frac{h}{3}(f_{i+1} + 4f_i + f_{i-1}) - \frac{h^5 f_i^{iv}}{90} + \dots, \tag{2.11.4}$$

showing that Simpson's $\tfrac{1}{3}$ rule [Eq. (2.10.2)] has an error of order h^5. The error in Simpson's $\tfrac{3}{8}$ rule can also be shown to be of order h^5.

Similarly if both $h^2 f_i''$ and $h^4 f_i^{iv}$ are expressed in terms of central differences, I_4 is obtained by means of a five-point formula with an error of order h^7:

$$D_4 = \frac{2h}{45}(7f_{i-2} + 32f_{i-1} + 12f_i + 32f_{i+1} + 7f_{i+2}) + 0(h^7). \tag{2.11.5}$$

Formulas for I_2 (area under two strips) with errors of order 9, 11, $\dots$, may similarly be obtained. The seven-point formula, with error of order h^9, has a set of rather complicated coefficients, and the more convenient *Weddle's formula* is often preferred, although it has an error of order h^8:

$$E_6 = \frac{3h}{10}(f_{i-3} + 5f_{i-2} + f_{i-1} + 6f_i + f_{i+1} + 5f_{i+2} + f_{i+3}) + 0(h^8). \tag{2.11.6}$$

One-sided formulas with errors of any order may be easily derived by integration of Newton's interpolation formulas between a and $a + h$:

$$I_1 = h \int_0^1 \left[1 + x\Delta + \frac{x(x-1)}{2!}\Delta^2 + \frac{x(x-1)(x-2)}{3!}\Delta^3 + \dots \right] y(a)\, dx$$

$$= h \left[1 + \frac{1}{2}\Delta - \frac{1}{12}\Delta^2 + \frac{1}{24}\Delta^3 - \frac{19}{720}\Delta^4 + \dots \right] y(a). \tag{2.11.7}$$

Taking two terms of the series, Eq. (2.11.7) gives

$$A_1 = h \left[1 + \frac{1}{2}\Delta \right] y(a) = \frac{h}{2}(y_i + y_{i+1}) + 0(h^3).$$

With three terms of the series, we obtain

$$B_1 = h \left[1 + \frac{1}{2}\Delta - \frac{1}{12}\Delta^2 \right] y(a) = \frac{h}{12}[5y_i + 8y_{i+1} - y_{i+2}] + 0(h^4). \tag{2.11.8}$$

With four terms, Eq. (2.11.7) gives

$$C_1 = h \left[1 + \frac{1}{2}\Delta - \frac{1}{12}\Delta^2 + \frac{1}{24}\Delta^3 \right] y(a)$$

$$= \frac{h}{24}(9y_i + 19y_{i+1} - 5y_{i+2} + y_{i+3}) + 0(h^5). \tag{2.11.9}$$

Whenever the numerical integration must be extended to a large number of strips of width h, the above-derived formulas may be added and the resulting combinations of pivotal ordinates presented in the form of "mathematical molecules" together with the order of the accumu-

(a) Trapezoidal Rule

(b) Simpson's Rule

Figure 2.10

lated error. For example, by the trapezoidal rule [Eq. (2.11.3)], an integral extended to n strips from $x = a$ to $x = b$ is given by

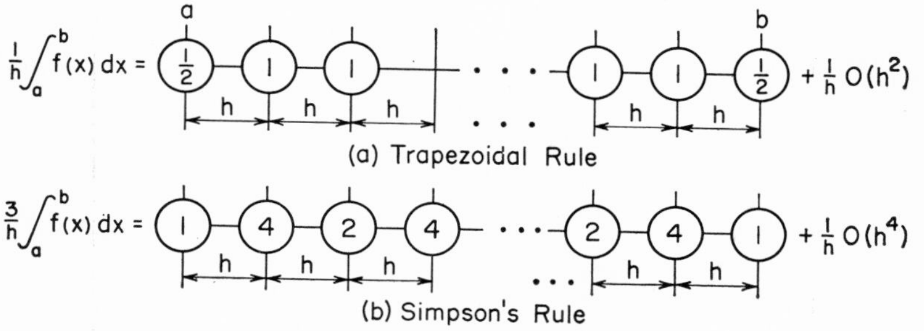

$$A = h[\tfrac{1}{2}f_0 + f_1 + f_2 + \ldots + f_{n-1} + \tfrac{1}{2}f_n] + e_t, \qquad (2.11.10)$$

where the accumulated error, by the theorem of the mean, becomes approximately

$$e_t \doteq -\frac{h^3}{12}(f_0'' + f_1'' + \ldots + f_{n-1}'') = -h^2\frac{nh}{12}f''(\bar{x}_n) = -h^2\frac{b-a}{12}f''(\bar{x}_n)$$
$$(2.11.11)$$

and is of order h^2.

The same area extended to an *even* number n of strips is, by Simpson's $\tfrac{1}{3}$ rule [Eq. (2.11.4)],

$$A = \frac{h}{3}[f_0 + 4f_1 + 2f_2 + 4f_3 + \ldots + 4f_{n-1} + f_n] + e_S, \quad (2.11.12)$$

where the error is given approximately by

$$e_S \doteq -\frac{h^5}{90}[f_1^{\mathrm{iv}} + f_3^{\mathrm{iv}} + \ldots + f_{n-1}^{\mathrm{iv}}]$$

$$= -\frac{h^4}{90}\frac{n}{2}hf^{\mathrm{iv}}(\bar{x}_n) = -h^4\frac{b-a}{180}f^{\mathrm{iv}}(\bar{x}_n) \qquad (2.11.13)$$

and is of order h^4.

Figure 2.10 gives the "molecules" for the trapezoidal and Simpson's $\tfrac{1}{3}$ rules.

The integral

$$A = \int_0^\pi \sin x\, dx = -\cos x\Big]_0^\pi = 2 \qquad (c)$$

is evaluated in Table 2.9 by the trapezoidal rule and in Table 2.10 by Simpson's $\frac{1}{3}$ rule.

Table 2.9
Numerical Integration by the Trapezoidal Rule

x	$\sin x$	$n = 2$ $h = \pi/2$ M		$n = 4$ $h = \pi/4$ M	
0	0	1/2	0	1/2	0
$\pi/4$	0.707			1	0.707
$\pi/2$	1.000	1	1.000	1	1.000
$3\pi/4$	0.707			1	0.707
π	0	1/2	0	1/2	0
		$\Sigma_2 =$	1.000	$\Sigma_4 =$	2.414

x	$\sin x$	$n = 6$ $h = \pi/6$ M	
0	0	1/2	0
$\pi/6$	0.500	1	0.500
$\pi/3$	0.866	1	0.866
$\pi/2$	1.000	1	1.000
$2\pi/3$	0.866	1	0.866
$5\pi/6$	0.500	1	0.500
π	0	1/2	0
		$\Sigma_6 =$	3.732

$$A_2 = \left(\frac{\pi}{2}\right) \cdot 1.000 = 1.571; \qquad e_2 = \frac{2 - 1.571}{2} \cdot 100 = 21 \text{ per cent.}$$

$$A_4 = \left(\frac{\pi}{4}\right) \cdot 2.414 = 1.896; \qquad e_4 = \frac{2 - 1.896}{2} \cdot 100 = 5.2 \text{ per cent.}$$

$$A_6 = \left(\frac{\pi}{6}\right) \cdot 3.732 = 1.954; \qquad e_6 = \frac{2 - 1.954}{2} \cdot 100 = 2.3 \text{ per cent.}$$

If one strip of width $h = \pi/4$ were to be added to the integration by Simpson's rule for $n = 4$, Eq. (2.10.5) would give for the last three strips, with

$$f_3 = -0.707; \qquad f_2 = 0; \qquad f_1 = 0.707; \qquad f_0 = 1.000;$$

$$\Delta A = \frac{3\pi}{8 \times 4} (1.000 + 3 \times 0.707 + 3 \times 0 - 0.707) = 0.631 \ (e = 14\%)$$

Table 2.10
Numerical Integration by Simpson's 1/3 Rule

x	$\sin x$	$n = 2$ $h = \pi/2$ M		$n = 4$ $h = \pi/4$ M	
0	0	1	0	1	0
$\pi/4$	0.707			4	2.828
$\pi/2$	1.000	4	4	2	2.000
$3\pi/4$	0.707			4	2.828
π	0	1	0	1	0
		$\Sigma_2 =$	4	$\Sigma_4 =$	7.656

$$A_2 = \frac{\pi/2}{3} \cdot 4 = 2.094; \qquad e_2 = 4.7 \text{ per cent.}$$

$$A_4 = \frac{\pi/4}{3} \cdot 7.656 = 2.004; \qquad e_4 = 0.23 \text{ per cent.}$$

(This fairly large error is due to the relatively large coefficient of h^5 in the error for this formula.)

Adding the area of the first two strips;

$$\Delta A_2 = \frac{\pi}{3 \times 4} (0 + 4 \times 0.707 + 1.000) = 1.002 \ (e = 0.2\%);$$

the area under five strips becomes:

$$A = 1.633 \ (e = 4.3\%)$$

2.12 Integration with Unevenly Spaced Pivotal Points

Integration with *unevenly spaced pivotal points* is performed by the trapezoidal rule with a varying h:

$$A = \tfrac{1}{2}[h_{1/2}f_0 + (h_{1/2} + h_{3/2})f_1 + (h_{3/2} + h_{5/2})f_2 + \ldots + h_{n-1/2}f_n] \quad (2.12.1)$$

or by a Simpson-type formula obtained by means of three ordinates spaced by h and αh.

By Eq. (b) of Sec. 2.11, with αh and $-h$ instead of h,

$$y(x + \alpha h) = y(x) + \frac{\alpha h}{1!} f(x) + \frac{\alpha^2 h^2}{2!} f'(x) + \frac{\alpha^3 h^3}{3!} f''(x) + \ldots$$

$$y(x - h) = y(x) - \frac{h}{1!} f(x) + \frac{h^2}{2!} f'(x) - \frac{h^3}{3!} f''(x) + \ldots,$$

Table 2.11

i	x_i	h	f_i	$(h_{i-\frac{1}{2}} + h_{i+\frac{1}{2}})f_i$	$3f_{i+1} + f_{i-1}$	$h_{i-\frac{1}{2}}(3f_{i+1} + f_{i-1})$	$3f_i + f_{i-1}$	$h_{i-\frac{1}{2}}(3f_i + f_{i-1})$	i
0	0		1.000	0.100					4
		0.1							
1	0.1		0.905	0.272	3.223	0.322	3.456	0.691	3
		0.2							
2	0.3		0.741	0.445					2
		0.4							
3	0.7		0.497	0.596	1.410	0.564	1.714	1.371	1
		0.8							
4	1.5		0.223	0.178					0
			Σ	1.591	Σ	0.886	Σ	2.062	

$$A = 0.795 \qquad\qquad A = 0.664 \qquad\qquad A = 0.773$$
$$e\% = 2.3 \qquad\qquad e\% = 14.5 \qquad\qquad e\% = 0.5$$

the area over two unequal strips becomes

$$y(x + \alpha h) - y(x - h) = h\left[(\alpha + 1)f(x) + \frac{\alpha^2 - 1}{2!} hf'(x) \right.$$

$$\left. + \frac{(\alpha^3 + 1)}{3!} h^2 f''(x) + \cdots \right],$$

and substituting for $hf'(x)$ and $h^2 f''(x)$ their central difference expansions,

$$B_2 = \frac{h}{2}\left[\left(\frac{\alpha^3 + 1}{3} + \frac{\alpha^2 - 1}{2} \right) f_{i+1} - 2\left(\frac{\alpha^3 + 1}{3} - \alpha - 1 \right) f_i \right.$$

$$\left. + \left(\frac{\alpha^3 + 1}{3} - \frac{\alpha^2 - 1}{2} \right) f_{i-1} \right] + 0(h^3). \quad (2.12.2)$$

Table 2.11 gives the integral of the function $y = e^{-x}$ between 0 and 1.5 by Eq. (2.12.1), by Eq. (2.12.2) with $\alpha = 2$ so that:

$$B_2 = \tfrac{3}{4}h(3f_{i+1} + f_{i-1}),$$

and by Eq. (2.12.2) with $\alpha = \tfrac{1}{2}$, i.e., integrating from $x = 1.5$ to $x = 0$ so that

$$B_2 = \tfrac{3}{8}h(3f_i + f_{i-1}).$$

2.13 Richardson's Extrapolations

It was shown in the previous sections that the error in the difference formulas for differentiation and integration depends on the spacing h

of the pivotal points, and that it is of order h^2 or h^4 in the better approximated formulas.

Thus, derivative values obtained by one term of their central difference expansions, and integrals obtained by the trapezoidal rule, have errors of order h^2, while derivatives obtained by two terms of their central difference expansions, and integrals obtained by Simpson's $\frac{1}{3}$ rule, have errors of order h^4.

The order of these errors is obtained by taking into account the higher terms of the expansions, but the reader will notice that in all the above cases the error in central difference expressions for the derivatives at a point x is represented by a series of the type

$$e(x) = f_1(x)h^2 + f_2(x)h^4 + f_3(x)h^6 + \ldots. \tag{2.13.1}$$

Hence, for example, errors of order h^4 have expansions with $f_1(x) \equiv 0$.

When the expression evaluated by differences is independent of x, as is the case for definite integrals, or when the error is computed with various values of the spacing h *at the same point* x, the error series has constant coefficients and may be written as

$$e = c_1 h^2 + c_2 h^4 + c_3 h^6 + \ldots. \tag{2.13.2}$$

It will now be shown that the knowledge of the form of the error series allows the evaluation of better approximations of the derivatives and of the integrals with a minimum amount of added labor.

Let us assume, for example, that the value A of an integral has been computed numerically by using n_1 and n_2 strips in the trapezoidal rule; that is, by taking

$$h_1 = \frac{b-a}{n_1}; \qquad h_2 = \frac{b-a}{n_2},$$

and let us call A_{n_1} and A_{n_2} the corresponding approximations. If h_1 and h_2 are small enough to allow us to neglect all the terms except the first in Eq. (2.13.2), we may write

$$e_1 \equiv A - A_{n_1} \doteq \frac{c_1(b-a)^2}{n_1^2}; \qquad e_2 \equiv A - A_{n_2} \doteq \frac{c_1(b-a)^2}{n_2^2},$$

where c_1 is unknown. Eliminating the unknown constant $c_1(b-a)^2$ between these two equations and solving for the true value A, we obtain the so-called h^2-*extrapolation formula:*

$$A_{n_1,n_2} = \frac{n_2^2}{n_2^2 - n_1^2} A_{n_2} - \frac{n_1^2}{n_2^2 - n_1^2} A_{n_1} = \alpha_1 A_{n_1} + \alpha_2 A_{n_2}, \tag{2.13.3}$$

which gives an excellent approximation of A whenever the higher terms of the error series are negligible.

For example, taking $A_2 = 1.571$ and $A_4 = 1.896$ from Table 2.9, the value of the integral (c) of Sec. 2.11 given by Eq. (2.13.3) is

$$A_{2,4} = \frac{4^2}{4^2 - 2^2} \, 1.896 \, - \, \frac{2^2}{4^2 - 2^2} \, 1.571$$

$$= \tfrac{4}{3} \cdot 1.896 \, - \, \tfrac{1}{3} \cdot 1.571 = 2.004,$$

with an error of 0.2 per cent as against errors of 21 per cent and 5.2 per cent in A_2 and A_4, respectively. Repeating the computation for $n = 4$, $n = 6$, we obtain similarly

$$A_{4,6} = \frac{6^2}{6^2 - 4^2} \, 1.954 \, - \, \frac{4^2}{6^2 - 4^2} \, 1.896 = 2.0004,$$

with an error of 0.02 per cent.

Table 2.12 gives the coefficients

$$\alpha_1 = - \frac{n_1^2}{n_2^2 - n_1^2}; \qquad \alpha_2 = \frac{n_2^2}{n_2^2 - n_1^2} \tag{2.13.4}$$

of the h^2-extrapolation formula [Eq. (2.13.3)] for the most commonly encountered ratios of the values of n_1 and n_2, as Eqs. (2.13.4) depend only on the ratio n_2/n_1.

Table 2.12
h^2—Extrapolation Coefficients

n_2/n_1	α_1	α_2
2/1	-0.3333333333	1.3333333333
3/2	-0.8	1.8
4/3	-1.2857142857	2.2857142857
5/4	-1.7777777778	2.7777777778
6/5	-2.2727272727	3.2727272727
7/6	-2.7692307692	3.7692307692
8/7	-3.2666666667	4.2666666667
3/1	-0.125	1.125
5/3	-0.5625	1.5625
7/5	-1.0416666667	2.0416666667

When three approximations A_{n_1}, A_{n_2}, A_{n_3} of A have been obtained by means of three spacings h_1, h_2, h_3 inversely proportional to n_1, n_2, n_3, we may take into account two terms of the error equation (2.13.2) and write

$$e_1 \equiv A - A_{n_1} = \frac{c_1(b-a)^2}{n_1^2} + \frac{c_2(b-a)^4}{n_1^4};$$

$$e_2 \equiv A - A_{n_2} = \frac{c_1(b-a)^2}{n_2^2} + \frac{c_2(b-a)^4}{n_2^4};$$

$$e_3 \equiv A - A_{n_3} = \frac{c_1(b-a)^2}{n_3^2} + \frac{c_2(b-a)^4}{n_3^4}.$$

Eliminating the two unknown constants $c_1(b-a)^2$ and $c_2(b-a)^4$ between these equations and solving for the true value A, we obtain the (h^2, h^4)-*extrapolation formula*

$$A_{n_1,n_2,n_3} = \frac{n_1^4}{(n_2^2 - n_1^2)(n_3^2 - n_1^2)} A_{n_1} - \frac{n_2^4}{(n_2^2 - n_1^2)(n_3^2 - n_2^2)} A_{n_2}$$

$$+ \frac{n_3^4}{(n_3^2 - n_1^2)(n_3^2 - n_2^2)} A_{n_3} \equiv \beta_1 A_{n_1} + \beta_2 A_{n_2} + \beta_3 A_{n_3}, \quad (2.13.5)$$

whose coefficients are given in Table 2.13 for the most common ratios of $n_3/n_2/n_1$.

Table 2.13
(h^2, h^4)—Extrapolation Coefficients

$n_3/n_2/n_1$	β_1	β_2	β_3
3/2/1	0.0416666667	−1.0666666667	2.025
4/2/1	0.0222222222	−0.4444444444	1.4222222222
4/3/2	0.2666666667	−2.3142857143	3.0476190476
5/4/2	0.6349206349	−2.3703703704	3.3068783069
5/4/3	0.7232142857	−4.0634920635	4.3402777778
6/5/4	1.4222222222	−6.3131313131	5.8909090909
7/6/5	2.3674242424	−9.0629370629	7.6955128205
8/7/6	3.5604395604	−12.3128205128	9.7523809524
5/3/1	0.0052083333	−0.6328125	1.6276041667
7/5/3	0.1265625	−1.6276041667	2.5010416667

For example, using the three approximations A_2, A_4, A_6 of the integral (c) of Sec. 2.11 in Table 2.9 and the coefficients β corresponding to the ratios $6/4/2 = 3/2/1$ from Table 2.13, we obtain: $A_{2,4,6} = 0.04167 \cdot 1.571 - 1.06667 \cdot 1.896 + 2.025 \cdot 1.954 = 1.99991$, with an error of 0.005 per cent.

When the order of the error is h^4, $c_1 = 0$ in Eq. (2.13.2), and the errors in two successive approximations with n_1 and n_2 subintervals take the form:

$$e_1 \equiv A - A_{n_1} = \frac{c_2(b-a)^4}{n_1^4} + \frac{c_3(b-a)^6}{n_1^6} + \cdots$$

$$e_2 \equiv A - A_{n_2} = \frac{c_2(b-a)^4}{n_2^4} + \frac{c_3(b-a)^6}{n_2^6} + \cdots .$$

Neglecting all but the first term of the error series and solving for A, we obtain the h^4-*extrapolation formula:*

$$A_{n_1,n_2} = \frac{n_2^4}{n_2^4 - n_1^4} A_{n_2} - \frac{n_1^4}{n_2^4 - n_1^4} A_{n_1} = \gamma_1 A_{n_1} + \gamma_2 A_{n_2}, \quad (2.13.6)$$

whose coefficients are given in Table 2.14.*

Table 2.14
h^4—**Extrapolation Coefficients**

n_2/n_1	γ_1	γ_2
2/1	-0.0666666667	1.0666666667
3/2	-0.2461538462	1.2461538462
4/3	-0.4628571429	1.4628571429
5/4	-0.6937669377	1.6937669377
6/5	-0.9314456036	1.9314456036
7/6	-1.1728506787	2.1728506787
8/7	-1.4165191740	2.4165191740
3/1	-0.0125	1.0125
5/3	-0.1488970588	1.1488970588
7/5	-0.3519144144	1.3519144144

For example, using the values A_2 and A_4 of the integral (c) of Sec. 2.11 obtained in Table 2.10 by means of Simpson's rule, whose error is of order h^4, and the coefficients of Table 2.14 for $n_2/n_1 = 2/1$, we obtain the extrapolation

$$A_{2,4} = -0.06667 \cdot 2.094 + 1.06667 \cdot 2.004 = 1.998,$$

with an error of 0.1 per cent.

As another example of extrapolation consider the approximate values of the first derivative of the Bessel function $J_{\frac{1}{4}}(x)$ at $x = 0.5$, which

---

* Tables 2.12, 2.13, and 2.14 have been computed by the Istituto Nazionale per le Applicazioni del Calcolo, the mathematical laboratory of the Italian National Research Council, directed by Prof. Mauro Picone. More complete tables of this type have been published by the author in *Proc.*, "First U.S. Congress of Applied Mechanics," *A.S.M.E.*, Chicago, 1952.

may be easily computed by the central difference operator [Eq. (2.7.16)]

$$J'_{\frac{1}{4}}(0.5) \doteq \frac{1}{2h} [J_{\frac{1}{4}}(0.5 + h) - J_{\frac{1}{4}}(0.5 - h)]$$

for $h = 0.4, 0.2, 0.1, 0.05$. These values appear in Table 2.15, column 3. Since the approximation of derivatives by central differences involves

Table 2.15

Approximations				h^2—Extrapolations		
h	n	$J'_{\frac{1}{4}}(0.5)$	$e(\%)$	n	$J'_{\frac{1}{4}}(0.5)$	$e(\%)$
0.4	1	0.30377	+38.6	2/1	0.20994	−4.2
0.2	2	0.23340	+6.5	4/2	0.21873	−1.6
0.1	4	0.22240	+1.5	8/4	0.21906	−0.013
0.05	8	0.21990	+0.37	...	...	...

(h^2, h^4)—Extrapolations		
n	$J'_{\frac{1}{4}}(0.5)$	$e(\%)$
4/2/1	0.21931	+0.10
8/4/2	0.21908	−0.004

errors of the type of Eq. (2.13.1), h^2-, and (h^2, h^4)-extrapolations may be evaluated in this case *at a given x* for $n_2/n_1 = 2/1$ and for $n_3/n_2/n_1 = 4/2/1$ by means of the coefficients of Tables 2.12 and 2.13. They appear in Table 2.15 together with the corresponding percentage of error evaluated from the true value of $J'_{\frac{1}{4}}(0.5) = 0.21909$. The table proves again that a reduction in error may be obtained by extrapolation with very little additional labor.

The extrapolations of this section should not be used when the successive approximations do not approach the true value monotonically, since in this case the higher terms of the error series cannot be neglected.

PROBLEMS

2.1 Given three evenly spaced pivotal values y_0, y_1, y_2, determine by means of interpolating parabolas the first and second derivatives of y at (a) 0, (b) 1, and (c) 2 in terms of the pivotal values at all three points.

Ans. (a) $y'_0 = \frac{1}{2h} (-3y_0 + 4y_1 - y_2)$. (b) $y'_1 = \frac{1}{2h} (-y_0 + y_2)$.

(c) $y'_2 = \frac{1}{2h} (y_0 - 4y_1 + 3y_2)$; $y''_{0,1,2} = \frac{y_0 - 2y_1 + y_2}{h^2}$.

2.2 Given four evenly spaced pivotal values y_0, y_1, y_2, y_3, determine by use of interpolating parabolas the following derivatives of y in terms of the pivotal values at all four points.

(a) y_2'.　(b) y_1'.　(c) y_0'.　(d) y_0''.　(e) y_2''.　(f) y_3''.

Ans.　(b) $y_1' = (1/6h)(-2y_0 - 3y_1 + 6y_2 - y_3)$.
　　　　(d) $y_0'' = (1/h^2)(2y_0 - 5y_1 + 4y_2 - y_3)$.
　　　　(f) $y_3'' = (1/h^2)(-y_0 + 4y_1 - 5y_2 + 2y_3)$.

2.3 Determine an approximate expression for y_i' by means of an interpolating parabola passing through the points of Fig. 2.2.

Ans.　$y_i' = \dfrac{y_r - (1 - \alpha^2)y_i - \alpha^2 y_l}{h\alpha(1 + \alpha)}$.

2.4 Determine an approximate expression for y_i''' by means of an interpolating parabola passing through the points of Fig. 2.3a.

2.5 Given evenly spaced pivotal values y_0, y_1, y_2, y_3, ..., determine by means of Taylor series expansions the following derivatives, with errors of the indicated order. Determine the first term of the error series.

(a) y_0'; $e = 0(h^2)$.　　　　　　　　(b) y_1'; $e = 0(h^2)$.
(c) y_2'; $e = 0(h^2)$.　　　　　　　　(d) y_0''; $e = 0(h)$.
(e) y_1''; $e = 0(h^2)$.　　　　　　　　(f) y_2'; $e = 0(h^3)$.
(g) y_1'; $e = 0(h^3)$.　　　　　　　　(h) y_0'; $e = 0(h^3)$.
(i) y_0''; $e = 0(h^2)$.　　　　　　　　(j) y_3''; $e = 0(h^2)$.

Ans.　(a) $y_0' = \dfrac{-3y_0 + 4y_1 - y_2}{2h}$; $e \doteq \dfrac{h^2 y_0'''}{3}$.

　　　　(c) $y_2' = \dfrac{y_0 - 4y_1 + 3y_2}{2h}$; $e \doteq \dfrac{h^2 y_2'''}{3}$.

　　　　(e) $y_1'' = \dfrac{y_0 - 2y_1 + y_2}{h^2}$; $e \doteq -\dfrac{h^2 y_1^{iv}}{12}$.

　　　　(g) $y_1' = \dfrac{-2y_0 - 3y_1 + 6y_2 - y_3}{6h}$; $e \doteq \dfrac{h^3 y_1^{iv}}{12}$.

　　　　(i) $y_0'' = \dfrac{2y_0 - 5y_1 + 4y_2 - y_3}{h^2}$; $e \doteq \dfrac{11h^2 y_0^{iv}}{12}$.

2.6 Given five evenly spaced values y_0, y_1, y_2, y_3, y_4, determine, by means of Taylor series expansions, the following derivatives of y in terms of all five pivotal values. Give the first term of the error in each case.

(a) y_1'; $e = 0(h^4)$.　　　　　　　　(b) y_2''; $e = 0(h^4)$.
(c) y_0'''; $e = 0(h^2)$.　　　　　　　(d) y_0''; $e = 0(h^3)$.
(e) y_2'''; $e = 0(h^2)$.

Ans. (a) $y_1' = \dfrac{1}{24h}(-6y_0 - 20y_1 + 36y_2 - 12y_3 + 2y_4);$

   $e \doteq -\frac{1}{20}h^4 y_1^{\mathrm{v}}.$

(c) $y_0''' = \dfrac{1}{4h^3}(-10y_0 + 36y_1 - 48y_2 + 28y_3 - 6y_4);$

   $e \doteq \frac{2\,1}{12}h^2 y_0^{\mathrm{v}}.$

(e) $y_2''' = \dfrac{1}{4h^3}(-2y_0 + 4y_1 - 4y_3 + 2y_4);$

   $e \doteq -\frac{1}{4}h^2 y_2^{\mathrm{v}}.$

2.7 Given six evenly spaced pivotal values y_0, y_1, y_2, y_3, ..., determine by means of Taylor series expansions the following derivatives in terms of all six pivotal values. Give the first term of the error series in each case.

(a) y_4''; $e = 0(h^4)$.
(b) y_3^{iv}; $e = 0(h^2)$.
(c) y_2'; $e = 0(h^5)$.

Ans. (a) $y_4'' = \dfrac{1}{60h^2}(5y_0 - 30y_1 + 70y_2 - 20y_3 - 75y_4 + 50y_5);$

   $e \doteq -\frac{13}{180}h^4 y_4^{\mathrm{iv}}.$

(b) $y_3^{\mathrm{iv}} = \dfrac{1}{5h^4}(5y_1 - 20y_2 + 30y_3 - 20y_4 + 5y_5);\; e \doteq -\frac{1}{6}h^2 y_3^{\mathrm{vi}}.$

(c) $y_2' = \dfrac{1}{120h}(6y_0 - 60y_1 - 40y_2 + 120y_3 - 30y_4 + 4y_5);$

   $e \doteq -\frac{1}{60}h^5 y_2^{\mathrm{vi}}.$

2.8 Derive Eq. (2.3.6) of Sec. 2.3 by a Taylor series expansion and prove that the error is of order h^2. Use the points of Fig. 2.3a.

2.9 Derive Eq. (2.3.7) of Sec. 2.3 by a Taylor series expansion and prove that the error is of order h^2. Use the points of Fig. 2.3b.

2.10 Determine by Taylor series an approximate four-point formula for y_i''' and the first term of the corresponding error series by means of the points of Fig. 2.3a.

Ans. $y_i''' = \dfrac{6y_r + 6\alpha(2 + \alpha)y_l - 3\alpha(1 + \alpha)y_{ll} - 3(1 + \alpha)(2 + \alpha)y_i}{h^3\alpha(1 + \alpha)(2 + \alpha)};$

   $e \doteq \dfrac{7(1 + \alpha) - (1 + \alpha^3)}{4\alpha(1 + \alpha)(2 + \alpha)} h y_i^{\mathrm{iv}}.$

2.11 Determine by Taylor series an approximate five-point formula for y_i''' and the first term of the corresponding error series by means of the points of Fig. 2.11.

Ans. $y_i''' = [36y_r + (\alpha^4 - 25\alpha^2 - 60\alpha - 36)y_i + (-3\alpha^4 + 57\alpha^2 + 90\alpha)y_l$
$+ (3\alpha^4 - 39\alpha^2 - 36\alpha)y_{ll} + (-\alpha^4 + 7\alpha^2 + 6\alpha)y_{lll}] \Big/ h^3(\alpha^4 + 18\alpha^3 +$
$11\alpha^2 - 6\alpha);$

$$e \doteq \frac{h^2(12\alpha^5 + 50\alpha^4 - 170\alpha^2 - 132\alpha)y_i^{\mathrm{v}}}{40(\alpha^4 + 18\alpha^3 + 11\alpha^2 - 6\alpha)}.$$

2.12 Determine by Taylor series an approximate five-point formula for y_i^{iv} and the first term of the corresponding error series by means of the points of Fig. 2.11.

Ans. $y_i^{\mathrm{iv}} = [24y_r - (12\alpha^3 + 24\alpha^2 + 36\alpha + 24)y_i + (36\alpha^3 + 60\alpha^2 + 48\alpha)y_l$
$- (36\alpha^3 + 48\alpha^2 + 12\alpha)y_{ll} + (12\alpha^3 + 12\alpha^2)y_{lll}] \Big/ h^4(\alpha^4 + 18\alpha^3 + 11\alpha^2$
$- 6\alpha);$

$$e \doteq \frac{h(-12\alpha^5 + 900\alpha^3 + 720\alpha^2 - 168\alpha)y_i^{\mathrm{v}}}{6(\alpha^4 + 18\alpha^3 + 11\alpha^2 - 6\alpha)}.$$

2.13 Given evenly spaced pivotal y_i, y_{i-1}, y_{i-2}, ..., determine approximate expressions for (a) y_i''', (b) y_i^{iv}, and (c) y_i^{v} with errors of order h by means of

(1) Backward difference expansions.
(2) Interpolating parabolas passing through four, five, and six points, respectively, to the left of i.
(3) Taylor series expansions.

Obtain, where possible, the first term of the error series.

Ans. (a) $y_i''' = \dfrac{1}{h^3}(y_i - 3y_{i-1} + 3y_{i-2} - y_{i-3}).$

(b) $y_i^{\mathrm{iv}} = \dfrac{1}{h^4}(y_i - 4y_{i-1} + 6y_{i-2} - 4y_{i-3} + y_{i-4}).$

(c) $y_i^{\mathrm{v}} = \dfrac{1}{h^5}(y_i - 5y_{i-1} + 10y_{i-2} - 10y_{i-3} + 5y_{i-4} - y_{i-5}).$

2.14 Determine approximate expressions for the following derivatives using two terms of their backward difference expansions. Determine the first terms of the corresponding error series.

(a) y_i'. (b) y_i''. (c) y_i'''. (d) y_i^{iv}.

Ans. (b) $y_i'' = \dfrac{1}{h^2}(2y_i - 5y_{i-1} + 4y_{i-2} - y_{i-3}); e \doteq \frac{11}{12}h^2 y_i^{\mathrm{iv}}.$

(d) $y_i^{\mathrm{iv}} = \dfrac{1}{h^4}(3y_i - 14y_{i-1} + 26y_{i-2} - 24y_{i-3} + 11y_{i-4} - 2y_{i-5});$

$e \doteq \frac{34}{12}h^2 y_i^{\mathrm{vi}}.$

2.15 Given evenly spaced pivotal points y_i, y_{i+1}, y_{i+2}, ..., determine approximate expressions for (a) y_i''', (b) y_i^{iv}, and (c) y_i^{v} with errors of order h by means of

(1) Forward difference expansions.

(2) Interpolating parabolas passing through four, five, and six points, respectively, to the right of i.

(3) Taylor series expansions.

Obtain, where possible, the first term of the error series.

Ans. (a) $y_i''' = \dfrac{1}{h^3}(y_{i+3} - 3y_{i+2} + 3y_{i+1} - y_i)$.

(b) $y_i^{iv} = \dfrac{1}{h^4}(y_{i+4} - 4y_{i+3} + 6y_{i+2} - 4y_{i+1} + y_i)$.

(c) $y_i^v = \dfrac{1}{h^5}(y_{i+5} - 5y_{i+4} + 10y_{i+3} - 10y_{i+2} + 5y_{i+1} - y_i)$.

2.16 Determine approximate expressions for the following derivatives using two terms of their forward difference expansions. Determine the first term of the error series in each case.

(a) y_i'. (b) y_i''. (c) y_i'''. (d) y_i^{iv}.

Ans. (b) $y_i'' = \dfrac{1}{h^2}(2y_i - 5y_{i+1} + 4y_{i+2} - y_{i+3}); e \doteq \tfrac{11}{12}h^2 y_i^{iv}$.

(d) $y_i^{iv} = \dfrac{1}{h^4}(3y_i - 14y_{i+1} + 26y_{i+2} - 24y_{i+3} + 11y_{i+4} - 2y_{i+5})$;

$e \doteq \tfrac{34}{12}h^2 y_i^{vi}$.

2.17 Derive by direct substitution of difference expansions in the Taylor series (a) of Sec. 2.6, (a) the forward, and (b) the backward Gregory-Newton interpolation formulas.

2.18 Given $\tan x$ for $x = 23°(1°)28°$, evaluate by means of the Gregory-Newton forward and backward interpolation formulas, to five significant figures:

(a) $\tan 23°15'$. (b) $\tan 27°13'$.

Ans. (a) Forward, $\tan 23°15' = 0.42963$. (b) Backward, $\tan 27°13' = 0.51433$. *Note:* The symbol $x = a(h)b$ stands for the values of x from a to b in steps of h.

2.19 Evaluate from the following table:

(a) $f(3.8)$ to three significant figures, using the Gregory-Newton backward interpolation formula.

(b) $f(1.2)$ to three significant figures, using the Gregory-Newton forward interpolation formula.

(c) $f(5.12)$ to three significant figures, using the Gregory-Newton forward interpolation formula.

x_i	0	1	2	3	4
$f(x_i)$	1.00	1.50	2.20	3.10	4.60

Ans. (b) 1.63.

2.20 Given sin x for $x = 5°(5°)30°$, evaluate to five significant figures by interpolation:

(a) sin 5°14′.   (b) sin 25°25′.   (c) sin 17°30′.

Ans.   (b) 0.42917.

2.21 Given x^3 for $x = 1(1)5$, find by interpolation the cubes of:

(a) 4.37.   (b) 1.35.   (c) 3.46.

Ans.   (a) $(4.37)^3 = 83.45$ (backward).   (c) $(3.46)^3 = 41.42$ (backward and forward).

2.22 Given evenly spaced pivotal values ..., y_{ll}, y_l, y_i, y_r, y_{rr}, ..., determine approximate expressions for (a) y_i'', (b) y_i''', (c) y_i^{iv}, and (d) y_i^{v} with errors of order h^2 by means of:

(1) Central difference expansions, expressing derivatives in both averaged and unaveraged forms.
(2) Interpolating parabolas passing through pivotal points symmetrically located with respect to i.
(3) Taylor series expansions.

Obtain, where possible, the first term of the error series.

Ans.   See Fig. 2.8a.

2.23 Determine approximate expressions for the following derivatives using two terms of their central difference expansions:

(a) y_i'.   (b) y_i''.   (c) y_i'''.   (d) y_i^{iv}.

Ans.   See Fig. 2.8b.

2.24 Form tables of backward, forward, and central differences for the following functions:

(a) $\tan x$; $x = 1°(1°)6°$.   (b) $\cosh x$; $x = 0.1(0.1)0.7$.
(c) e^x; $x = 0(0.5)3.0$.   (d) $J_0(x)$; $x = 0(0.1)1.0$.
(e) $x^3 - 4x^2 + 5x + 3$; $x = 0(1)4$.   (f) $\log \sin x$; $x = 5°(5°)25°$.
(g) e^{-x}; $x = 0(0.5)3.0$.   (h) $\tanh x$; $x = 0.1(0.1)0.7$.

2.25 Locate the error in one of the pivotal values of the following tables and correct it by central differences.

(a)

x_i	0.50	0.52	0.54	0.56	0.58	0.60	0.62
y_i	0.5211	0.5438	0.5666	0.5987	0.6131	0.6367	0.6605

(b)

x_i	1	2	3	4	5	6	7	8	9
y_i	0.01746	0.03492	0.05241	0.07154	0.08749	0.10510	0.12278	0.14054	0.15838

(c)

x_i	1	2	3	4	5	6	7	8
y_i	1.733	1.822	1.916	2.100	2.117	2.226	2.340	2.460

(d)

x	0	0.1	0.2	0.3	0.4	0.5	0.6	0.7
e^{-x}	1.000	0.905	0.819	0.741	0.640	0.607	0.549	0.497

Ans. (b) $y_4 = 0.06993$. (d) $e^{-0.4} = 0.670$.

2.26 Given tan x for $x = 23°(1°)(28°)$, evaluate by means of Sterling's interpolation formula to five significant figures:

(a) tan 23°15′. (b) tan 27°13′.

Ans. (a) tan 23°15′ = 0.42963.

2.27 Given sin x for $x = 5°(5°)30°$, evaluate by means of Sterling's interpolation formula to five significant figures:

(a) sin 5°14′. (b) sin 25°25′. (c) sin 17°30′.

Ans. (b) sin 25°25′ = 0.42920.

2.28 Evaluate, using Lagrange's interpolation, the function defined by the following tables.

(a)

x	0	1.2	2.5	4.0	5.1	6.0	6.5	7.0
$f(x)$	3.00	6.84	14.25	27.00	39.21	51.00	58.25	66.00

Evaluate $f(2.00); f(4.50); f(6.30)$.

(b)

x	0	1.4	2.5	3.8	5.4	6.0	6.7	7.0
$f(x)$	5.00	1.36	1.25	4.24	7.56	17.00	23.09	26.00

Evaluate $f(2.00); f(3.00); f(6.40)$.

Ans. (a) $f(2.00) = 11.00; f(6.30) = 55.25$.
(b) $f(3.00) = 2.00$.

2.29 Obtain the following derivatives of the Bessel function $J_0(x)$ at the indicated points, with errors of the indicated order, using one term of their backward, central, or forward difference expansions.

x	0.0	0.1	0.2	0.3	0.4
$J_0(x)$	1.0000	0.9975	0.9900	0.9776	0.9604

(a) $\left. \dfrac{dJ_0}{dx} \right]_{x=0.1}$; $e = 0(h^2)$.

(b) $\left. \dfrac{d^2J_0}{dx^2} \right]_{x=0.1}$; $e = 0(h)$.

(c) $\left. \dfrac{d^2J_0}{dx^2} \right]_{x=0.1}$; $e = 0(h^2)$.

(d) $\left. \dfrac{d^4J_0}{dx^4} \right]_{x=0.2}$; $e = 0(h^2)$.

(e) $\left. \dfrac{d^3J_0}{dx^3} \right]_{x=0}$; $e = 0(h)$.

(f) $\left. \dfrac{d^2J_0}{dx^2} \right]_{x=0.4}$; $e = 0(h)$.

(g) $\left. \dfrac{dJ_0}{dx} \right]_{x=0.4}$; $e = 0(h)$.

Ans. (a) -0.0500. (c) -0.5000. (e) 0.1000. (g) -0.1720.

2.30 Obtain the following derivatives of the Bessel function $Y_1(x)$ at the indicated points, with errors of the indicated order, using the first term of their backward, forward, or central difference expansions.

x	6.0	6.1	6.2	6.3	6.4
$Y_1(x)$	0.1750	-0.1998	-0.2223	-0.2422	-0.2596

(a) $\left. \dfrac{d^4Y_1}{dx^4} \right]_{x=6.2}$; $e = 0(h^2)$.

(b) $\left. \dfrac{dY_1}{dx} \right]_{x=6.0}$; $e = 0(h)$.

(c) $\left. \dfrac{d^3Y_1}{dx^3} \right]_{x=6.3}$; $e = 0(h)$.

(d) $\left. \dfrac{d^2Y_1}{dx^2} \right]_{x=6.3}$; $e = 0(h^2)$.

(e) $\left. \dfrac{dY_1}{dx} \right]_{x=6.4}$; $e = 0(h)$.

Ans. (b) -0.2480. (d) 0.2500.

2.31 Given the following table, evaluate approximate expressions for the given derivatives at the indicated points. Use formulas for unevenly spaced pivotal points.

x	0.0	1.2	2.4	3.9
y	3.41	2.68	1.37	-1.48

(a) $\left. y' \right]_{x=2.4}$; $e = 0(h)$.

(b) $\left. y' \right]_{x=2.4}$; $e = 0(h^2)$.

(c) $\left. y' \right]_{x=1.2}$; $e = 0(h^2)$.

(d) $\left. y'' \right]_{x=2.4}$; $e = 0(h)$.

(e) $y''\Big]_{x=2.4}$; $e = 0(h^2)$.

Ans. (b) -1.451. (d) -0.5988.

2.32 Evaluate the given derivatives at the indicated points with errors of the indicated order. Use formulas for unevenly spaced pivotal points.

x	0.0	0.1	0.2	0.4
$J_0(x)$	1.0000	0.9975	0.9900	0.9604

(a) $\dfrac{dJ_0}{dx}\Big]_{x=0.2}$; $e = 0(h^2)$.

(b) $\dfrac{dJ_0}{dx}\Big]_{x=0.2}$; $e = 0(h)$.

(c) $\dfrac{d^2J_0}{dx^2}\Big]_{x=0.2}$; $e = 0(h^2)$.

(d) $\dfrac{d^2J_0}{dx^2}\Big]_{x=0.2}$; $e = 0(h)$.

(e) $\dfrac{d^2J_0}{dx^2}\Big]_{x=0.1}$; $e = 0(h^2)$.

Ans. (a) -0.0993. (c) -0.4900. (e) -0.5000.

2.33 Assuming that the error series of a formula of order h^4 may be stopped after the second term,

$$e \doteq c_2 h^4 + c_3 h^6,$$

derive the expressions for the coefficients of the so-called (h^4, h^6)-extrapolation formula and compute the values of these coefficients for values of h inversely proportional to (a) 3, 2, 1; (b) 4, 3, 2; (c) 5, 4, 3.

Ans. $K_{ijk} = \dfrac{n_k^6(n_j^2 - n_i^2)k_k - n_j^6(n_k^2 - n_i^2)k_j + n_i^6(n_k^2 - n_j^2)k_i}{n_k^6(n_j^2 - n_i^2) - n_j^6(n_k^2 - n_i^2) + n_i^6(n_k^2 - n_j^2)}$.

  (a) 1.301786; 0.304762; 0.002976. (b) 1.681445; 0.718227; 0.036782.
  (c) 2.170139; 1.300317; 0.130179.

2.34 Evaluate the second derivative of $J_0(x)$ at (a) $x = 0.2$, and (b) $x = 0.5$ by central differences with error of order h^2, using the table of Problem 2.24(d), with $h = 0.2$ and $h = 0.1$. Extrapolate and compare with the value obtained by the central difference formula with error of order h^4 and $h = 0.1$.

2.35 (a) Evaluate the second derivative of $\sin x$ at $x = \pi/4$ by central difference expansions, with error of order (1) h^2, and (2) h^4, taking $h = \pi/4$, $\pi/8$, and $\pi/16$. Extrapolate and compare with the true value.

(b) Evaluate the first derivative of $\sin x$ at $x = \pi/4$ using expressions with errors as above and $h = \pi/8$ and $\pi/16$.

Ans. (a) $e = 0(h^2)$; $h = \pi/4$; $y'' = -0.67151$;
                $h = \pi/8$; $y'' = -0.69813$;
                $h = \pi/16$; $y'' = -0.70500$;
        $e = 0(h^4)$; $h = \pi/8$; $y'' = -0.70702$;
                $h = \pi/16$; $y'' = -0.70729$.

(b) $e = 0(h^2)$; $h = \pi/4$; $y' = 0.63662$;
                    $h = \pi/8$; $y' = 0.68908$;
                    $h = \pi/16$; $y' = 0.70257$;
    $e = 0(h^4)$; $h = \pi/8$; $y' = 0.70656$;
                    $h = \pi/16$; $y' = 0.70707$.

2.36 Derive the integration formula of Eq. (2.11.5) by Taylor series.

2.37 Derive a seven-point integration formula with an error of order h^9 by Taylor series and compare it with Weddle's formula of Eq. (2.11.6).

2.38 Evaluate the following integrals by the trapezoidal rule for the indicated values of n and extrapolate.

(a) $\int_0^\pi \sin^3 x \, dx$ $(n = 2,4,6)$.

(b) $\int_0^2 \sqrt{4x - x^2} \, dx$ $(n = 2,4)$.

(c) $\int_0^2 e^{-x^2} \, dx$ $(n = 2,4)$.

Ans.   (a) $n = 2$; 1.571; $n = 4$; 1.342; $n = 6$; 1.335; $n = 2, 4$; 1.266; $n = 4, 6$; 1.330; true = 1.333.   (c) $n = 2$; 0.877; $n = 4$; 0.881; $n = 2, 4$; 0.8823; true = 0.8821.

2.39 Evaluate the following integrals by Simpson's $\frac{1}{3}$ rule for the indicated values of n, and extrapolate.

(a) $\int_0^2 \sqrt{4x - x^2} \, dx$ $(n = 2,4)$.   (b) $\int_2^6 x \sqrt{3 + 4x} \, dx$ $(n = 2,4)$.

(c) $\int_0^4 \sqrt{16 - x^2} \, dx$ $(n = 2,4)$.   (d) $\int_1^3 x^2 \sinh x \, dx$ $(n = 2,4)$.

(e) $\int_1^5 \frac{dx}{x}$ $(n = 2,4,6)$.   (f) $\int_0^\pi \sin^3 x \, dx$ $(n = 2,4,6)$.

(g) $\int_0^4 \frac{dx}{\sqrt{25 + x^2}}$ $(n = 2,4)$.   (h) $\int_0^4 \frac{dx}{(25 - x^2)^{3/2}}$ $(n = 2,4)$.

Ans.   (b) $A_2 = 71.702$;   (d) $A_2 = 49.796$;
                $A_4 = 71.691$; $A_4 = 48.464$;
                $A_{2,4} = 71.690$; $A_{2,4} = 48.375$;
                $A = 71.693$. $A = 48.371$.
        (f) $A_2 = 2.094$;   (h) $A_2 = 0.0577$;
                $A_4 = 1.268$; $A_4 = 0.0541$;
                $A_6 = 1.330$; $A_{2,4} = 0.0538$;
                $A_{2,6} = 1.3205$;* $A = 0.05333$.
                $A = 1.333$.

* The h^2 and the h^4 extrapolations can be applied only to a monotonic sequence of values.

2.40 Evaluate the following integrals, using the trapezoidal rule, for $n = 2$ and $n = 4$ subintervals, and extrapolate.

(a) $\displaystyle \int_0^{\pi/2} \cos x \, dx.$ (b) $\displaystyle \int_3^7 x^2 \log x \, dx.$

(c) $\displaystyle \int_1^{11} \sqrt{1 + x^2} \, dx.$ (d) $\displaystyle \int_0^{0.8} \cosh x^2 \, dx.$

(e) $\displaystyle \int_3^7 \log x \, dx.$ (f) $\displaystyle \int_4^8 \frac{dx}{\sqrt{16x - x^2}}.$

(g) $\displaystyle \int_1^5 \frac{dx}{\sqrt{x + 2}}.$ (h) $\displaystyle \int_0^4 \frac{dx}{\sqrt{25 - x^2}}.$

(i) $\displaystyle 4 \int_0^1 \frac{dx}{1 + x^2}.$

Ans.   (b) $A_2 = 185.7090$; $A_4 = 179.5385$; $A_{2,4} = 177.4819$;
           $A = 177.4836.$
       (d) $A_2 = 0.848$; $A_4 = 0.837$; $A_{2,4} = 0.834.$
       (f) $A_2 = 0.5275$; $A_4 = 0.5244$; $A_{2,4} = 0.5234$; $A = 0.5236.$
       (h) $A_2 = 0.9695$; $A_4 = 0.9389$; $A_{2,4} = 0.9286$; $A = 0.9267.$

2.41 Evaluate the integrals of Problem 2.40 by Simpson's $\frac{1}{3}$ rule and extrapolation for $n = 2$ and $n = 4$ subintervals.

Ans.   (b) $A_2 = 177.454$; $A_4 = 177.481$; $A_{2,4} = 177.483.$
       (d) $A_2 = 0.835$; $A_4 = 0.834$; $A_{2,4} = 0.834.$
       (f) $A_2 = 0.5238$; $A_4 = 0.5234$; $A_{2,4} = 0.5234.$
       (h) $A_2 = 0.9372$; $A_4 = 0.9286$; $A_{2,4} = 0.9280.$
       (i) $A_2 = 3.1333$; $A_4 = 3.1413$; $A_{2,4} = 3.1419$; $A = \pi.$

2.42 Evaluate the integrals of Problem 2.38 by Simpson's $\frac{3}{8}$ rule for $n = 3,6$ and extrapolate when $A_{3,6}$ is valid.

Ans.   (a) $A_3 = 1.530$; $A_6 = 1.305$; $A = 1.333.$
       (c) $A_3 = 0.8623$; $A_6 = 0.8820$; $A_{3,6} = 0.8886$; $A = 0.8821.$

2.43 Evaluate the integrals of Problem 2.40 by Simpson's $\frac{3}{8}$ rule and extrapolation for $n = 3$ and $n = 6$ subintervals.

Ans.   (b) $A_3 = 177.457$; $A_6 = 177.472$; $A_{36} = 177.477$; $A = 177.4836.$
       (f) $A_3 = 0.5237$; $A_6 = 0.5236$; $A_{3,6} = 0.5236$; $A = 0.5236.$

2.44 Evaluate the integrals of Problem 2.38 by Eq. (2.11.5) with $n = 4$.

Ans.   (b) $A_4 = 177.485.$ (f) $A_4 = 0.5236.$

2.45 Evaluate the integrals of Problem 2.38 by Weddle's rule with $n = 6$.

Ans.   (a) $I = 1.343.$

2.46 Evaluate the integrals from x_0 to x_n of the functions given in the following tables by Eq. (2.12.1).

(a)

x	0	1.2	2.5	4.0	5.1	6.0	6.5	7.0
$f(x)$	3.00	6.84	14.25	27.00	39.21	51.00	58.25	66.00

(b)

x	0.00	0.20	0.38	0.50	0.75	0.90	1.00
$f(x)$	6.00	5.24	4.62	4.25	3.56	3.21	3.00

Ans. (b) $I = 4.34$.

2.47 Evaluate the integrals from x_0 to x_n of the functions of Problems 2.46(a) and (b) by Eq. (2.12.2).

Ans. (b) $I = 4.23$.

III

The Numerical Integration of Initial Value Problems

3.1 Introduction

Consider an nth order differential equation

$$y^{(n)}(x) = f(x,y,y',\ldots,y^{(n-1)}) \qquad (3.1.1)$$

with the n initial conditions at a point arbitrarily chosen as origin

$$y(0) = y_0; \quad y'(0) = y'_0; \quad \ldots; \quad y^{(n-1)}(0) = y^{(n-1)}. \qquad (3.1.2)$$

The numerical solution of this initial value problem consists in the evaluation of the integral $y(x)$ at pivotal points of its interval of definition, evenly spaced by h units. These values are obtained step by step, starting at the initial point, which is usually taken to be the origin, as indicated by Eq. (3.1.2).

The evaluation of y at the pivotal point $x_i = ih$ (i = integer) is performed by *recurrence equations* as soon as y is known at a certain number of preceding pivotal points $x_{i-1}, x_{i-2}, x_{i-3}, \ldots$. In order to apply these equations, it is therefore necessary to evaluate accurately $y(x)$

at the first few (one to four) pivotal points; this is usually done by a Taylor expansion of $y(x)$.

3.2 Starting the Solution by Taylor Series

The successive derivatives of order n, $n + 1$, $n + 2$, ... of y at the origin can be evaluated by means of Eqs. (3.1.1) and (3.1.2):

$$y_0^{(n)} = f(0,y_0,y_0',\ldots,y_0^{(n-1)})$$

$$y_0^{(n+1)} = \frac{\partial f}{\partial x} + \frac{\partial f}{\partial y} y' + \frac{\partial f}{\partial y'} y'' + \cdots + \frac{\partial f}{\partial y^{(n-1)}} y^{(n)}\bigg]_{x=0}$$

$$y_0^{(n+2)} = \frac{\partial^2 f}{\partial x^2} + \frac{\partial^2 f}{\partial y^2} y'^2 + \frac{\partial f}{\partial y} y'' + \frac{\partial^2 f}{\partial y'^2} y''^2 + \frac{\partial f}{\partial y'} y''' + \cdots\bigg]_{x=0}$$

(3.2.1)

. . . .

By means of these derivatives the first terms of the Taylor expansion of y about the origin

$$y(x) = y_0 + \frac{y_0'}{1!} x + \frac{y_0''}{2!} x^2 + \frac{y_0'''}{3!} x^3 + \cdots \tag{3.2.2}$$

allow the evaluation of y at the first few pivotal points, provided h be small enough for the series to be rapidly convergent at $x = ih$ $(i = 1,2,\ldots,4)$.

Consider, for example, the first-order nonlinear equation

$$y' = -\frac{0.9}{1 + 2x} y \tag{a}$$

with the initial condition

$$y(0) = y_0 = 1. \tag{b}$$

The initial values of the successive derivatives of y are

$$y'(0) = -0.9[(1 + 2x)^{-1}y]_{x=0} = -0.9;$$

$$y''(0) = -0.9[(1 + 2x)^{-1}y' - 2(1 + 2x)^{-2}y]_{x=0}$$

$$= -0.9(y_0' - 2y_0) = +2.610;$$

$$y'''(0) = -0.9[(1 + 2x)^{-1}y'' - 4(1 + 2x)^{-2}y' + 8(1 + 2x)^{-3}y]_{x=0}$$

$$= -0.9(y_0'' - 4y_0' + 8y_0) = -12.79;$$

$$y^{iv}(0) = -0.9[(1 + 2x)^{-1}y''' - 6(1 + 2x)^{-2}y'' + 24(1 + 2x)^{-3}y'$$

$$- 48(1 + 2x)^{-4}y]_{x=0}$$

$$= -0.9(y_0''' - 6y_0'' + 24y_0' - 48y_0) = +88.24.$$

The first five terms of the Taylor expansion $y_T(x)$ of $y(x)$ about $x = 0$ thus become

$$y_T(x) = y_0 + \frac{y_0'}{1!} x + \frac{y_0''}{2!} x^2 + \frac{y_0'''}{3!} x^3 + \frac{y_0^{iv}}{4!} x^4$$

$$= 1 - 0.9x + 1.305x^2 - 2.132x^3 + 3.677x^4.$$

Table 3.1 gives the values of $y_T(x)$ for $x = 0(0.02)0.10$ and for $x = 0.20$ and 0.30, together with the corresponding values of $y(x)$

Table 3.1

x	$y_T(x)$	$y(x)$
0	1.0000	1.0000
0.02	0.9825	0.9825
0.04	0.9660	0.9660
0.06	0.9503	0.9503
0.08	0.9354	0.9354
0.10	0.9213	0.9212
0.20	0.8610	0.8595
0.30	0.8197	0.8094

obtained by integrating Eq. (a) by separation of the variables:

$$\frac{dy}{y} = -0.9 \frac{dx}{1 + 2x},$$

$$\int_{y_0}^{y} \frac{dy}{y} = \ln \frac{y}{y_0} = -0.9 \int_0^x \frac{dx}{1 + 2x} = -0.45 \ln (1 + 2x).$$

$$y(x) = (1 + 2x)^{-0.45}.$$

The value $y_T(0.3)$ is in error by $+1.27$ per cent.

As an example of the starting of a second-order equation, consider the mathematical pendulum of Fig. 3.1.

The oscillations in a vacuum of a mathematical pendulum released from rest at $t = 0$ from an angle θ_0 satisfy the well-known nonlinear differential equation:*

$$\frac{d^2\theta}{dt^2} + \frac{g}{L} \sin \theta = 0 \tag{c}$$

and the initial conditions

$$\theta(0) = \theta_0; \qquad \dot{\theta}(0) = 0, \tag{d}$$

* See, for example, *Differential Equations*, Sec. 2.7.

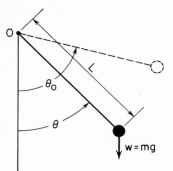

Figure 3.1

where θ is the angle between the pendulum and the vertical, t the time, g the acceleration of gravity, and L the length of the pendulum.

A rigorous solution of the initial value problem (c), (d), may be obtained in terms of nonelementary functions called *elliptic integrals** and shows that the period of oscillation of the pendulum is given by

$$T = 4K\left(\frac{\theta_0}{2}\right)\sqrt{\frac{L}{g}}, \qquad \text{(e)}$$

where K is the *complete elliptic integral of the first kind* and is tabulated, for example, in Peirce's *A Short Table of Integrals.* For $\theta_0 = 120°$, $K(\theta_0/2) = 2.1565$, and, with $g = 32.2$ ft/sec², $L = 3.22$ ft, the pendulum period equals $T = 2.7276$ sec.

To solve the same problem by numerical methods, the solution is started in nondimensional form, by setting

$$t = \frac{T}{4}\tau; \qquad \therefore \qquad dt = \frac{T}{4}d\tau;$$

$$(dt)^2 = \left(\frac{T}{4}\right)^2 (d\tau)^2 = (0.6819)^2(d\tau)^2 = 0.46499d\tau^2.$$

Equation (c), with $g/L = 10$ sec⁻², then becomes

$$\frac{d^2\theta}{d\tau^2} \equiv \ddot{\theta} = -4.6499 \sin \theta, \qquad \text{(f)}$$

while the initial conditions require that

$$\theta(0) = \theta_0 = 120° = 2.0944 \text{ radians};$$
$$\dot{\theta}(0) = \dot{\theta}_0 = 0, \qquad \text{(g)}$$

where dots indicate differentiation with respect to τ. From Eq. (f) and its derivatives, we obtain

$$\ddot{\theta}_0 = -4.6499 \sin \theta_0 = -4.0268;$$

$$\dddot{\theta}_0 = -4.6499 \cos \theta_0 \cdot \dot{\theta}_0 = 0;$$

$$\theta_0^{iv} = -4.6499(\cos \theta_0 \cdot \ddot{\theta}_0 - \sin \theta_0 \cdot \dot{\theta}_0^2) = -9.3623,$$

and hence the Taylor series

$$\theta(\tau) \doteq 2.0944 - 2.0134\tau^2 - 0.3901\tau^4. \qquad \text{(h)}$$

* See, for example, *Differential Equations,* Secs. 9.3 and 9.4.

Table 3.2 gives the values of θ derived from this series for $\tau = 0(0.1)0.4$.

Table 3.2

$\tau = t/0.6819$	θ	θ_L
0	2.0944	2.0944
0.1	2.0742	2.0458
0.2	2.0132	1.9026
0.3	1.9100	1.6713
0.4	1.7623	1.3624

The linearized equation, valid for values of the angle θ small enough to have $\sin \theta \doteq \theta$, is

$$\ddot{\theta} = -4.6499\theta$$

and yields the solution

$$\theta_L(\tau) = 2.0944 \cos 2.1564\tau. \tag{i}$$

The values of θ_L are given, for comparison, in the third column of Table 3.2.

The solution of the same problem when the pendulum oscillates in a viscous medium, which cannot be obtained by elliptic integrals, involves no increased difficulties when a Taylor series is used.

The differential equation of the pendulum in a viscous medium contains an additional damping term, $\mu \, d\theta/dt$, where μ is the frictional resistance per unit mass. With $\mu = 0.5875$ sec^{-1}, for example, and $g/L = 10$ sec^{-2} as before, Eq. (c) is transformed* into the equation

$$\frac{d^2\theta}{dt^2} + 0.5875 \frac{d\theta}{dt} + 10 \sin \theta = 0. \tag{j}$$

If we again let $t = (T/4)\tau = 0.6819\tau$ (where T is the period of the undamped pendulum), this equation takes the form

$$\ddot{\theta} + 0.4\dot{\theta} + 4.6499 \sin \theta = 0 \tag{k}$$

(where dots indicate differentiation with respect to τ), while the initial conditions remain those of Eqs. (g). By means of Eq. (k) and its successive derivatives,

$$\ddot{\theta}_0 = -0.4\dot{\theta}_0 - 4.6499 \sin \theta_0 = -4.0268;$$

$$\dddot{\theta}_0 = -0.4\ddot{\theta}_0 - 4.6499 \cos \theta_0 \cdot \dot{\theta}_0 = 1.6107;$$

$$\theta_0^{iv} = -0.4\dddot{\theta}_0 - 4.6499 \cos \theta_0 \cdot \ddot{\theta}_0 + 4.6499 \sin \theta_0 \cdot \dot{\theta}_0^2 = -10.006,$$

* See, for example, *Differential Equations*, Sec. 2.7.

we obtain, as before, the Taylor series solution:

$$\theta(\tau) = 2.0944 - 2.0134\tau^2 + 0.2685\tau^3 - 0.4169\tau^4, \tag{1}$$

which is tabulated in Table 3.3 for $\tau = 0(0.1)0.4$.

Table 3.3

τ	θ	θ_L	$\dot\theta$
0	2.0944	2.0944	0
0.1	2.0745	2.0465	-0.3963
0.2	2.0153	1.9076	-0.7865
0.3	1.9171	1.6875	-1.1806
0.4	1.7788	1.3994	-1.5886

The solution of the corresponding linearized equation

$$\ddot\theta + 0.4\dot\theta + 4.6499\theta = 0$$

(whose characteristic roots are $-0.2 \pm 2.1471i$) equals

$$\theta_L(\tau) = e^{-0.2\tau}(2.0944 \cos 2.1471\tau + 0.1951 \sin 2.1471\tau) \tag{m}$$

and is tabulated for comparison in the third column of Table 3.3.

The fourth column of this table contains the values of $\dot\theta$ evaluated by differentiating Eq. (1):

$$\dot\theta = -4.0268\tau + 0.8054\tau^2 - 1.6677\tau^3,$$

which will be used in a later section.

The methods used in this section on low-order differential equations can be extended to equations of any order and are of practical value in determining the solution in the neighborhood of the origin (or initial point). As the distance from the origin increases, the accuracy of the Taylor solution decreases, and a large number of terms of the series must be taken into account for a given accuracy. Since this may become quite laborious, it is more practical to prolong the solution by other methods, some of which are illustrated in the following sections.

3.3 Euler Forward Integration Methods

An elementary method of step-by-step integration of first-order equations, due to Euler, has limited value because of its low accuracy but is useful in illustrating forward integration processes and does not require the starting of the solution.

Given the initial value problem

$$y' = f(x,y); \qquad y(0) = y_0, \tag{3.3.1}$$

the increment Δy_i may be computed stepwise by the equation

$$\Delta y_i = y_{i+1} - y_i = f(x_i, y_i)h. \qquad (3.3.2)$$

Table 3.4 illustrates the application of Eq. (3.3.2) to the problem of Eqs. (a), (b) of Sec. 3.2.

Table 3.4

x	y_i	f_i	Δy_i
0	1.0000	−0.9000	−0.0180
0.02	0.9820	−0.8498	−0.0170
0.04	0.9650	−0.8042	−0.0161
0.06	0.9489	−0.7625	−0.0153
0.08	0.9336	−0.7243	−0.0145
0.10	0.9191	−0.6893	−0.0689
0.20	0.8402	−0.5401	−0.0540
0.30	0.7862		

The value at $x = 0.10$ is in error by 0.24 per cent; the value at $x = 0.3$ by 2.86 per cent.

The error in Euler's method is of order h since it uses the first term on the right-hand member of Eq. (2.11.1). The accuracy of Euler's method may be improved by using Eq. (3.3.2) to obtain y_{i+1} and hence y'_{i+1} by Eq. (3.3.1), and by then evaluating a corrected $\Delta'y_i$ by means of the average of y'_i and y'_{i+1}, i.e., by means of the trapezoidal rule:

$$\Delta'y_i = \frac{h}{2}\left[f(x_i, y_i) + f(x_{i+1}, y_{i+1})\right]. \qquad (3.3.3)$$

Equation (3.3.2) is called the *predictor* and Eq. (3.3.3) the *corrector* of *Euler's modified method*. The modified Euler method has an error of order h^3 since it is based on Eq. (2.11.3) for the trapezoidal rule.

Table 3.5 applies this method to the problem of Table 3.4.

Table 3.5

x_i	y_i	f_i	Δy_i	y_{i+1}	f_{i+1}	$\Delta'y_i$	$\dfrac{-0.9}{1+2x}$
0	1.0000	−0.90000	−0.0180	0.9820	−0.8498	−0.0175	−0.9000
0.02	0.9825	−0.8503	−0.0170	0.9655	−0.8046	−0.0165	−0.8654
0.04	0.9660	−0.8050	−0.0161	0.9499	−0.7633	−0.0157	−0.8333
0.06	0.9503	−0.7637	−0.0153	0.9350	−0.7255	−0.0149	−0.8036
0.08	0.9354	−0.7258	−0.0145	0.9209	−0.6907	−0.0142	−0.7759
0.10	0.9212	−0.6909	−0.0691	0.8521	−0.5478	−0.0619	−0.7500
0.20	0.8593	−0.5524	−0.0552	0.8041	−0.4523	−0.0502	−0.6429
0.30	0.8091						−0.5625

The error at $x = 0.10$ is now zero and at $x = 0.3$ is 0.04 per cent.

3.4 Milne's Method

A predictor-corrector method for first-order equations with error of order h^5, the *Milne method*, requires the knowledge y and y' at the first four pivotal points in order to start.

Given the equation and the pivotal values

$$y' = f(x,y); \qquad y_0, y_1, y_2, y_3; \qquad f_0, f_1, f_2, f_3, \qquad (3.4.1)$$

Eq. (2.10.3), shifted to the left by one step,

$$B_4 = y_{i+1} - y_{i-3} = \int_{x_{i-3}}^{x_{i+1}} f(x,y)\, dx = \frac{4h}{3}\,(2f_{i-2} - f_{i-1} + 2f_i) + \frac{14}{15}\,h^5 f^{iv}(\xi),$$
$$(a)$$

gives rise to Milne's predictor:

$$y_{i+1} = y_{i-3} + \frac{4h}{3}\,(2f_{i-2} - f_{i-1} + 2f_i), \qquad (3.4.2)$$

by means of which one evaluates f_{i+1} from Eq. (3.4.1). The corrected value of y_{i+1} is then obtained by Simpson's $\frac{1}{3}$ rule of Eq. (2.11.4):

$$y_{i+1} = y_{i-1} + \frac{h}{3}\,(f_{i-1} + 4f_i + f_{i+1}), \qquad (3.4.3)$$

which has an error $-\dfrac{h^5}{90}\,f^{iv}(\xi)$.

Table 3.6 gives the integration from $x = 0$ to $x = 2.4$ of the equation

$$y' = x + y; \qquad y_0 = 0, \qquad (b)$$

whose initial values were obtained by a Taylor expansion, with a spacing $h = 0.3$. The last column in Table 3.6 gives the correct values of $y = e^x - (1 + x)$.

Table 3.6

x_i	$y_{i,p}$	$f_{i,p}$	$y_{i,c}$	$f_{i,c}$	y_i
0				0.000	0.000
0.3				0.350	0.050
0.6				0.822	0.222
0.9				1.460	0.560
1.2	1.119	2.319	1.119	2.319	1.119
1.5	1.979	3.479	1.982	3.482	1.981
1.8	3.248	5.048	3.249	5.049	3.249
2.1	5.062	7.162	5.066	7.166	5.066
2.4	7.618	10.018	7.622		7.623

3.5 Adams's Method

The continuation of a solution started by a Taylor series may be obtained by the backward difference *Adams's recurrence equation*.

To obtain Adams's formula one substitutes in the Taylor expansion of Eq. (2.11.1) the expansions of the derivatives in terms of backward differences of Eqs. (2.4.16), (2.4.17):

$$y_{i+1} = y_i + h[f_i + \tfrac{1}{2}(\nabla + \tfrac{1}{2}\nabla^2 + \tfrac{1}{3}\nabla^3 + \tfrac{1}{4}\nabla^4 + \tfrac{1}{5}\nabla^5 + \ldots)f_i$$
$$+ \tfrac{1}{6}(\nabla^2 + \nabla^3 + \tfrac{11}{12}\nabla^4 + \tfrac{5}{6}\nabla^5 + \ldots)f_i$$
$$+ \tfrac{1}{24}(\nabla^3 + \tfrac{3}{2}\nabla^4 + \tfrac{7}{4}\nabla^5 + \ldots)f_i + \tfrac{1}{120}(\nabla^4 + 2\nabla^5 + \ldots)f^i$$
$$+ \tfrac{1}{720}(\nabla^5 + \ldots)f_i + \ldots]$$

or

$$y_{i+1} = y_i + h[1 + \tfrac{1}{2}\nabla + \tfrac{5}{12}\nabla^2 + \tfrac{3}{8}\nabla^3 + \tfrac{251}{720}\nabla^4 + \tfrac{95}{288}\nabla^5 + \ldots]f_i. \quad (3.5.1)$$

The number of terms to be taken into account in the series of Eq. (3.5.1) depends on the number of pivotal values computed by the Taylor series and on the accuracy required in the solution.

To illustrate the use of Adams's formula consider the electric circuit of Fig. 3.2. The circuit contains a coil with an iron core whose magnetization curve is given by

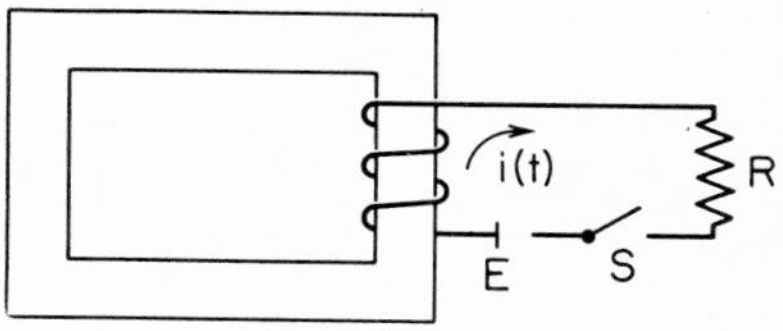

Figure 3.2

$$Ni = 0.6\phi + 0.0033 \times 10^{10}\phi^3, \quad (a)$$

where ϕ is the flux in the core (in kilolines), N the number of turns of the coil, and i the current (in amperes) setting up the flux.

Kirchhoff's voltage law applied to the circuit gives:*

$$E = Ri + L\frac{di}{dt} = Ri + N\frac{d\phi}{dt},$$

where ϕ is in webers (10^5 kilolines) and t is in seconds, or, by means of Eq. (a),

$$E = \frac{R}{N}(0.6\phi + 0.0033\phi^3) + N\frac{d\phi}{dt} \cdot 10^{-5},$$

where ϕ is now expressed in kilolines. Hence with $E = 18$ volts, $N = 100$, $R = 3000$ ohms, and t in milliseconds, the flux is governed by the *nonlinear*, first-order equation:

$$\frac{d\phi}{dt} + 1.8\phi + 0.01\phi^3 = 18. \quad (b)$$

* See, for example, *Differential Equations*, Sec. 1.7.

If the switch S is closed at $t = 0$, the initial condition requires that

$$\phi(0) = 0. \tag{c}$$

The flux ϕ approaches asymptotically its maximum value ϕ_m as t increases; hence ϕ_m is defined by the condition $d\phi/dt = 0$ and, by Eq. (b), is a root of the cubic equation

$$0.01\phi^3 + 1.8\phi - 18 = 0.$$

The only real root of this equation equals 7.5802; hence $\phi_m = 7.5802$.

To reduce Eq. (b) to nondimensional form, we set in this equation

$$\phi(t) = \phi_m y(t), \tag{d}$$

and obtain the equation for the nondimensional function $y(t)$:

$$\phi_m \dot{y} = 18 - 1.8\phi_m y - 0.01\phi_m^3 y^3,$$

where $\dot{y}$ stands for dy/dt. With $\phi_m = 7.5802$ this equation becomes, finally,

$$\dot{y} = 2.3746 - 1.8y - 0.5746y^3, \tag{e}$$

while the initial condition (c) requires that

$$y(0) = 0. \tag{f}$$

To start the solution of the initial value problem (e), (f) by series, we differentiate Eq. (e) successively, obtaining

$\dot{y}_0 = 2.3746;$

$\ddot{y}_0 = -1.8\dot{y}_0 - 0.5746 \cdot 3y_0^2 \dot{y}_0 = -4.2743;$

$\dddot{y}_0 = (-1.8 - 0.5746 \cdot 3y_0^2)\ddot{y}_0 - 0.5746 \cdot 6y_0 \dot{y}_0^2 = 7.6937;$

$y_0^{iv} = (-1.8 - 0.5746 \cdot 3y_0^2)\dddot{y}_0 - 0.5746 \cdot 6(3y_0 \ddot{y}_0 + \dot{y}_0^2)\dot{y}_0 = -60.011;$

$y_0^{v} = (-1.8 - 0.5746 \cdot 3y_0^2)y_0^{iv} - 0.5746 \cdot 6(4y_0 \dot{y}_0 \dddot{y}_0 + 3y_0 \ddot{y}_0^2 + 6\dot{y}_0^2 \ddot{y}_0)$

$\quad = 606.58.$

With these values of the derivatives at zero the Taylor series for $y(t)$ becomes:

$$y(t) = 2.3746t - 2.1372t^2 + 1.2823t^3 - 2.5005t^4 + 5.0548t^5$$

and gives the values of Table 3.7 for $t = 0(0.05)0.20$ and $t = 0.30$. The third column of Table 3.7 contains the approximate values $y_L(t)$ of $y(t)$ obtained by linearizing Eq. (e); that is, by dropping the cubic term $-0.5746y^3$, in which case the solution reduces to

$$y_L(t) = 1.3192(1 - e^{-1.8t}). \tag{g}$$

In Table 3.8 Adams's formula is used to prolong the solution. The first four rows of Table 3.8 contain: (a) the values of y and y^3 at $t = 0$,

Table 3.7

t	$y(t)$	$y_L(t)$
0	0	0
0.05	0.1135	0.1136
0.10	0.2172	0.2173
0.15	0.3116	0.3121
0.20	0.3973	0.3988
0.30	0.5476	0.5505

0.1, 0.2, 0.3 obtained from Table 3.7, (b) the value of $\dot{y} = f(y)$* given by Eq. (e) at the same points, and (c) the values of the first three backward differences of $f(y)$.

Table 3.8

i	t	y_i	y_i^3	f_i	∇f_i	$\nabla^2 f_i$	$\nabla^3 f_i$	y_L
0	0	0	0	2.3746				0
1	0.1	0.2172	0.0103	1.9777	−0.3969			0.2173
2	0.2	0.3973	0.0627	1.6234	−0.3543	0.0426		0.3988
3	0.3	0.5476	0.1642	1.2946	−0.3288	0.0255	−0.0171	0.5505
4	0.4	0.6610	0.2888	1.0189	−0.2757	0.0531	0.0276	0.6770
5	0.5	0.7523	0.4258	0.7758	−0.2431	0.0326	−0.0205	0.7828
6	0.6	0.8183	0.5479	0.5868	−0.1890	0.0541	0.0215	0.8712
7	0.7	0.8706	0.6598	0.4284	−0.1584	0.0306	−0.0235	0.9449
8	0.8	0.9059	0.7435	0.3168	−0.1116	0.0468	0.0162	1.0067
9	0.9	0.9346	0.8164	0.2232	−0.0936	0.0180	−0.0288	1.0581
10	1.0	0.9519						1.1011
	∞	1.0000						1.3192

Adams's formula, cut after its fourth term and with $h = 0.1$, takes the form

$$y_{i+1} = y_i + 0.1[f_i + \tfrac{1}{2}\nabla f_i + \tfrac{5}{12}\nabla^2 f_i + \tfrac{3}{8}\nabla^3 f_i], \tag{h}$$

and allows the determination of y_4 at $t = 0.4$ in terms of y, f, and its differences at $t = 0.3$. Once y_4 is known, f_4 is evaluated by Eq. (e), and its differences are computed by means of Table 3.8. Equation (h) is

* Notice that in the present problem the differential equation takes the simplified form $y' = f(y)$, since the independent variable does not appear in f.

then used to evaluate y_5, and so on. The pivotal values up to y_{10}, obtained step by step, are shown in Table 3.8.

The column y_L of Table 3.8 contains, for comparison, the values of the linearized solution of the same problem computed from Eq. (g) by letting the coefficient of y^3 equal zero.

The rigorous solution of Eqs. (e), (f) may be obtained by the method of the separation of the variables,* which gives t as a function of y in the form

$$t = 0.2838 \left[- \ln (1 - y) + \tfrac{1}{2} \ln \frac{y^2 + y + 4.1326}{4.1326} \right.$$

$$\left. + 0.7613 \left(\tan^{-1} \frac{2y + 1}{3.9409} - \tan^{-1} 0.2537 \right) \right]. \quad \text{(i)}$$

By means of this result, we find that for $y = 0.7523$, t equals 0.5040 rather than 0.5 as shown in Table 3.8, and that for $y = 0.9519$, t equals 0.9974 rather than 1.0000. Conversely, interpolating from the values of Table 3.8 by the forward Gregory-Newton interpolation formula [Eq. (2.6.1)], we obtain the results of Table 3.9, in which y_i are the interpolated values, y the true values, and ϵ the per cent errors.

Table 3.9

t	0.5040	0.9974
y_i	0.7552	0.9513
y	0.7523	0.9519
$\epsilon(\%)$	0.38	0.06

These results not only prove the small discrepancies between the true and the extrapolated values of the solution after 10 steps, but show that *in many cases it is actually economical to evaluate the solution of a differential equation by numerical methods even if a rigorous solution is available.* In the present problem, for example, it is certainly simpler to proceed as in Table 3.8 than first to derive the rigorous solution (i) and then to evaluate it numerically; the evaluation of Eq. (i) is burdensome and, moreover, does not give the pivotal values of y.

3.6 The Euler-Fox Method for Linear Equations

A simple and efficient method of step-by-step integration, due to Fox and based upon the classical formula of Euler, allows the integration of first-order linear differential equations *without starting the solution by means of a Taylor expansion.*

---

* See, for example, *Differential Equations*, Sec. 4.2b.

Consider the Euler modified equation [Eq. (3.3.3)]:

$$y_{i+1} = y_i + \frac{h}{2}[y_i' + y_{i+1}'] + \epsilon_{i+1}, \tag{3.6.1}$$

where

$$\epsilon_{i+1} = -(\tfrac{1}{12}h^3 y_i''' + \tfrac{1}{24}h^4 y_i^{iv} + \tfrac{1}{80}h^5 y_i^{v} + \ldots). \tag{a}$$

The error ϵ_{i+1} of Eq. (a) may be expressed in terms of *unaveraged* central differences in the form*

$$\epsilon_{i+1}^{(n)} = -(\tfrac{1}{12}\delta^3 - \tfrac{1}{120}\delta^5 + \tfrac{1}{840}\delta^7 - \ldots)y_{i+\frac{1}{2}}^{(n)}\dagger \tag{3.6.2}$$

and is *Fox's correction* to the *modified Euler formula*.

The modified Euler formula with Fox's correction will now be used to obtain a recurrence formula for the solution of first-order linear differential equations.

* For this purpose, note that the unaveraged central difference of odd order $2n + 1$ at $i + \frac{1}{2}$ may also be written as the forward difference of the central difference of order $2n$ at i, since

$$\delta^{2n+1} y_{i+\frac{1}{2}} = \Delta(\delta^{2n} y_i). \tag{b}$$

For example,

$$\delta^3 y_{i+\frac{1}{2}} = \delta(\delta^2 y_{i+\frac{1}{2}}) = \delta^2 y_{i+1} - \delta^2 y_i = \Delta(\delta^2 y_i).$$

By means of the symbolical expressions for the forward and central unaveraged differences [Eqs. (2.5.2) and (2.7.11)],

$$\Delta = (e^{hD} - 1); \qquad \delta^{2n} = 2^{2n} \sinh^{2n}(hD/2),$$

the left-hand member of Eq. (b) becomes

$$\delta^{2n+1} y_{i+\frac{1}{2}} = 2^{2n}(e^{hD} - 1) \sinh^{2n}(hD/2)y_i.$$

Substitution of these expressions in Eq. (3.6.2) reduces this equation to Eq. (a). For example,

$$\delta^3 y_{i+\frac{1}{2}} = \left[2^2(e^{hD} - 1)\sinh^2\left(\frac{hD}{2}\right) \right] y_i$$

$$= 2^2\left[hD + \frac{h^2 D^2}{2!} + \frac{h^3 D^3}{3!} + \ldots \right]\left[\frac{h^2 D^2}{4} + \frac{h^4 D^4}{48} + \ldots \right] y_i$$

$$= \left[h^3 D^3 + \frac{h^4 D^4}{2} + \frac{h^5 D^5}{4} + \ldots \right] y_i;$$

$$\delta^5 y_{i+\frac{1}{2}} = \left[h^5 D^5 + \frac{h^6 D^6}{2} + \ldots \right] y_i,$$

by means of which Eq. (3.6.2) gives

$$\epsilon_{i+1} = -\left[\frac{1}{12}\left(h^3 D^3 + \frac{h^4 D^4}{2} + \frac{h^5 D^5}{4} + \ldots \right) - \frac{1}{120}(h^5 D^5 + \ldots) + \ldots \right] y_i$$

$$= -\left(\frac{1}{12}h^3 D^3 + \frac{1}{24}h^4 D^4 + \frac{1}{80}h^5 D^5 + \ldots \right) y_i,$$

which is identical with Eq. (a).

† In this and the following sections the symbol $y_i^{(n)}$ will often be used to indicate the nth approximation of y at i.

Given a first-order *linear* differential equation

$$y' = f(x)y + g(x) \tag{3.6.3}$$

and the initial condition

$$y(0) = y_0, \tag{3.6.4}$$

let

$$x = ih; \qquad f(x) = f_i; \qquad f(x + h) = f_{i+1};$$

$$g(x) = g_i; \qquad g(x + h) = g_{i+1}.$$

Substituting Eq. (3.6.3) in Eq. (3.6.1),

$$y_{i+1} = y_i + \frac{h}{2}\left(f_i y_i + g_i + f_{i+1}y_{i+1} + g_{i+1}\right) + \epsilon_{i+1},$$

and solving this equation for y_{i+1}, we obtain the *Euler-Fox recurrence equation:*

$$y_{i+1}^{(n)} = \frac{1}{1 - \dfrac{h}{2}f_{i+1}}\left[\left(1 + \frac{h}{2}f_i\right)y_i^{(n)} + \frac{h}{2}(g_i + g_{i+1}) + \epsilon_{i+1}^{(n-1)}\right], \tag{3.6.5}$$

where the error $\epsilon_{i+1}^{(n-1)}$, given by Eq. (3.6.2), is of order h^3.

The Euler-Fox recurrence equation will now be applied to the solution of problem (a), (b) of Sec. 3.2, which is governed by the equation:

$$y' = -\frac{0.9}{1 + 2z}\,y \tag{c}$$

and the condition:

$$y(0) = 1. \tag{d}$$

In this case, with $h = 0.1$, $f(z) = -\dfrac{0.9}{1 + 2z}$, $g(z) = 0$, Eq. (3.6.5) becomes

$$y_{i+1}^{(n)} = \frac{1}{1 - 0.05f_{i+1}}[(1 + 0.05f_i)y_i^{(n)} + \epsilon_{i+1}^{(n-1)}]. \tag{e}$$

The values of $y_i^{(1)}$ in the third column of Table 3.10 were computed

Table 3.10

z	f_i	$y_i^{(1)}$	$\delta y_{i+\frac{1}{2}}$	$\delta^2 y_i$	$\delta^3 y_{i+\frac{1}{2}}$	$\dfrac{\epsilon_{i+1}^{(1)}}{1 - 0.05f_{i+1}}$	$y_i^{(2)}$
0	-0.9000	1.0000					1.0000
			-0.0795		(-0.0056)	$+0.0005$	
0.1	-0.7500	0.9205		0.0174			0.9210
			-0.0621		-0.0056	$+0.0005$	
0.2	-0.6428	0.8584		0.0118			0.8594
			-0.0503		(-0.0056)	$+0.0005$	
0.3	-0.5625	0.8081					0.8096

by means of Eq. (e) starting with $y_0 = 1$ and ignoring the correction ϵ_{i+1}. The value of $y(0.3)$ has an error of 0.16 per cent.

The successive columns of Table 3.10 contain the central unaveraged differences of $y_{i+\frac{1}{2}}$, the correction $\epsilon_{i+1}^{(1)}$, and the second approximation $y_i^{(2)}$ of y, evaluated by means of Eq. (e) with the correction. Since the value of $\delta^3 y_{i+\frac{1}{2}}$ can be computed only at the point $z = 0.15$, it was assumed that the third difference is constant and equal to -0.0056 at all points $i + \frac{1}{2}$. Hence,

$$\epsilon_{i+1}^{(1)} \doteq -\tfrac{1}{12}\delta^3 y_{i+\frac{1}{2}} = -\tfrac{1}{12} \cdot 0.0056 = 0.0005,$$

whatever i, and

$$y_i^{(2)} = y_i^{(1)} + \frac{0.0005}{1 - 0.05 f_{i+1}}.$$

The last value $y^{(2)}(0.3)$, has an error of only 0.02 per cent.

3.7 The Solution of Simultaneous First-order Equations

Adams's formula [Eq. (3.5.1)] may be conveniently used to solve systems of simultaneous first-order differential equations. Consider the simple case of two simultaneous equations:

$$y' = f(x,y,z); \qquad z' = \phi(x,y,z), \tag{3.7.1}$$

where y and z are functions of the same independent variable x, with the two initial conditions

$$y(0) = y_0; \qquad z(0) = z_0. \tag{3.7.2}$$

Applying Adams's formula to both equations, we obtain the recurrence equations

$$\begin{aligned}
y_{i+1} &= y_i + h[1 + \tfrac{1}{2}\nabla + \tfrac{5}{12}\nabla^2 + \ldots]f_i; \\
z_{i+1} &= z_i + h[1 + \tfrac{1}{2}\nabla + \tfrac{5}{12}\nabla^2 + \ldots]\phi_i,
\end{aligned} \tag{3.7.3}$$

which can be used as soon as sufficient initial values for y and z have been obtained by Taylor series.

For example, the particularly simple set of simultaneous equations

$$y' = f(x,y,z) = z; \qquad z' = \phi(x,y,z) = y \tag{a}$$

with the conditions

$$y(0) = y_0 = 1; \qquad z(0) = z_0 = 2 \tag{b}$$

give by differentiation

$$y_0 = 1; \qquad z_0 = 2,$$
$$y_0' = z_0 = 2; \qquad z_0' = y_0 = 1,$$
$$y_0'' = z_0' = 1; \qquad z_0'' = y_0' = 2,$$

$$\dots\dots\dots\dots\dots\dots\dots\dots$$

and hence the Taylor series,

$$y = 1 + 2x + \frac{x^2}{2} + \dots; \qquad z = 2 + x + x^2 + \dots.$$

From these series we obtain the values of y, ∇y, $\nabla^2 y$, z, ∇z, $\nabla^2 z$ of the first three lines of Table 3.11 for $x = 0$, 0.1, 0.2. The values of y and z for $x = 0.3$ and 0.4 are then obtained by Eqs. (3.7.3) with $h = 0.1$, $f = z$, and $\phi = y$. The true values of y and z at $x = 0.4$ are 1.903 and 2.573, respectively.

Table 3.11

x	y	∇y	$\nabla^2 y$	z	∇z	$\nabla^2 z$
0	1			2		
0.1	1.205	0.205		2.110	0.110	
0.2	1.420	0.215	0.010	2.240	0.130	0.020
0.3	1.651	0.231	0.016	2.393	0.153	0.023
0.4	1.899	0.248	0.017	2.570	0.177	0.024

The procedure may obviously be extended to any number of simultaneous equations and to the other methods of step-by-step integration.

In particular, the Euler-Fox method may also be extended to solve simultaneous *linear* equations. The reader may derive the recurrence equations for systems of two or more equations following the pattern of this section (see Problem 3.19).

The solution of an nth-order equation,

$$y^{(n)} = f(x,y,y',y'',\dots,y^{(n-1)}), \qquad (3.7.4)$$

is reduced to the solution of n simultaneous first-order equations by the substitutions

$$y' = f_1(x,y)$$
$$y'' = f_1' = f_2(x,y,y') = f_2(x,y,f_1)$$
$$y''' = f_2' = f_3(x,y,y',y'') = f_3(x,y,f_1,f_2) \qquad (3.7.5)$$

$$\dots\dots\dots\dots\dots\dots\dots\dots\dots\dots\dots$$

$$y^{(n)} = f_{n-1}' = f(x,y,y',\dots,y^{(n-1)}) = f(x,y,f_1,f_2,\dots,f_{n-1}).$$

Thus any method for the solution of first-order equations may be extended to solve nth-order equations.

3.8 Milne's Method for Second-order Equations

Milne's predictor-corrector method for first-order equations is easily extended to second-order equations. Given

$$y'' = f(x,y,y'); \qquad y(0) = y_0; \qquad y'(0) = y'_0, \qquad (3.8.1)$$

one starts the solution by a Taylor series and obtains the first four pivotal values of y_i, y'_i, and $y''_i = f_i$. The use of Eq. (2.10.3) as a predictor at $i - 1$ gives:

$$y'_{i+1} = y'_{i-3} + \frac{4h}{3} (2f_i - f_{i-1} + 2f_{i-2}). \qquad (3.8.2)$$

The knowledge of y'_{i+1} allows the use of Simpson's $\frac{1}{3}$ rule to predict y_{i+1}:

$$y_{i+1} = y_{i-1} + \frac{h}{3} (y'_{i+1} + 4y'_i + y'_{i-1}). \qquad (3.8.3)$$

The value of $y''_{i+1} = f_{i+1}$ is obtained from the differential equation by means of the predicted values of y_{i+1} and y'_{i+1}, and the corrected value of y'_{i+1} is evaluated by means of Simpson's $\frac{1}{3}$ rule:

$$y'_{i+1} = y'_{i-1} + \frac{h}{3} (f_{i+1} + 4f_i + f_{i-1}). \qquad (3.8.4)$$

The corrected value of y_{i+1} is finally computed by Eq. (3.8.3). The procedure may be iterated, but this is seldom required if h is suitably small.

Table 3.12 illustrates the application of Milne's method to the problem

$$y'' - \tfrac{3}{2}y' + \tfrac{1}{2}y = 0; \qquad y_0 = 0; \qquad y'_0 = 1. \qquad (a)$$

The solution of this problem, $y = 2(e^x - e^{x/2})$, $y' = 2e^x - e^{x/2}$, was used to obtain the first four values of y_i and y'_i in Table 3.12, as well as the correct values of y in its last row.

Table 3.12

x	0	0.3	0.6	0.9	1.2 p	1.2 c	1.5 p	1.5 c	1.8 p	1.8 c
y	0	0.3762	0.9444	1.7826	2.9957	2.9959	4.7285	4.7289	7.1790	7.1793
y'	1.0	1.5380	2.9243	3.3509	4.8154	4.8167	6.8412	6.8451	9.6339	9.6369
y''	1.5	2.1189	2.9692	4.1350	5.7252	5.7274	7.8976	7.9032	10.8614	10.8657
				y		2.9960		4.7294		7.1800

3.9 The Adams-Störmer Method for Second-order Equations

[a] COMPLETE EQUATION

The solution of a second-order equation

$$y'' = f(x,y,y')$$

$$(3.9.1)$$

with initial conditions

$$y(0) = y_0; \qquad y'(0) = y_0'$$

$$(3.9.2)$$

is reduced to the integration of two simultaneous first-order equations by setting

$$y' = z(x,y),$$

$$(3.9.3)$$

so that Eq. (3.9.1) becomes

$$y'' = z' = f(x,y,z).$$

$$(3.9.4)$$

Applying Adams's formula [Eq. (3.5.1)] to the two first-order equations (3.9.3) and (3.9.4), we obtain the recurrence formulas

$$z_{i+1} = z_i + h[1 + \tfrac{1}{2}\nabla + \tfrac{5}{12}\nabla^2 + \ldots]f_i;$$

$$y_{i+1} = y_i + h[1 + \tfrac{1}{2}\nabla + \tfrac{5}{12}\nabla^2 + \ldots]z_i.$$

$$(3.9.5)$$

The solution is started, as usual, by a Taylor series, and the integration is then continued as indicated in Table 3.13, in which the values

Table 3.13

i	x	y	z	∇z	$\nabla^2 z$	$\ldots$	f	∇f	$\nabla^2 f$	$\ldots$
$i-2$	x_{i-2}	y_{i-2}	z_{i-2}				f_{i-2}			
$i-1$	x_{i-1}	y_{i-1}	z_{i-1}	∇z_{i-1}			f_{i-1}	∇f_{i-1}		
i	x_i	y_i	z_i	∇z_i	$\nabla^2 z_i$	$\ldots$	f_i	∇f_i	$\nabla^2 f_i$	$\ldots$
$i+1$	x_{i+1}	y_{i+1}	z_{i+1}	∇z_{i+1}	$\nabla^2 z_{i+1}$	$\ldots$	f_{i+1}	∇f_{i+1}	$\nabla^2 f_{i+1}$	$\ldots$
$i+2$	x_{i+2}	y_{i+2}	z_{i+2}	∇z_{i+2}	$\nabla^2 z_{i+2}$	$\ldots$	f_{i+2}	∇f_{i+2}	$\nabla^2 f_{i+2}$	$\ldots$

above the double line are known from the Taylor series, and the values below the double line are obtained by means of Eqs. (3.9.5) moving from left to right.

A certain simplification of the procedure may be obtained, when the derivative y' is not needed, by eliminating z between the two Eqs. (3.9.5) and hence saving the labor of differencing z. For this purpose, applying the second of Eqs. (3.9.5) at y_{i+1} and y_i,

$$y_{i+1} - y_i = h[1 + \tfrac{1}{2}\nabla + \tfrac{5}{12}\nabla^2 + \ldots]z_i;$$

$$y_i - y_{i-1} = h[1 + \tfrac{1}{2}\nabla + \tfrac{5}{12}\nabla^2 + \ldots]z_{i-1},$$

and subtracting the second from the first equation, we obtain

$$y_{i+1} - 2y_i + y_{i-1} = h[1 + \tfrac{1}{2}\nabla + \tfrac{5}{12}\nabla^2 + \ldots](z_i - z_{i-1})$$
$$= h[1 + \tfrac{1}{2}\nabla + \tfrac{5}{12}\nabla^2 + \ldots]\nabla z_i. \tag{3.9.6}$$

But, by Eqs. (2.4.11) and (3.9.4),

$$\nabla z_i = [1 - \tfrac{1}{2}hD + \tfrac{1}{6}h^2D^2 + \ldots]hDz_i = [1 - \tfrac{1}{2}hD + \tfrac{1}{6}h^2D^2 + \ldots]hf_i,$$

and substituting in the bracket for the powers of hD the difference expansions of Eqs. (2.4.16) to (2.4.17),

$$\nabla z_i = [1 - \tfrac{1}{2}\nabla - \tfrac{1}{12}\nabla^2 - \ldots]hf_i.$$

Hence, substituting this value of ∇z_i in Eq. (3.9.6), we obtain the *Adams-Störmer recurrence formula:*

$$y_{i+1} = -y_{i-1} + 2y_i + h^2[1 + \tfrac{1}{12}\nabla^2 + \tfrac{1}{12}\nabla^3$$
$$+ \tfrac{19}{240}\nabla^4 + \tfrac{3}{40}\nabla^5 + \ldots]f_i. \tag{3.9.7}$$

[b] INCOMPLETE EQUATION

Whenever the right-hand member of Eq. (3.9.1) does not depend on y', the integration of the equation can be performed by means of Eq. (3.9.7) alone; however, when y'' is a function of y', Eq. (3.9.7) must be used together with the first of Eqs. (3.9.5).

Equation (3.9.7) will now be applied to the extrapolation of the solution of the frictionless pendulum problem, governed by Eq. (f) of Sec. 3.2:

$$\ddot{\theta} = -4.6499 \sin \theta, \tag{a}$$

with the initial conditions

$$\theta_0 = 2.0944; \qquad \dot{\theta}_0 = 0, \tag{b}$$

which was started in Sec. 3.2 (Table 3.2). In this case

$$\ddot{\theta} = f(\theta) = -4.6499 \sin \theta$$

does not depend on either τ or $\dot{\theta}$, and only Eq. (3.9.7) is needed for the solution. Table 3.14 gives the results of the extrapolation started with three values of θ for $h = 0.1$, taking into account second differences of f.

Interpolating linearly from Table 3.14, we obtain $\theta = 0$ at $\tau = 0.9978$ with an error of 0.2 per cent in the period of the oscillations obtained rigorously by an elliptic integral solution (see Sec. 3.2).

The simultaneous use of the first of Eqs. (3.9.5) and of Eq. (3.9.7) is illustrated in Table 3.15, which gives the solution of the friction pendulum problem of Sec. 3.2, governed by Eq. (k),

$$\ddot{\theta} + 0.4\dot{\theta} + 4.6499 \sin \theta = 0, \tag{c}$$

Table 3.14

τ	θ_i	f_i	∇f_i	$\nabla^2 f_i$
0	2.0944	-4.0268		
0.1	2.0742	-4.0728	-0.0460	
0.2	2.0132	-4.2021	-0.1293	-0.0833
0.3	1.9101	-4.3849	-0.1828	-0.0535
0.4	1.7631	-4.5643	-0.1794	$+0.0034$
0.5	1.5705	-4.6499	-0.0856	0.0938
0.6	1.3313	-4.5174	$+0.1325$	0.2181
0.7	1.0467	-4.0259	0.4915	0.3590
0.8	0.7215	-3.0713	0.9546	0.4631
0.9	0.3652	-1.6605	1.4108	0.4562
1.0	-0.0081			

and conditions (b) of this section, using $h = 0.1$ and three initial values from the Taylor solution of Table 3.3. In this case,

$$\ddot{\theta} = f(\theta,\dot{\theta}) = -0.4\dot{\theta} - 4.6499 \sin \theta$$

and the recurrence equations become

$$\dot{\theta}_{i+1} = \dot{\theta}_i + 0.1[1 + 0.5\nabla + 0.4167\nabla^2]f_i;$$

$$\theta_{i+1} = -\theta_{i-1} + 2\theta_i + 0.01[1 + 0.0833\nabla^2]f_i. \qquad (d)$$

A linear interpolation between $\tau = 1.0$ and $\tau = 1.1$ gives $\tau = 1.0763$

Table 3.15

τ	θ_i	$\dot{\theta}_i$	f_i	∇f_i	$\nabla^2 f_i$
0	2.0944	0	-4.0268		
0.1	2.0745	-0.3963	-3.9139	0.1129	
0.2	2.0153	-0.7865	-3.8833	$+0.0306$	-0.0823
0.3	1.9172	-1.1767	-3.9030	-0.0197	-0.0503
0.4	1.7800	-1.5701	-3.9205	-0.0175	$+0.0022$
0.5	1.6036	-1.9629	-3.8624	$+0.0581$	0.0756
0.6	1.3886	-2.3431	-3.6355	0.2269	0.1688
0.7	1.1374	-2.6883	-3.1445	0.4910	0.2641
0.8	0.8550	-2.9672	-2.3219	0.8226	0.3316
0.9	0.5497	-3.1444	-1.1713	1.1506	0.3280
1.0	0.2330	-3.1903	$+1.0452$	2.2165	1.0659
1.1	-0.0724	-2.9305			

for the passage of the pendulum through the vertical position, an increase of 7.63 per cent over the time for the undamped pendulum.

3.10 Fox's Methods for Second-order Linear Equations

A simple formula for the step-by-step integration of the second-order *linear* differential equation

$$y'' + f(x)y' + g(x)y = F(x) \qquad (3.10.1)$$

with the initial conditions

$$y(0) = y_0; \qquad y'(0) = y_0' \qquad (3.10.2)$$

may be obtained as suggested by Fox. The equation is multiplied by h^2:

$$h^2 y'' + h f(x)(h y') + h^2 g(x)y = h^2 F(x)$$

and the terms $h^2 y''$ and $h y'$ are expressed by means of their *central* difference expansions of Eqs. (2.7.16), letting $x = ih$ and calling y_i, f_i, g_i, F_i the values of y, f, g, and F at x_i:

$$y_{i+1} - 2y_i + y_{i-1} + \frac{h}{2} f_i(y_{i+1} - y_{i-1}) + h^2 g_i y_i$$

$$= h^2 F_i + \left(\frac{\delta^4}{12} - \frac{\delta^6}{90} + \ldots \right) y_i + h f_i \mu \left(\frac{\delta^3}{6} - \frac{\delta^5}{30} + \ldots \right) y_i.$$

Solving this equation for y_{i+1}, we obtain *Fox's formula for second-order linear equations:*

$$y_{i+1}^{(n)} = \frac{1}{1 + \frac{h}{2} f_i} \left[-\left(1 - \frac{h}{2} f_i \right) y_{i-1}^{(n)} + (2 - h^2 g_i) y_i^{(n)} + h^2 F_i + \epsilon_{i+1}^{(n-1)} \right],$$

$$(3.10.3)$$

where the correction $\epsilon_{i+1}^{(n-1)}$ equals

$$\epsilon_{i+1}^{(n-1)} = \left(\frac{\delta^4}{12} - \frac{\delta^6}{90} + \ldots \right) y_i^{(n-1)} + h f_i \mu \left(\frac{\delta^3}{6} - \frac{\delta^5}{30} + \ldots \right) y_i^{(n-1)}, \quad (3.10.4)$$

and is of order h^4.

The solution y is started by means of a Taylor series in order to obtain y_1 and is then extrapolated by means of Eq. (3.10.3), neglecting the correction. The differences of the first approximation $y^{(1)}$ thus obtained are then used to evaluate $\epsilon^{(1)}$, and Eq. (3.10.3) is used again with these $\epsilon^{(1)}$ to obtain a second approximation $y^{(2)}$ of y. The procedure is repeated until the corrections have identical values in two successive approximations.

To illustrate this procedure, consider the electric circuit of Fig. 3.3 in which the inductance L, the variable conductance $G(t)$, and the capacitance C are connected in parallel. If $G(t)$ varies according to the law

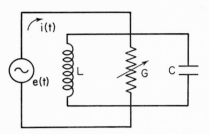

$$G(t) = G_0(1 + a \sin 10^3 t), \quad \text{(a)}$$

Kirchhoff's second law* yields for the voltage e the equation

$$C \frac{de}{dt} + G(t)e + \frac{1}{L} \int e \, dt = i$$

Figure 3.3

or, after differentiation with respect to t and division by C,

$$\frac{d^2e}{dt^2} + \frac{G(t)}{C} \frac{de}{dt} + \left(\frac{1}{LC} + \frac{1}{C} \frac{dG(t)}{dt}\right) e = \frac{1}{C} \frac{di}{dt}.$$

With $C = 1$ microfarad (10^{-6} farad), $L = 0.02778$ henry, $G_0 = 0.007$ mho, $a = 0.5$, $i = (10^{-9}/6) \sin 6 \cdot 10^3 t$, and neglecting the time-varying part, $\frac{1}{C} \frac{dG}{dt} = 3.5 \cdot 10^6 \cos 10^3 t$, in comparison with the constant term $1/LC = 36 \cdot 10^6$,† the equation for the voltage becomes

$$\frac{d^2e}{dt^2} + 7000(1 + 0.5 \sin 10^3 t) \frac{de}{dt} + 36 \cdot 10^6 e = \cos 6 \cdot 10^3 t.$$

A change in the time unit from t seconds to τ milliseconds $(\tau = 10^3 t)$ changes the equation to

$$\ddot{e} + 7(1 + 0.5 \sin \tau)\dot{e} + 36e = \cos 6\tau, \qquad \text{(b)}$$

where a dot denotes differentiation with respect to τ. Initial rest conditions require that

$$e(0) = e_0 = 0; \qquad \dot{e}(0) = \dot{e}_0 = 0. \qquad \text{(c)}$$

To start the solution we write

$$\ddot{e} = -7(1 + 0.5 \sin \tau)\dot{e} - 36e + \cos 6\tau; \qquad \ddot{e}_0 = 1$$

and find by differentiation

$$\dddot{e} = -7(1 + 0.5 \sin \tau)\ddot{e} - (3.5 \cos \tau + 36)\dot{e} - 6 \sin 6\tau; \qquad \dddot{e}_0 = -7;$$

* See, for example, *Differential Equations*, Sec. 1.7.

† In order to solve the complete equation without neglecting the term involving dG/dt, set $e = dv/dt$ and write the circuit equation in terms of v:

$$\frac{d^2v}{dt^2} + \frac{G(t)}{C} \frac{dv}{dt} + \frac{1}{L} v = i.$$

Once this equation has been solved for v, $e(t)$ is obtained by differentiation.

$$e^{\mathrm{iv}} = -7(1 + 0.5 \sin \tau)\ddot{e} - (7 \cos \tau + 36)\ddot{e} + (3.5 \sin \tau)\dot{e} - 36 \cos 6\tau;$$

$$e_0^{\mathrm{iv}} = -30.$$

We thus obtain the series expansion for $e(\tau)$ in the neighborhood of the origin:

$$e(\tau) = \tfrac{1}{2}\tau^2 - \tfrac{7}{6}\tau^3 - \tfrac{5}{4}\tau^4 = 0.5\tau^2 - 1.1667\tau^3 - 1.25\tau^4,$$

from which

$$e(0.05) = 0.00110; \qquad e(0.10) = 0.00371.$$

The application of Eq. (3.10.3) to the initial value problem of Eqs. (b), (c), with

$$h = 0.1; \qquad f(\tau) = 7(1 + 0.5 \sin \tau); \qquad g(\tau) = 36; \qquad F(\tau) = \cos 6\tau,$$

gives the recurrence equation for the first approximation $e^{(1)}$ of e:

$$e_{i+1}^{(1)} = \frac{1}{1 + 0.05f_i} [-(1 - 0.05f_i)e_{i-1}^{(1)} + 1.64e_i^{(1)} + 0.01F_i], \qquad \text{(d)}$$

in which ϵ is neglected. Starting with $e_0^{(1)} = 0$ and $e_1^{(1)} = 0.00371$, we obtain the results of Table 3.16.

Table 3.16

τ	f_i	$1 + 0.05f_i$	$1 - 0.05f_i$	$0.01F_i$	$e_i^{(1)}$
0	7.00000				0
0.1	7.34944	1.36747	0.63253	0.00825	0.00371
0.2	7.69534	1.38477	0.61523	+0.00362	0.01048
0.3	8.03432	1.40172	0.59828	−0.00227	0.01337
0.4	8.36297	1.41815	0.58185	−0.00737	0.00955
0.5	8.67801	1.43390	0.56610	−0.00990	+0.00036
0.6	8.97624	1.44881	0.55119	−0.00897	−0.01026
0.7	9.25477	1.46274	0.53726	−0.00490	−0.01794
0.8	9.51076	1.47554	0.52446	+0.00087	−0.01969
0.9	9.74166	1.48708	0.51292	0.00635	−0.01491
1.0	9.94514	1.49726	0.50274	0.00960	−0.00538
1.1	10.11924	1.50596	0.49404		+0.00552

To evaluate a second approximation by Fox's correction ϵ, we difference $e^{(1)}$ and compute the correction by means of its first two terms:

$$\epsilon_{i+1}^{(1)} = \left(\frac{\delta^4}{12} + hf_i \frac{\mu\delta^3}{6} \right) e_i^{(1)} = (0.08333\delta^4 + 0.01667f_i\mu\delta^3)e_i^{(1)}. \qquad \text{(e)}$$

The results of this computation appear in Table 3.17.

Table 3.17

τ	$e_i^{(1)}$	$10^5\delta e_{i+1/2}^{(1)}$	$10^5\delta^2 e_i^{(1)}$	$10^5\delta^3 e_i^{(1)}$ and $10^5\mu\delta^3 e_i^{(1)}$	$10^5\delta^4 e_i^{(1)}$	ϵ_{i+1}^1	$e_i^{(2)}$	$e_i^{(3)}$
0	0						0	0
		371						
0.1	0.00371		+306	(−250)	(250)	−0.00010	0.00371	0.00371
		677		−694				
0.2	0.01048		−388	(−488)	411	−0.00028	0.01040	0.01040
		+289		−283				
0.3	0.01337		−671	(−75)	417	+0.00025	0.01308	0.01305
		−382		+134				
0.4	0.00955		−537	(264)	260	0.00058	0.00942	0.00938
		−919		394				
0.5	+0.00036		−143	(415)	+43	0.00064	+0.00073	+0.00096
		−1062		437				
0.6	−0.01026		+294	(368)	−138	0.00044	−0.00934	−0.00909
		−768		299				
0.7	−0.01794		593	(180)	−239	+0.00008	−0.01673	−0.01656
		−175		+60				
0.8	−0.01969		653	(−59)	−238	−0.00029	−0.01862	−0.01851
		+478		−178				
0.9	−0.01491		475	(−258)	−160	−0.00055	−0.01435	−0.01468
		953		−338				
1.0	−0.00538		137	(−400)	(0)	−0.00066	−0.00550	−0.00588
		1090						
1.1	+0.00552			(−250)	(200)	−0.00026	+0.00476	+0.00445

The values (in parentheses) of $\mu\delta^3$ and δ^4 for $\tau = 0.1$, 1.0, and 1.1 are obtained by extrapolation at sight. The values (in parentheses) of $\mu\delta^3$ for $\tau = 0.2$ to $\tau = 0.9$ are the averages of the adjoining value of δ^3.

The values of $e_i^{(2)}$ are obtained by means of the recurrence equation

$$e_{i+1}^{(2)} = \frac{1}{1 + 0.05f_i}[-(1 - 0.05f_i)e_{i-1}^{(2)} + 1.64e_i^{(2)} + 0.01F_i + \epsilon_{i+1}^{(1)}], \quad (f)$$

where $\epsilon_{i+1}^{(1)}$ is taken from Table 3.17. Differencing the values $e_i^{(2)}$, one computes the new corrections and hence the values of $e_i^{(3)}$ which are given in the last column of Table 3.17. The differencing of $e^{(3)}$ shows that the corrections of $e^{(3)}$ are identical with the corrections of $e^{(2)}$, and the process is therefore stopped at this point.

The time-consuming starting of the solution by a Taylor series may be avoided, at the cost of some accuracy, by expressing the second initial condition of Eq. (3.10.2) in terms of central averaged differences and by applying Eq. (3.10.3) at the origin, without correction:

$$y_1 - y_{-1} = 2hy_0';$$

$$\left(1 + \frac{h}{2}f_0\right)y_1 + \left(1 - \frac{h}{2}f_0\right)y_{-1} = (2 - h^2 g_0)y_0 + h^2 F_0.$$

Elimination of the fictitious pivotal value y_{-1} gives

$$y_1 = \left(1 - \frac{h}{2} f_0\right) h y_0' + \left(1 - \frac{h^2}{2} g_0\right) y_0 + \frac{h^2}{2} F_0. \qquad (3.10.5)$$

For the case of Eqs. (b), (c), one obtains

$$e_1 = \frac{h^2}{2} F_0 = \frac{(0.1)^2}{2} \cos 0 = 0.005,$$

and by Eq. (d),

$$e_2 = 0.01048; \qquad e_3 = 0.01280; \qquad e_4 = 0.00888.$$

The accuracy of this solution depends on the relative importance of the step h on the value of e_1.

Fox's methods of Sec. 3.6 and this section are well adapted to use on computers capable of automatic differencing.

3.11 Noumerov's Methods

When a second-order *linear* differential equation lacks the first derivative term and hence is of the form

$$y'' + f(x)y = F(x), \qquad (3.11.1)$$

its integration may be performed by another very powerful procedure, due to Noumerov. Multiplying Eq. (3.11.1) by h^2 and substituting for the second derivative its expansion in terms of central differences [Eq. (2.7.15)], Eq. (3.11.1) becomes

$$\left(\delta^2 - \frac{\delta^4}{12} + \frac{\delta^6}{90} + \cdots\right) y_i + h^2 f_i y_i = h^2 F_i.$$

Operating on both sides of this equation with $\left(1 + \dfrac{\delta^2}{12}\right)$, the term in δ^4 is eliminated and the equation takes the form

$$\left(\delta^2 + \frac{\delta^6}{240} - \frac{13\delta^8}{15,120} + \cdots\right) y_i + h^2 f_i y_i + \frac{h^2\delta^2}{12}(f_i y_i) = h^2 F_i + \frac{h^2\delta^2}{12} F_i$$

or $\quad y_{i+1} - 2y_i + y_{i-1} + h^2 f_i y_i + \dfrac{h^2}{12}(f_{i+1}y_{i+1} - 2f_i y_i + f_{i-1}y_{i-1})$

$$= h^2 F_i + \frac{h^2}{12}(F_{i+1} - 2F_i + F_{i-1}) - \left(\frac{\delta^6}{240} - \frac{13\delta^8}{15,120} + \cdots\right) y_i.$$

Solving this equation for y_{+1}, we obtain the *Noumerov recurrence formula:*

$$y_{i+1}^{(n)} = \frac{1}{1 + \frac{h^2}{12} f_{i+1}} \left[-\left(1 + \frac{h^2}{12} f_{i-1}\right) y_{i-1}^{(n)} + \left(2 - \frac{5h^2}{6} f_i\right) y_i^{(n)} \right.$$

$$\left. + \frac{h^2}{12} (F_{i-1} + 10 F_i + F_{i+1}) + \epsilon_{i+1}^{(n-1)} \right], \qquad (3.11.2)$$

where
$$\epsilon_{i+1}^{(n-1)} = -\left(\frac{\delta^6}{240} - \frac{13\delta^8}{15{,}120} + \cdots\right) y_i^{(n-1)}. \qquad (3.11.3)$$

Only y_0 and y_1 are needed to start the solution, and the correction, being of the order of h^6, is often negligible even for fairly large values of h.

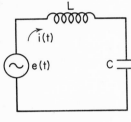

Figure 3.4

To illustrate the use of Eq. (3.11.2), consider the electric circuit of Fig. 3.4 with an inductance and a capacitance in series, in which the capacitance varies according to the law

$$\frac{1}{C} = \frac{1}{C_0} (1 + a \cos 10^3 t). \qquad (a)$$

The charge $q(t)$ on the capacitor satisfies the equation:*

$$\frac{d^2 q}{dt^2} + \frac{1}{LC} q = \frac{1}{L} e(t).$$

If $1/(LC_0) = 36 \cdot 10^6$ in practical units, the equation becomes

$$\frac{d^2 q}{dt^2} + 36 \cdot 10^6 (1 + 0.4 \cos 10^3 t) q = \cos 6 \cdot 10^3 t$$

or, with $\tau = 1000t$,

$$\ddot{q} + 36(1 + 0.4 \cos \tau)q = \cos 6\tau, \qquad (b)$$

where dots denote differentiation with respect to τ. Initial rest conditions require that

$$q(0) = q_0 = 0; \qquad \dot{q}(0) = \dot{q}_0 = i(0) = 0. \qquad (c)$$

To start the solution, we write, by differentiation,

$$\ddot{q} = -36(1 + 0.4 \cos \tau)q + \cos 6\tau; \qquad \ddot{q}_0 = 1$$

$$\dddot{q} = -36(1 + 0.4 \cos \tau)\dot{q} + 14.4 (\sin \tau)q - 6 \sin 6\tau; \qquad \dddot{q}_0 = 0$$

$$q^{iv} = -36(1 + 0.4 \cos \tau)\ddot{q} + 28.8 (\sin \tau)\dot{q} + 14.4 (\cos \tau)q - 36 \cos 6\tau;$$

$$q_0^{iv} = -86.4,$$

---

* See, for example, *Differential Equations*, Sec. 2.8.

and obtain the series expansion valid in the neighborhood of zero:

$$q(\tau) = \frac{\tau^2}{2} - \frac{86.4\tau^4}{24} = 0.5\tau^2 - 3.6\tau^4,$$

by means of which $q(0.1) = q_1 = 0.00464$. The application of Eq. (3.11.2) without correction to the initial value problem of Eqs. (b), (c), with

$$h = 0.1; \qquad f(\tau) = 36(1 + 0.4 \cos \tau); \qquad F(\tau) = \cos 6\tau,$$

gives the recurrence equation

$$q_{i+1}^{(1)} = \frac{1}{1 + \frac{0.01}{12} f_{i+1}} \left[-\left(1 + \frac{0.01}{12} f_{i-1}\right) q_{i-1}^{(1)} + \left(2 - \frac{5}{6} 0.01 f_i\right) q_i^{(1)} \right.$$

$$\left. + \frac{0.01}{12} (F_{i-1} + 10F_i + F_{i+1}) \right]. \quad \text{(d)}$$

Starting with $q_0 = 0$, $q_1 = 0.00464$, Eq. (d) gives the results of Table 3.18, which also contains the solution of the equation with constant

Table 3.18

τ	f_i	$1 + \dfrac{0.01}{12} f_i$	$2 - \dfrac{5}{6} 0.01 f_i$	$\dfrac{0.01}{12} (F_{i-1} + 10F_i + F_{i+1})$	q	q_c
0	50.4	1.04200	1.58002		0	0
0.1	50.328	1.04194	1.58062		0.00464	0.00471
0.2	50.11308	1.04176	1.58241	0.00801	0.01475	0.01553
0.3	49.75704	1.04146	1.58537	+0.00352	0.02115	0.02435
0.4	49.26312	1.04105	1.58949	−0.00221	+0.01532	0.02252
0.5	48.63708	1.04053	1.59471	−0.00716	−0.00465	+0.00588
0.6	47.88504	1.03990	1.60097	−0.00961	−0.03171	−0.00221
0.7	47.01384	1.03918	1.60823	−0.00871	−0.05258	−0.05084
0.8	46.03248	1.03836	1.61641	−0.00476	−0.05426	+0.06641
0.9	44.95104	1.03746	1.62542	+0.00085	−0.03105	−0.05796
1.0	43.78032	1.03648	1.63518	0.00616	+0.01161	−0.00233
1.1	42.53184	1.03544		0.00932	0.05845	+0.02856

coefficients corresponding to Eq. (b):

$$\ddot{q} + 36q = \cos 6\tau,$$

satisfying the conditions (c), that is,

$$q_c = \frac{\tau}{12} \sin 6\tau. \qquad \text{(e)}$$

The corrections ϵ evaluated by means of Eq. (3.11.3) change by one or two units the last figure of q and hence are negligible.

Noumerov's method may be generalized to solve equations with even-order derivatives of any order in which *only y has a variable coefficient*. For example, given the fourth-order equation

$$y^{iv} + cy'' + f(x)y = F(x), \tag{3.11.4}$$

a multiplication through by h^4 and the substitution of $h^4 y^{iv}$ and $h^2 y''$ by their central difference expansions leads to the corresponding difference equation

$$\left[\left(\delta^4 - \frac{\delta^6}{6} + \frac{7}{240}\delta^8 - \cdots\right) + ch^2\left(\delta^2 - \frac{\delta^4}{12} + \frac{\delta^6}{90} - \cdots\right) + h^4 f_i\right] y_i = h^4 F_i. \tag{f}$$

Operating on this equation with $1 + \alpha\delta^2$, where α is an undetermined constant, we obtain

$$\left[\left(\delta^4 - \frac{\delta^6}{6} + \cdots\right) + \alpha(\delta^6 - \delta^8 + \cdots) + ch^2\left(\delta^2 - \frac{\delta^4}{12} + \frac{\delta^6}{90} - \cdots\right)\right.$$
$$\left. + \alpha ch^2\left(\delta^4 - \frac{\delta^6}{12} + \cdots\right) + h^4 f_i\right] y_i + \alpha h^4\delta^2(f_i y_i) = h^4(1 + \alpha\delta^2)F_i. \tag{g}$$

The undetermined constant α may be so chosen as to reduce to zero the coefficient of $\delta^6 y_i$ in Eq. (g):

$$\alpha = \frac{2}{15}\left[\frac{15 - ch^2}{12 - ch^2}\right]. \tag{3.11.5}$$

With this value of α and neglecting differences of order higher than 6, Eq. (g) becomes

$$[1 + ch^2(\alpha - \tfrac{1}{12})]\delta^4 y_i + ch^2\delta^2 y_i + h^4(1 + \alpha\delta^2)f_i y_i = h^4(1 + \alpha\delta^2)F_i. \tag{3.11.6}$$

This equation can be solved for y_{i+2} in terms of y_{i+1}, y_i, y_{i-1}, and y_{i-2}, permitting the step-by-step integration with only four starting values and an error of order h^6.

The four starting values may be obtained by a Taylor expansion or by means of the four difference equations derivable from the three initial conditions on y', y'', y''' and from the differential equation at the origin, involving the five points y_{-2}, y_{-1}, y_0, y_1, y_2, of which y_0 is known.

Table 3.19 gives the solution of the problem

$$y^{iv} - 10^4 y = 0; \quad y_0 = 1; \quad y_0' = 0; \quad y_0'' = -100; \quad y_0''' = 0, \tag{h}$$

with the four starting values taken from the true solution $y = \cos 10x$.

The recurrence equation for this problem, with

$$c = 0; \quad f(x) = -10^4; \quad \alpha = \tfrac{1}{6}; \quad F(x) = 0,$$

becomes

$$y_{i+2}^{(1)} = (4 + \tfrac{1}{6}10^4 h^4)y_{i+1} - (6 - \tfrac{2}{3}10^4 h^4)y_i + (4 + \tfrac{1}{6}10^4 h^4)y_{i-1} - y_{i-2} \quad \text{(i)}$$

Table 3.19 contains also the solution obtained by the recurrence equation

$$y_{i+2}^{(2)} = 4y_{i+1} - (6 - 10^4 h^4)y_i + 4y_{i-1} - y_{i-2} \quad \text{(j)}$$

derived by means of the first terms of central difference expansions, i.e., by Eq. (f), and the correct value of y.

Table 3.19

x	$y_i = \cos 10x$	$y_i^{(1)}$	$e\%$	$y_i^{(2)}$	$e\%$
0.4	-0.6536	-0.6546	0.15	-0.7183	9.8
0.5	0.2837	0.2784	1.90	-0.1279	

Operating on Eq. (f) with $(1 + \alpha\delta^2 + \beta\delta^4)$ and choosing α and β so as to set equal to zero the coefficients of $\delta^4 y_i$ and $\delta^6 y_i$, one may derive a recurrence equation with an error of order h^8. Table 3.20 illustrates this procedure applied to the problem

$$y'' + 100y = 0; \quad y_0 = 1; \quad y_0' = 0.$$

In this case,

$$\alpha = \frac{1 + \tfrac{2}{15}ch^2}{12 + ch^2}; \quad \beta = -\frac{\tfrac{1}{20}}{12 + ch^2}. \quad \text{(k)}$$

The recurrence equations for $h = 0.1$ with errors of order h^4, h^6, and h^8 are, respectively,

$$y_{i+1}^{(1)} = -y_{i-1}^{(1)} + y_i^{(1)};$$
$$y_{i+1}^{(2)} = -y_{i-1}^{(2)} + \tfrac{14}{13}y_i^{(2)}; \quad \text{(l)}$$
$$y_{i+1}^{(3)} = -y_{i-1}^{(3)} + \tfrac{229}{212}y_i^{(3)}.$$

Table 3.20

x	$y_i = \cos 10x_i$	$y_i^{(1)}$	$e\%$	$y_i^{(2)}$	$e\%$	$y_i^{(3)}$	$e\%$
0	1.0000						
0.1	0.5403						
0.2	-0.4162	-0.4957	10	-0.4182	0.48	-0.4164	0.05
0.3	-0.9900	-1.0000	1	-0.9907	0.07	-0.9901	0.01
0.4	-0.6536	-0.5403	17	-0.6487	0.75	-0.6531	0.08
0.5	0.2837	0.4597	62	0.2921	3.00	0.2847	0.35

3.12 Solution of Characteristic Value Problems by Forward Integration

One-dimensional characteristic value problems are governed by *homogeneous* ordinary differential equations with *homogeneous* boundary conditions. Nonzero solutions of such problems exist for certain values of a parameter, which must be determined (*characteristic values*). The numerical solution of characteristic value problems is one of the important branches of modern numerical analysis.* It is essential in the field of vibrations and elastic stability. A forward integration procedure will be illustrated here, while a solution by central differences and simultaneous equations is given in Section 4.7.

The Euler buckling of a simply supported beam is governed by the characteristic value problem†

$$y'' + \frac{PL^2}{EI}\, y = 0; \qquad y(0) = y(1) = 0, \tag{3.12.1}$$

where L is the beam length, EI its flexural rigidity, P the thrust, and prime signs indicate differentiation with respect to the nondimensional variable $z = x/L$. Multiplying Eq. (3.12.1) by $h^2 = 1/n^2$ and substituting central differences of order h^2 for $h^2 y''$, we obtain the recurrence equation

$$y_{i+1} = -y_{i-1} + (2 - k^2 h^2)y_i, \tag{3.12.2}$$

where

$$k^2 = \frac{PL^2}{EI}. \tag{3.12.3}$$

The integration is started with a trial value k_0^2 for k^2 and a $y_1 = 1$, since

Table 3.21

i	z_i	y_i
0	0.00	0.0000
1	0.25	1.0000
2	0.50	1.2500
3	0.75	0.5625
4	1.00	-0.5469

the homogeneous problem of Eq. (3.12.1) defines y within a multiplying constant. Table 3.21 gives the results of this integration for $k_0^2 = 12$ and

---

* See L. Collatz, *Eigenwertprobleme und ihre numerische Behandlung*, Chelsea Publishing Company, New York, 1948.

† See, for example, *Differential Equations*, Sec. 1.7.

$n = 4$; i.e., for the recurrence equation

$$y_{i+1} = -y_{i-1} + 1.25y_i. \tag{a}$$

A linear interpolation shows that y is zero at $z = 0.8768$. Since it may be shown that the parameter k^2 is proportional to $1/L^2$ and the true nondimensional length of the beam is $z = 1$, the value of k^2 is

$$k^2 = (0.8768)^2 k_0^2 = 9.2256$$

with an error of 6.5 per cent with respect to $k^2 = \pi^2$.

Table 3.22 gives the integration for $k_0^2 = 9$ and $n = 10$; i.e., for the equation

$$y_{i+1} = -y_{i-1} + 1.91y_i. \tag{b}$$

A linear interpolation gives $y = 0$ at $z = 1.0433$ and hence a $k^2 = (1.0433)^2 \times 9 = 9.7965$, with an error of 0.74 per cent.

Table 3.22 also contains the values of $y_{i+1} - y_{i-1}$ that are proportional to y_i'. A linear interpolation shows that $y_i' = 0$ at $z = 0.5218$. Considering this to be the length of a cantilever beam, we obtain the corresponding k^2:

$$k^2 = (0.5218)^2 \times 9 = 2.4507,$$

with an error of 0.67 per cent in comparison with $\pi^2/4$.

Table 3.22

i	z_i	y_i	$y_{i+1} - y_{i-1}$
0	0.0	0.0000	
1	0.1	1.0000	1.9100
2	0.2	1.9100	1.6481
3	0.3	2.6481	1.2379
4	0.4	3.1479	0.7163
5	0.5	3.3644	0.1302
6	0.6	3.2781	-0.4676
7	0.7	2.8968	-1.0233
8	0.8	2.2548	-1.5769
9	0.9	1.4099	-1.8167
10	1.0	0.4381	-1.9830
11	1.1	-0.5731	

To use a more powerful integration formula, apply Noumerov's Eq. (3.11.2) to the problem

$$y'' + k^2(1 + \sin \pi z)y = 0; \qquad y(0) = y(1) = 0, \tag{3.12.4}$$

which governs the buckling of a simply supported beam with variable moment of inertia $I(z) = I_0/(1 + \sin \pi z)$. The recurrence equation becomes in this case

$$y_{i+1} = \frac{1}{1 + \dfrac{k^2 h^2}{12}(1 + \sin \pi z_{i+1})} \left\{ \left[2 - 10 \frac{k^2 h^2}{12}(1 + \sin \pi z_i) \right] y_i \right.$$
$$\left. - \left[1 + \frac{k^2 h^2}{12}(1 + \sin \pi z_{i-1}) \right] y_{i-1} \right\}. \quad (3.12.5)$$

Table 3.23 gives the integration for $k_0^2 = PL^2/EI_0 = 8$, $n = 4$.

Table 3.23

i	z_i	$1 + \dfrac{k^2 h^2}{12}(1 + \sin \pi z_i)$	$2 - \dfrac{10}{12} k^2 h^2 (1 + \sin \pi z_i)$	y_i
0	0.00	1.0417	1.5833	0
1	0.25	1.0711	1.2887	1.0000
2	0.50	1.0833	1.1667	1.1896
3	0.75	1.0711	1.2887	0.2957
4	1.00	1.0417	1.5833	−0.8713

A linear interpolation gives $y = 0$ at $z = 0.8133$ and hence

$$k^2 = (0.8133)^2 \times 8 = 5.2920,$$

with an error $e = 0.71$ per cent with respect to the true solution 5.33 obtained by iteration.

3.13 Difference Equations

In previous sections finite differences have been used to transform differential equations into recurrence equations, involving the values of the unknown integral at pivotal points, in order to solve initial value problems. The recurrence equations were then used to determine a given y_i once the preceding pivotal values y_{i-1}, y_{i-2}, ... were known. The same technique will be applied to boundary value problems in following chapters, where it will be seen that the pivotal values y_i satisfy a set of simultaneous linear algebraic equations.

The solution of *finite difference recurrence equations*, relating a certain number of pivotal values evenly spaced along the x-axis, is such an essential process in numerical calculus that a complete theory of difference equations has been established, which parallels the corresponding theory of differential equations.*

For the purposes of this book it is only necessary to develop the theory of *homogeneous linear difference equations with constant coefficients*, i.e.,

---

* See *Differential Equations*, Chap. 3.

of equations of the type

$$y_{k+n} + A_{n-1}y_{k+n-1} + A_{n-2}y_{k+n-2} + \ldots + A_1 y_{k+1} + A_0 y_k = 0, \quad (3.13.1)$$

in which k and n* are integers and the coefficients A are constants.

Introducing the *step-operator* $E \equiv e^{hD}$,

$$E y_k = y_{k+1} \quad (3.13.2)$$

and its powers

$$E^2 y_k = y_{k+2}; \qquad E^3 y_k = y_{k+3}; \qquad \ldots; \qquad E^n y_k = y_{k+n}, \quad (3.13.3)$$

which is analogous to the D-operator, the difference equation (3.13.1) may be written in the form:

$$(E^n + A_{n-1}E^{n-1} + A_{n-2}E^{n-2} + \ldots + A_1 E + A_0)y_k = 0. \quad (3.13.4)$$

The solution of Eq. (3.13.4) is obtained by means of the trial function

$$y_k = z^k, \quad (3.13.5)$$

in which z is a complex (or a real) number. Substitution of Eq. (3.13.5) in Eq. (3.13.4) gives

$$(z^n + A_{n-1}z^{n-1} + A_{n-2}z^{n-2} + \ldots + A_1 z + A_0)z^k = 0, \quad (3.13.6)$$

so that, if y_k is to be a solution of the difference equation whatever the integer k, z must be a root of the algebraic equation (*characteristic equation*)

$$z^n + A_{n-1}z^{n-1} + A_{n-2}z^{n-2} + \ldots + A_1 z + A_0 = 0. \quad (3.13.7)$$

(a) When the roots z_j $(j = 1,2,\ldots,n)$ of Eq. (5.13.7) are all real and separate, Eq. (3.13.6) may be written in factored form:

$$(z - z_1)(z - z_2)(z - z_3)\ldots(z - z_n)z^k = 0$$

and its general solution is given by

$$y_k = C_1 z_1^k + C_2 z_2^k + \ldots + C_n z_n^k, \quad (3.13.8)$$

where the C_j are arbitrary constants to be determined by the conditions of the problem.

For example, given the difference equation

$$y_{k+2} - 4y_{k+1} + 3y_k = 0 \quad \text{(a)}$$

with the conditions

$$y_0 = 0; \qquad y_4 = 10, \quad \text{(b)}$$

---

* The running integer k is used here instead of i, in order to avoid confusion with the imaginary unit, while n is the order of the equation.

its characteristic equation

$$z^2 - 4z + 3 = 0$$

has the real roots $z_1 = 1$, $z_2 = 3$. Therefore the general solution of Eq. (a) is

$$y_k = C_1 \cdot 1^k + C_2 \cdot 3^k \tag{c}$$

The two conditions (b) require that

$$C_1 + C_2 = 0; \qquad C_1 \cdot 1^4 + C_2 \cdot 3^4 = 10; \qquad C_1 = -C_2 = -\tfrac{1}{8},$$

and the particular solution of the problem (a), (b) becomes

$$y_k = \tfrac{1}{8}(3^k - 1^k). \tag{d}$$

It is sometimes preferable to write the general solution of the difference equation in an exponential form by introducing the logarithms of the root z_j:

$$r_j = \ln z_j; \qquad z_j = e^{r_j} \tag{3.13.9}$$

so that Eq. (3.13.8) becomes

$$y_k = C_1 e^{r_1 k} + C_2 e^{r_2 k} + \ldots + C_n e^{r_n k}. \tag{3.13.10}$$

(b) When the characteristic equation has a real root, say z_1, repeated twice, Eq. (3.13.4) has a factor

$$y_{k+2} - 2z_1 y_{k+1} + z_1^2 y_k. \tag{e}$$

It is easy to check by substitution that

$$y_k = k z_1^k \tag{f}$$

is the second independent solution of the repeated factor (e):

$$(k + 2)z_1^{k+2} - 2z_1(k + 1)z_1^{k+1} + z_1^2 k z_1^k = z_1^{k+2}(k + 2 - 2k - 2 + k) = 0.$$

Thus the terms of the general solution stemming from a repeated real root z_1 are

$$y_k = (C_1 + C_2 k)z_1^k \tag{g}$$

and, in general, the terms of the general solution stemming from a real root z_j repeated m times are

$$y_k = (C_1 + C_2 k + C_3 k^2 + \ldots + C_m k^{m-1})z_j^k. \tag{3.13.11}$$

For example, the equation

$$y_{k+3} - 8y_{k+2} + 21y_{k+1} - 18y_k = 0 \tag{h}$$

has the characteristic equation

$$(z - 2)(z - 3)^2 = 0$$

and hence real roots $z_1 = 2$ and $z_2 = z_3 = 3$. Its general solution is

$$y_k = C_1 2^k + (C_2 + C_3 k) 3^k. \tag{i}$$

(c) When the characteristic equation contains two complex conjugate roots

$$z_1 = \rho e^{i\theta}; \qquad z_2 = \rho e^{-i\theta}, \tag{3.13.12}$$

the corresponding terms of the general solution are

$$y_k = \bar{C}_1 (\rho e^{i\theta})^k + \bar{C}_2 (\rho e^{-i\theta})^k = \rho^k (C_1 \cos k\theta + C_2 \sin k\theta), \tag{3.13.13}$$

where $\bar{C}_1$, $\bar{C}_2$ and C_1, C_2 are arbitrary constants.

For example, the equation

$$y_{k+1} - 2y_k + 2y_{k-1} = 0 \tag{j}$$

has a characteristic equation

$$z^2 - 2z + 2 = 0,$$

with roots $z_{1,2} = 1 \pm i = \sqrt{2}\, e^{\pm(\pi/4)i}$. Hence its general solution is

$$y_k = 2^{k/2} \left(C_1 \cos k \frac{\pi}{4} + C_2 \sin k \frac{\pi}{4} \right). \tag{k}$$

(d) When the complex conjugate roots of the characteristic equation are repeated m times, the constants C_1, C_2 of Eq. (3.13.13) become, respectively,

$$C_1 + C_2 k + C_3 k^2 + \ldots + C_m k^{m-1};$$
$$C_{m+1} + C_{m+2}k + C_{m+3}k^2 + \ldots + C_{2m}k^{m-1}. \tag{3.13.14}$$

3.14 Accumulation of Error in Step-by-step Integration

The integration formulas of this chapter show the error ϵ inherent in their use, that is, the difference between the true and the approximate solutions of a differential equation due to *one* step in the numerical integration process. These errors are usually called *truncation errors* and may be reduced by using a larger number of terms in the expansion of derivatives into finite differences or by reducing the spacing h. On the other hand, truncation errors are bound to accumulate in step-by-step procedures both because the starting point at each step is incorrect and because each step introduces an additional error.

Both the truncation and the accumulated errors depend on the spacing h only, once the differential equation is given and the integration formula is chosen. It will be shown in this section, on an elementary example, that unless h is smaller than a given value the solution of the difference equation may diverge more and more from the solution of the corresponding differential equation; i.e., that the solution of the difference equation may become *unstable* unless h is properly chosen.

Consider the initial value problem

$$\ddot{y} + \omega^2 y = 0;$$
$$y_0 = 1; \qquad \dot{y}_0 = 0,$$

(3.14.1)

whose rigorous solution is

$$y = \cos \omega t,$$

(3.14.2)

and apply to Eq. (3.14.1) the Noumerov procedure [Eq. (3.11.2)].

Multiplying Eq. (3.14.1) by h^2, substituting $(\delta^2 - \delta^4/12)y_k$ for $h^2\ddot{y}$,* and operating on the whole equation with $(1 + \delta^2/12)$, we obtain the difference equation

$$\delta^2 y_k + \frac{\omega^2 h^2}{12}(12 + \delta^2)y_k = 0$$

or

$$y_{k+1} + 2cy_k + y_{k-1} = 0,$$

(3.14.3)

where

$$2c = \frac{\frac{5}{6}\omega^2 h^2 - 2}{1 + \frac{1}{12}\omega^2 h^2}.$$

(3.14.4)

In solving Eq. (3.14.3) by the methods of Sec. 3.13 we shall consider separately three cases:

$$c > 1; \qquad c = 1; \qquad 1 > c > -1.$$

(a) When $c > 1$, let

$$c = \cosh \alpha$$

(a)

and substitute $y_k = z^k$ in Eq. (3.14.3):

$$[z^2 + 2(\cosh \alpha)z + 1]z^{k-1} = 0.$$

The roots of the characteristic equation are

$$z_{1,2} = -\cosh \alpha \pm \sqrt{\cosh^2 \alpha - 1}$$

$$= -\cosh \alpha \pm \sinh \alpha = \begin{cases} -e^{-\alpha} \\ -e^{\alpha} \end{cases}$$

and the general solution becomes

$$y_k = c_1(-1)^k e^{-\alpha k} + c_2(-1)^k e^{\alpha k}.$$

(b)

The initial conditions require that

$$y_0 = c_1 + c_2 = 1$$

---

* The running subscript i has been changed to k to avoid confusion with the imaginary unit.

and that $\dot{y}_0 \doteq (y_1 - y_{-1})/h = 0$; i.e., that

$$(-c_1 e^{-\alpha} - c_2 e^{\alpha}) - (-c_1 e^{\alpha} - c_2 e^{-\alpha}) = (e^{\alpha} - e^{-\alpha})(c_1 - c_2) = 0,$$

from which $c_1 = c_2 = \frac{1}{2}$. The particular solution thus becomes

$$y_k = \tfrac{1}{2}[(-1)^k e^{-\alpha k} + (-1)^k e^{\alpha k}] = (-1)^k \cosh \alpha k. \qquad (c)$$

This solution grows indefinitely, in an oscillatory manner, with k, and after a few steps cannot represent to any degree of accuracy the trigonometric solution $\cos \omega t$. Hence when $c > 1$, i.e., by Eq. (3.14.4) for

$$\omega^2 h^2 > 6 \qquad\qquad (3.14.5)$$

the solution of the difference equation becomes unstable.

(b) When $c = 1$, the characteristic equation of Eq. (3.14.3),

$$z^2 + 2z + 1 = 0,$$

has a repeated real root $z_1 = z_2 = -1$ and hence, by Eq. (3.13.11), a general solution:

$$y_k = (c_1 + c_2 k)(-1)^k.$$

The initial conditions require that

$$y_0 = 1 \quad \therefore \quad c_1 = 1;$$

$$y_1 = y_{-1} \quad \therefore \quad c_1 + c_2 = c_1 - c_2,$$

from which $c_2 = 0$. The particular solution is thus given by

$$y_k = (-1)^k = (e^{\pi i})^k = \cos k\pi \qquad (d)$$

and has an oscillatory behavior and the correct amplitude. In order to evaluate the frequency of this solution, let, in Eq. (d),

$$t = kh$$

so that

$$y_k = \cos \frac{\pi}{h} t = \cos \frac{\pi}{\omega h} \omega t. \qquad (e)$$

The frequency of this solution is $\pi/\omega h$ times the frequency ω of the correct solution. But for $c = 1$, Eq. (3.14.4) gives $\omega^2 h^2 = 6$; hence the frequency of the difference equation solution is $\pi/\sqrt{6} = 1.28$ times the frequency of the true solution, and the difference solution after a short while gets out of step.

(c) When $1 > c \geq -1$, let

$$c = \cos \alpha \qquad (0 < \alpha \leq \pi) \qquad (f)$$

so that the characteristic equation becomes

$$z^2 + 2\,(\cos\alpha)\,z + 1 = 0,$$

with roots

$$z_{1,2} = -\cos\alpha \pm i\sin\alpha = \begin{cases} e^{(\pi-\alpha)i} \\ e^{-(\pi-\alpha)i}. \end{cases}$$

Hence, the general solution of the equation becomes

$$y_k = c_1 e^{k(\pi-\alpha)i} + c_2 e^{-k(\pi-\alpha)i}.$$

The initial conditions require that

$$c_1 + c_2 = 1; \qquad c_1 - c_2 = 0,$$

from which $c_1 = c_2 = \frac{1}{2}$ and

$$y_k = \tfrac{1}{2}[e^{k(\pi-\alpha)i} + e^{-k(\pi-\alpha)i}] = \cos k(\pi - \alpha).$$

The frequency of this solution is $\omega(\pi - \alpha)/\omega h$. Table 3.24 gives the values of c, $\omega^2 h^2$, and $(\pi - \alpha)/\omega h$ corresponding to given values of α.

Table 3.24

α	0	$\pi/4$	$\pi/2$	$3\pi/4$	π
c	1	$\sqrt{2}/2$	0	-0.7071	-1
$\omega^2 h^2$	6	4.77	2.40	0.6161	0
$(\pi - \alpha)/\omega h$	1.28	1.08	1.01	1.0006	1

For $c = -1$, Eq. (3.14.4) gives $h = 0$, and hence the numerical solution approaches in the limit the correct solution of Eq. (3.14.1).

It is thus seen that the Noumerov method will not converge at all, in this simple problem, for $\omega^2 h^2 > 6$, that is, for a time interval

$$h > \frac{\sqrt{6}}{\omega} = \frac{\sqrt{6}}{2\pi}\,T = \frac{T}{2.56},$$

where T is the period of the solution. The method will converge for $h < T/2.56$ and will give good results for

$$\omega^2 h^2 < 2.40 = \tfrac{12}{5} \quad \therefore \quad h < 2\sqrt{\tfrac{3}{5}}\,\frac{1}{\omega} = \sqrt{\tfrac{3}{5}}\,\frac{T}{\pi} = \frac{T}{4.05}.$$

The Noumerov method gives, therefore, good results for a time interval less than one-quarter of the period.

Since in the solution of complex vibrational problems this method is often applied to the first few modes of vibration of a system, it is well to remember that the time interval must be smaller than one-quarter of the shortest period to be considered.

Similar results can be obtained for more complicated differential problems and for other integration procedures.

PROBLEMS

3.1 Evaluate, by means of a Taylor series expansion, the integral of the following problem at:

(a) $x = 0.1(0.1)0.3$ to three significant figures.
(b) $x = 1.0, 1.1$ to four significant figures.

$$y' - 2y = 3e^x; \qquad y(0) = 0.$$

Ans.   (a) $y(0.1) = 0.348; y(0.2) = 0.811; y(0.3) = 1.415.$
          (b) $y(1) = 13.91; y(1.1) = 17.87.$

3.2 Evaluate to four significant figures the integral of the following problem at $x = 2.1$ and 2.2 by means of a Taylor series expansion about $x = 2$:

$$y' + \frac{1}{x} y^2 = 0; \qquad y(2) = 1.442.$$

3.3 Evaluate the integrals of the following problems to four significant figures at $x = 0.1(0.1)0.3$, by Taylor series:

(a) $y'' = -xy; \quad y(0) = 1; \quad y'(0) = 0.5.$
(b) $y'' + yy' = x^2; \quad y(0) = 1; \quad y'(0) = 1.$

Ans.   (a) $y(0.1) = 1.050; y(0.2) = 1.099; y(0.3) = 1.145.$
          (b) $y(0.1) = 1.095; y(0.2) = 1.180; y(0.3) = 1.257.$

3.4 Evaluate to three significant figures the integral of the following problem at $x = 0.2$ and 0.4, by means of a Taylor series expansion:

$$y''y^2 + 1 = 0; \qquad y(0) = -1; \qquad y'(0) = 1.$$

3.5 Evaluate the integral of the following problem to four significant figures at $x = 1.1(0.1)1.3$, using a Taylor series expansion:

$$y'' + y^2y' = x^3; \qquad y(1) = 1; \qquad y'(1) = 1.$$

Ans. $y(1.1) = 1.100; y(1.2) = 1.201; y(1.3) = 1.306.$

3.6 A mathematical pendulum of length L (Fig. 3.1) is released from rest from an angle $\theta_0 = 160°$ and oscillates in a viscous medium of coefficient $\mu = 1.2$ sec^{-1} per unit mass. Determine θ in the interval $t = 0(0.1)0.2$ by Taylor series.

3.7 Evaluate the integrals of the following problems by Euler's predictor-corrector method at the given points:

(a) $y' - y = e^x$; $y(0) = 0$; $x = 0.2, 0.4$.
(b) $y' - y^2 = 0$; $y(0) = 1$; $x = 0.1, 0.2$.
(c) $y' - xy = 0$; $y(1) = 1$; $x = 1.1, 1.2$.

Ans. (b) $y(0.1) = 1.11$; $y(0.2) = 1.25$.

3.8 Evaluate the integrals of the following problems at $x = 0.4$, 0.5 by Milne's predictor-corrector method, given their value at the four points $x = 0$, $0.1, 0.2, 0.3$.

(a) $y' - 4y = 0$; $y_0 = 1$; $y_1 = 1.492$; $y_2 = 2.226$; $y_3 = 3.320$.
(b) $y' - 2y = 3e^x$; $y_0 = 0$; $y_1 = 0.348$; $y_2 = 0.811$; $y_3 = 1.415$.
(c) $y' + y = 2e^x$; $y_0 = 2$; $y_1 = 2.010$; $y_2 = 2.040$; $y_3 = 2.090$.

Ans. (a) $y_4 = 4.953$; $y_5 = 7.389$. (c) $y_4 = 2.162$; $y_5 = 2.256$.

3.9 Evaluate to three significant figures the integral of Problem 3.1 at $x = 0.4(0.1)0.6$, using Adams's formula with differences up to the third order. Use the starting values determined in Problem 3.1.

Ans. $y(0.4) = 2.20$; $y(0.5) = 3.20$; $y(0.6) = 4.49$.

3.10 Evaluate to three significant figures the integral of the following problem at $x = 1.0(0.1)1.6$, using Adams's method with differences up to the third order, after starting the solution by Taylor series:

$$y' + \frac{1}{x}y = \frac{1}{x^2}; \qquad y(1) = 1.$$

3.11 Evaluate to three significant figures the integral of Problem 3.2 using Adams's method with differences up to the third order.

Ans. $y(2.4) = 1.14$; $y(2.5) = 1.09$; $y(2.6) = 1.04$; $y(2.7) = 1.00$; $y(2.8) = 0.97$.

3.12 Evaluate to four significant figures the integral of the following problem at $x = 0(0.1)0.6$, using Adams's method with differences up to the third order, after starting the solution by Taylor series:

$$y' + y^2 = e^x; \qquad y(0) = 1.$$

3.13 A body of compact shape has a terminal velocity of 500 fps when falling freely through air. Determine its velocity v as a function of time in the interval $t = 0(1)6$ sec by Adams's method with second-order differences, if $v_0 = 200$ fps and air resistance is assumed proportional to v^2. *Note:* The equation of motion is $m\ddot{x} + \mu\dot{x}^2 = mg$, where m is the mass. The terminal velocity $\dot{x}_t$ is reached when $\dot{x} = $ constant:

$$(\dot{x})_t = \sqrt{mg/\mu}.$$

Ans.

t	0	1	2	3	4	5	6
v	200	226	251	274	296	316	334

3.14 A body is dropped from a plane with the help of a parachute. Its terminal velocity is 30 fps. Determine the velocity v in the interval $t = 0(0.1)0.5$, assuming $v_0 = 20$ fps and air resistance proportional to $v^{3\!/\!2}$. Use Adams's method with differences of the first order.

3.15 The shunt field of a d-c motor has an inductance of $L = 200$ henrys and is connected in series with a resistance R. The resistance increases slightly with current and may be expressed as $R = R_0 + ri$, where i is the current (amperes) flowing through R, and $R_0 = 100$ ohms, $r = 10$ ohms per ampere. A steady voltage $E = 120$ v is applied to the circuit by closing a switch. Find by Adams's method the current $i(t)$ in the interval $t = 0(0.5)2.5$ sec, and compare the result with the current in a linear circuit with $R = 106$ ohms, if $i(0) = 1.2$ a.

Ans.

t	1.5	2.0	2.5
i	1.129	1.117	1.108

3.16 Evaluate to three significant figures the first approximation of the integral of the following problem at $x = 1.1(0.1)1.3$, using the Euler-Fox method.

$$y' + \frac{1}{x} y = \frac{1}{x^2}; \qquad y(1) = 1.$$

Ans. $y(1.1) = 0.996; y(1.2) = 0.986; y(1.3) = 0.971.$

3.17 Evaluate to three significant figures the first and second approximations of the integral of the following problem at $x = 0.1(0.1)0.4$, using the Euler-Fox method with error corrections.

$$y' - 2y = 3e^x; \qquad y(0) = 0.$$

3.18 Evaluate to three significant figures the first and second approximations of the integral of the following problem at $x = 1.1(0.1)1.3$, using the Euler-Fox method with error corrections.

$$y' - x^2 y = x^2; \qquad y(1) = 1.$$

Ans. $y(1.1) = 1.24; y(1.2) = 1.58; y(1.3) = 2.10.$

3.19 Determine recurrence equations of the Euler-Fox type (see Secs. 3.6, 3.7) for the solution of the simultaneous equations:

$$y' = y + z; \qquad z' = z - y;$$

$$y_0 = 0.1; \qquad z_0 = 0.2.$$

and apply them to the evaluation of $y(x)$ and $z(x)$ in the interval $x = 0(0.1)0.3$, ignoring the corrections.

Ans. $y_1 = 0.1326; \quad y_2 = 0.1696, \quad y_3 = 0.2112; \quad z_1 = 0.2088, \quad z_2 = 0.2149,$
$z_3 = 0.2176.$

3.20 Evaluate to three significant figures by Adams's method in the interval $x = 0(0.1)0.4$ the functions $y(x)$ and $z(x)$, satisfying the following equations and conditions. Start the solution by a Taylor series and use differences up to the second order.

(a) $y' = 2z^2 - y$, $y(0) = 1$; $z' = zy$, $z(0) = 1$.
(b) $y' = z - y^2$, $y(0) = 1$; $z' = zy$, $z(0) = 1$.

Ans.   (a) $y(0.3) = 1.492$, $y(0.4) = 1.803$; $z(0.3) = 1.434$, $z(0.4) = 1.683$.
     (b) $y(0.3) = 1.041$, $y(0.4) = 1.072$; $z(0.3) = 1.355$, $z(0.4) = 1.506$.

3.21 Evaluate by Milne's predictor-corrector method the integrals of the following problems at $x = 0.8$, 1.0, given their values and the values of their first derivative at the four points $x = 0$, 0.2, 0.4, 0.6.

(a) $y'' + y = 0$; $y_0 = 1.00$; $y_1 = 0.980$; $y_2 = 0.921$; $y_3 = 0.825$.
   $y_0' = 0$; $y_1' = -0.199$; $y_2' = +0.389$; $y_3' = -0.565$.
(b) $y'' - y = 0$; $y_0 = 0$; $y_1 = 0.201$; $y_2 = 0.411$; $y_3 = 0.637$; $y_0' = 1$;
   $y_1' = 1.020$; $y_2' = 1.081$; $y_3' = 1.185$.

Ans.   (b) $y_4 = 0.8882$; $y_5 = 1.176$.

3.22 Evaluate by Milne's predictor-corrector method the integrals of the following problems at $x = 0.4$, 0.5, after obtaining their values and the values of their first derivative at $x = 0.1$, 0.2, 0.3 by a Taylor series.

(a) $y'' - y^2 = 0$; $y(0) = 1$; $y'(0) = 1$.
(b) $y'' - xy = 0$; $y(0) = 1$; $y'(0) = 1$.

Ans.   (b) $y_4 = 1.413$; $y_5 = 1.526$.

3.23 Evaluate to four significant figures the integral of the following problem at $x = 1.0(0.1)1.5$, using the Adams-Störmer method with differences up to the second order. Start the solution by a Taylor series.

$$y'' + 3xy' + x^2y = e^x; \qquad y(0) = 1; \qquad y'(0) = 1.$$

3.24 Evaluate to three significant figures the integral of the following problem at $x = 0(0.2)1.0$, using the Adams-Störmer method with differences up to the second order, after starting the solution by a Taylor series.

$$xy'' + y' + xy = 0; \qquad y(0) = 1; \qquad y'(0) = 0.$$

Ans. $y(0.6) = 0.912$; $y(0.8) = 0.847$; $y(1.0) = 0.766$.

3.25 Evaluate to four significant figures the integral of the following problem at $x = 0(0.1)0.6$, using the Adams-Störmer method with differences up to the second order. Start the solution by a Taylor series.

$$y'' + yy' = x^2; \qquad y(0) = 1; \qquad y'(0) = 1.$$

3.26 Evaluate to four significant figures the integral of the following problem at $x = 1.0(0.1)1.5$, using the Adams-Störmer method with differences up to the second order. Start the solution by a Taylor series.

$$y'' + y^2y' = x^3; \qquad y(1) = 1; \qquad y'(1) = 1.$$

Ans. $y(1.3) = 1.3053$; $y(1.4) = 1.4132$; $y(1.5) = 1.5266$.

3.27 Evaluate to four significant figures the integral of the following problem at $x = 0(0.1)0.5$, after starting the solution by a Taylor series.

$$y'' + 2xy = 3x^3 + 1; \qquad y(0) = 1; \qquad y'(0) = 1.$$

(a) Use the general Adams-Störmer method with differences of the second order.

(b) Use the Adams-Störmer recurrence equation valid when y' is absent.

3.28 Evaluate to four significant figures the integral of the following problem at $x = 0(0.1)0.5$.

$$y'' + x^2y = 3e^x; \qquad y(0) = 1; \qquad y'(0) = 0.$$

(a) Use the general Adams-Störmer method with differences up to the second order.

(b) Use the Adams-Störmer recurrence equation valid when y' is absent. Start the solutions by a Taylor series.

Ans. (a) $y(0.3) = 1.1488; y(0.4) = 1.2730; y(0.5) = 1.4400.$
        (b) $y(0.3) = 1.1489; y(0.4) = 1.2731; y(0.5) = 1.4400.$

3.29 An elastic sphere of mass 1 is pressed slightly against a rigid flat body and then released from rest at $t = 0$. Express the displacement of a point of the sphere away from the point of contact (the so-called *approach* α) in terms of the time t by means of a Taylor series. The differential equation of motion of the sphere is given by $m\ddot{\alpha} + k\alpha^{3/2} = 0$, where k is the elastic constant of the sphere,* and the initial conditions state that

$$\alpha(0) = \alpha_0; \qquad \dot{\alpha}(0) = 0.$$

Evaluate α at $t = 0.1$ and $t = 0.2$ by a Taylor series expansion, and prolong the solution to $t = 0.5$ by the Adams-Störmer formula, assuming $k = 10$ and $\alpha_0 = 1$.

3.30 A rocket of mass M is launched vertically from the earth's surface ($x = R$) with an initial speed V_0. Determine by the Adams-Störmer method, using first-order differences, the value of x for $t = 0(1)6$, assuming air resistance proportional to the velocity, and the earth's attraction inversely proportional to x^2, if in a consistent set of units.

$$R = 10; \qquad V_0 = 5; \qquad \mu = 0.1; \qquad k = 1,$$

where μ is the coefficient of air resistance per unit of mass, and k is the gravitational constant. *Note:* The equation governing the displacement is $M\ddot{x} + \mu M\dot{x} + Mk/x^2 = 0.$†

Ans.

t	0	1	2	3	4	5	6
x	10.00	14.75	19.03	22.90	26.41	29.58	32.45

* See, for example, S. Timoshenko and J. Goodier, *Theory of Elasticity*, McGraw-Hill Book Company Inc., New York, 1951, pp. 372 ff.
† See, for example, *Differential Equations*, Sec. 9.2.

3.31 Prolong the solution of Problem 3.6 to the interval 0.2(0.1)0.5 by the Adams-Störmer method using second-order differences.

3.32 A body of mass M oscillates freely on a horizontal frictionless slide under the action of a nonlinear spring, whose spring rate equals $k_0 + rx^2$. The body goes through the origin $x = 0$ with a velocity v_0. Determine the value of x for $t = 0(0.5)3$ by the Adams-Störmer method using second-order differences for the following values of the constants in a consistent system of units:

$$M = 1; \qquad k_0 = 1; \qquad r = \tfrac{1}{2}; \qquad v_0 = 1.$$

Note: The equation governing the motion is $M\ddot{x} + (k_0 + rx^2)x = 0.$*

	t	0	0.5	1.0	1.5	2.0	2.5	3.0
Ans.								
	x	0	0.478	0.823	0.892	0.658	0.236	-0.244

3.33 The body of Problem 3.32 oscillates under the action of a spring of spring rate $k_0 - rx^2$, where $k_0 = 1$, $r = \tfrac{1}{2}$, and starts at $x = 1$ with zero speed. Determine the value of x in the interval $t = 0(1)4$ by the Adams-Störmer method, using second-order differences.

3.34 The equation of motion for an electron placed in an electrostatic field due to an infinite positively charged wire is†

$$m\ddot{x} + \frac{k}{x} = 0,$$

where x is the distance of the electron from the wire. If $k/m = 2$, and the electron starts from rest at a distance of eight units from the wire at $t = 0$, determine x for $t = 0(2)10$ by the Adams-Störmer recurrence formula, using second-order differences. *Note:* Assume that the electron can cross the wire through an infinitesimal gap.

	t	0	2	4	6	8	10
Ans.							
	x	8.000	7.496	5.943	3.026	-2.620	-4.630

3.35 Evaluate to three significant figures the first and second approximations of the integral of the following problem at $x = 0(0.2)1.0$, using Fox's method and the first two terms of the error expansion

$$xy'' + y' + xy = 0; \qquad y(0) = 1; \qquad y'(0) = 0.$$

Ans. $y(0.4) = 0.960; y(0.6) = 0.912; y(0.8) = 0.847; y(1.0) = 0.766.$

3.36 Evaluate to four significant figures, the integral of the following problem at $x = 0(0.2)1.0$, using Fox's method.

$$y'' + 3xy' + x^2y = e^x; \qquad y(0) = 1; \qquad y'(0) = 1.$$

* See, for example, *Differential Equations*, Sec. 9.8.
† See, for example, *Differential Equations*, Sec. 7.5.

3.37 Evaluate to three significant figures, the first and second approximations of the integral of the following problem at $x = 0(0.4)2.0$, using Fox's method and the first two terms of the error expansion

$$xy'' + y' + xy = 0; \qquad y(0) = 1; \qquad y'(0) = 0.$$

Ans. $y(0.8) = 0.846; y(1.2) = 0.671; y(1.6) = 0.456; y(2.0) = 0.224.$

3.38 Evaluate to three significant figures the integral of the following problem at $x = 0(0.1)0.5$ by Noumerov's recurrence formula.

$$y'' + x^2 y = 3e^x; \qquad y(0) = 1; \qquad y'(0) = 1.$$

Evaluate $y(0.1)$ by Taylor series.

3.39 Evaluate to four significant figures the integral of the following problem at $x = 0(0.1)0.5$ by Noumerov's recurrence formula.

$$y'' + 2xy = 3x^3 + 1; \qquad y(0) = 1; \qquad y'(0) = 1.$$

Ans. Taylor series: $y(0) = 1; \ y(0.1) = 1.105. \quad y(0.2) = 1.217; \ y(0.3) = 1.335; \ y(0.4) = 1.456; \ y(0.5) = 1.577.$

3.40 A mathematical pendulum of length L (Fig. 3.1) moves through the origin $\theta = 0$ at $t = 0$ with an angular velocity $\dot{\theta} = 1$ radian per sec. Assuming small deflections, determine the values of θ in the interval $0(0.1)0.5$, by Noumerov's recurrence formula, assuming $g/L = 20 \ \text{sec}^{-2}$.

(a) Obtain θ at $t = 0.1$ and $t = 0.2$ by approximating $\dot{\theta}_0$ by $\mu \left(\delta - \dfrac{\delta^3}{6} \right) \theta_0$
and by applying the difference equation at $t = -0.1$, $t = 0$, and $t = 0.1$.

(b) Obtain θ at $t = 0.1$ by means of a Taylor series.

3.41 The pendulum of Problem 3.40 oscillates in a viscous medium of $\mu = 1.2$ per unit mass. Determine the values of θ in the interval $0(0.1)0.5$ by the Fox method. *Note:* Obtain θ at $t = 0.1$ by a Taylor series.

Ans.

t	0.1	0.2	0.3	0.4	0.5	0.6
θ	0.091	0.155	0.182	0.171	0.130	0.068

3.42 The series $R\text{-}L\text{-}C$ circuit of Fig. 3.5 contains an inductance L of 0.1 henry, a capacitance C of 0.05 microfarad ($0.05 \cdot 10^{-6}$ farad) and a resistance R

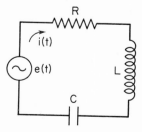

Figure 3.5

of 5000 ohms. The circuit elements are connected in series with a 22.5-volt battery and switch. There is no initial charge q on the capacitor, and no current i flows in the circuit at time $t = 0$.

(a) Find the charge q after the switch is closed by the Fox method in the interval $t = 0(0.01)0.04$ sec.

(b) Determine the charge q in the same circuit if $R = 0$.

(c) Determine the charge in the same circuit if $R = 2000$ ohms and a current of 5 milliamperes flows initially in the same direction in which the battery voltage is applied. *Note:* The differential equation of the circuit is given by

$$L\ddot{q} + R\dot{q} + (1/C)q = e,$$

where e is the battery voltage. The current i is the time derivative of the charge q.

Ans.   (b) True values of q:

$10^2 t$	1	2	3	4
q	0.0112	0.0439	0.0998	0.1753

3.43 Evaluate by Noumerov's generalized method the integral of the following equation at $x = 0.1(0.1)0.4$.

$$y^{\text{iv}} - (1 - x)y = 0; \qquad y_0 = 1; \qquad y_0' = 0; \qquad y_0'' = 1; \qquad y_0''' = 0.$$

Ans. $y(0.1) = 1.005$; $y(0.2) = 1.020$; $y(0.3) = 1.046$; $y(0.4) = 1.082$.

3.44 Derive a recurrence equation of order h^{10} for the integration of the following problem.

$$y'' + c^2 y = 0; \qquad y_0 = 0; \qquad y_0' = 1.$$

3.45 Evaluate the first characteristic value of the following problems by forward integration using $h = 0.2$ and $h = 0.1$, and assuming that k^2 is proportional to $1/L^2$.

(a) $y'' + k^2(x/L)^2 y = 0$; $y(0) = 0$; $y(L) = 0$.
(b) $y'' + k^2(1 - x/L)y = 0$; $y(0) = 0$; $y(L) = 0$.

Ans.   (a) $k_1 = 5.52$.

3.46 Prove that the step-by-step integration of the problem

$$y'' + \omega^2 y = 0; \qquad y(0) = 1; \qquad y'(0) = 0,$$

obtained by substituting $\delta^2 y$ for $h^2 y''$, leads to an oscillating solution with a frequency equal to 1.11ω when the time interval $h = T/4.44$, where $T = 2\pi/\omega$ is the period of the true solution; and that the solution diverges for $h > T/\pi$.

IV

The Numerical Integration of Ordinary Boundary Value Problems

4.1 *Boundary Value Problems*

The solution of ordinary boundary value problems by finite differences reduces the integration of a differential equation to the evaluation of the roots of a system of simultaneous algebraic equations. These roots are the values of the required solution at the pivotal points of its interval of definition, which is one-dimensional for ordinary differential equations.

Problems involving first-order, ordinary differential equations are necessarily of the initial value type. Boundary value problems lead, instead, to second- and higher-order equations; of these the odd-order equations, with different numbers of conditions at the two ends of the interval, are sometimes hard to handle numerically and are usually transformed into even-order equations by either integration or differentiation.

Whenever possible, the derivatives appearing in the differential

159

equation are expanded in terms of central differences, since the accuracy of these expansions is greater than the accuracy obtainable by lateral differences.

The derivatives involved in the boundary conditions of the problem may be expressed in terms of lateral or of central differences. For example, the following boundary conditions at the origin are translated by means of Eqs. (2.7.16) into the corresponding central difference conditions by using the first term of their expansions:

$$y(0) = 0; \qquad y_0 = 0;$$

$$y'(0) = 0; \qquad y_1 - y_{-1} = 0;$$

$$y''(0) = 0; \qquad y_1 - 2y_0 + y_{-1} = 0; \qquad (4.1.1)$$

$$y'''(0) = 0; \qquad y_2 - 2y_1 + 2y_{-1} - y_{-2} = 0;$$

$$y^{iv}(0) = 0; \qquad y_2 - 4y_1 + 6y_0 - 4y_{-1} + y_{-2} = 0.$$

These equations are actually used to define the values y_{-1} and y_{-2}, which lie beyond the interval of definition of y, in terms of y_0, y_1, y_2, and have errors of order h^2.

When central differences of order h^2 are used in the equations, and either forward or backward differences are used in the boundary conditions, these last should also have errors of order h^2, whenever possible. Hence, for example, the conditions of Eqs. (4.1.1) should be expressed in terms of the difference operators of Fig. 2.5b:

$$y(0) = 0; \qquad y_0 = 0;$$

$$y'(0) = 0; \qquad -y_2 + 4y_1 - 3y_0 = 0;$$

$$y''(0) = 0; \qquad -y_3 + 4y_2 - 5y_1 + 2y_0 = 0; \qquad (4.1.2)$$

$$y'''(0) = 0; \qquad -3y_4 + 14y_3 - 24y_2 + 18y_1 - 5y_0 = 0;$$

$$y^{iv}(0) = 0; \qquad -2y_5 + 11y_4 - 24y_3 + 26y_2 - 14y_1 + 3y_0 = 0.$$

4.2 Step-by-step Integration of Boundary Value Problems

Ordinary boundary value problems of the second order can be solved by the methods of Chapter III, that is, by step-by-step forward integration formulas, in conjunction with trial and error and/or interpolation procedures.

Consider, for example, the simple problem

$$y'' + y^2 = 0; \qquad y(0) = 2; \qquad y(1) = 0. \tag{a}$$

Multiplying the equation by h^2 and using central differences, we obtain the recurrence equation

$$y_{i+1} = 2y_i - h^2 y_i^2 - y_{i-1}, \tag{b}$$

which, for example, for $h = \frac{1}{4}$ becomes

$$y_{i+1} = 2y_i - \left(\frac{y_i}{4}\right)^2 - y_{i-1}. \tag{c}$$

To start the solution *assume* a value $y_1 = 1.5$ and integrate forward, as shown in the third column of Table 4.1. With $y_1 = 2.0$ we obtain the

Table 4.1

i	x_i	$y_1 = 1.5$	$y_1 = 2.0$	$y_1 = 1.70$	$y_1 = 1.6825$
0	0	2.00	2.00	2.00	2.0000
1	0.25	1.50	2.00	1.70	1.6825
2	0.50	0.86	1.75	1.22	1.1881
3	0.75	0.17	1.31	0.65	0.6055
4	1.00	−0.52	0.76	0.05	0.0000

results given in the fourth column of Table 4.1. A linear interpolation between $y_1 = 1.5$, $y_4 = -0.52$, and $y_1 = 2.0$, $y_4 = 0.76$ gives [Eq. (1.2.7)]

$$y_1 = \frac{1.5 \times 0.76 - 2.0 \times (-0.52)}{0.76 - (-0.52)} = 1.70$$

and with $y_1 = 1.70$, Eq. (c) gives the results of the fifth column of Table 4.1. Interpolating between 1.5 and 1.70,

$$y_1 = \frac{1.5 \times 0.05 - 1.70(-0.52)}{0.05 - (-0.52)} = 1.6825$$

and with $y_1 = 1.6825$ the y_i of column 6 in Table 4.1 are the correct answer for $n = 4$.

Similar procedures may be used to solve higher-order equations, using as parameters the first few ordinates y_i and computing the errors in the boundary conditions at the far end of the interval of integration. This method of solution becomes cumbersome as soon as the order of the equation is higher than third or fourth.

4.3 Solution of Second-order Problems by Central Differences

In order to illustrate the general method of solution of ordinary boundary value problems by central differences, we shall consider the heat-flow problem of determining the temperature u in a circular wire of length L and radius R, connecting two bodies kept at constant temperatures u_0 and u_n, respectively, and losing heat to the surrounding medium kept at a temperature $U(x)$ (Fig. 4.1).

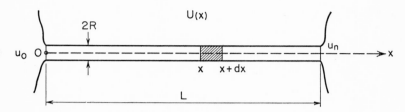

Figure 4.1

Equating the heat entering an element of length dx of the wire to the heat leaving its surface, it may be found* that the boundary value problem in question reduces to

$$u'' - \frac{2k_1}{kR} u = - \frac{2k_1}{kR} U; \qquad u(0) = u_0; \qquad u(L) = u_n, \quad (4.3.1)$$

where k = the thermal conductivity of the wire,
k_1 = the boundary conductance of the wire,
x = axis of wire with origin at its left end.
To reduce the problem to nondimensional form, let

$$z = \frac{x}{L}; \qquad v(z) = \frac{u(x)}{u_n}; \qquad F(z) = \frac{U(x)}{U(0)},$$

obtaining

$$v'' - \frac{2k_1 L^2}{kR} v = - \frac{2k_1 L^2}{kR} \frac{U(0)}{u_n} F(z);$$

$$v(0) = \frac{u_0}{u_n}; \qquad v(1) = 1, \tag{4.3.2}$$

where primes indicate differentiation with respect to z.

* See, for example, *Differential Equations*, Sec. 2.13.

In a particular case it will be assumed that

$$L = 100 \text{ cm}; \qquad R = 1 \text{ cm};$$

$$k = 1 \text{ cal/sec } °C \text{ cm}^2/\text{cm};$$

$$k_1 = 6 \cdot 10^{-4}(\tfrac{3}{2}z + \tfrac{1}{3}) \text{ cal/sec } °C \text{ cm}^{2*};$$

$$u_0 = 0; \qquad U(0)/u_n = 1;$$

$$F(z) = e^z,$$

so that the boundary value problem of Eqs. (4.3.2) reduces to

$$v'' - 2(9z + 2)v = -2(9z + 2)e^z;$$
$$v(0) = 0; \qquad v(1) = 1. \tag{4.3.3}$$

To transform Eqs. (4.3.3) into the corresponding difference problem, the interval of definition $(0,1)$ of the variable z is divided into n equal parts of width $h = 1/n$, the differential equation is multiplied by h^2, and $(\delta^2 v + \epsilon_2)$ is substituted for $h^2 v''$, according to Eq. (2.7.16). The equation thus becomes

$$v_l - 2v_i + v_r + \epsilon_{2i} - 2h^2(9z_i + 2)v_i = -2h^2(9z_i + 2)e^{z_i}$$

or

$$v_l - c_{hi}v_i + v_r = -(c_{hi} - 2)e^{z_i} - \epsilon_{2i} \quad (i = 1,2,\ldots,n-1), \tag{4.3.4}$$

where
$$c_{hi} = 2[1 + h^2(9z_i + 2)]. \tag{4.3.5}$$

The boundary conditions are in this case

$$v_0 = 0; \qquad v_n = 1. \tag{4.3.6}$$

Equation (4.3.4) holds and is applied at the $n - 1$ internal pivotal points, $i = 1, 2, \ldots, n - 1$, and leads to a set of $n - 1$ linear algebraic equations in the $n - 1$ unknown pivotal values v_i. Once this system is solved, v is known, as required, at the $n + 1$ pivotal points v_i $(i = 0,1,\ldots,n)$. By increasing the number of subintervals n, the accuracy of the solution can be indefinitely improved, at least theoretically.

The problem represented by Eqs. (4.3.4), (4.3.6) will now be solved for $n = 2,3,4$, successively, that is, for decreasing values of h. The correction ϵ_{2i} will be neglected at first.

---

* The boundary conductance k_1 is known to vary linearly between $0°C$ and $500°C$ to a first approximation.

Approximation n = 2. Equation (4.3.4) applied at $z_1 = \frac{1}{2}$ (Fig. 4.2a), with

$$v_0 = v_l = 0; \qquad v_n = v_r = v_2 = 1;$$

$$h = \tfrac{1}{2}; \qquad c_{h1} = 2[1 + \tfrac{1}{4}(9 \cdot 0.5 + 2)] = 5.25,$$

gives $0 - 5.25v_1 + 1 = -3.25e^{0.5} = -5.359;$

$$v(\tfrac{1}{2}) = v_1^{(1)} = 1.211. \tag{4.3.7}$$

Approximation n = 3. Equation (4.3.4) applied at $z_1 = \frac{1}{3}$, $z_2 = \frac{2}{3}$ (Fig. 4.2b), with

$$v_0 = 0; \qquad v_n = v_3 = 1;$$

$$h = \tfrac{1}{3}; \qquad c_{hi} = 2[1 + \tfrac{1}{9}(9z_i + 2)],$$

gives

at $z_1 = \frac{1}{3}$ $0 - 3.1111v_1 + v_2 = -1.1111e^{\frac{1}{3}} = -1.5507;$

at $z_2 = \frac{2}{3}$ $v_1 - 3.7778v_2 + 1 = -1.7778e^{\frac{2}{3}} = -3.4628;$

$$v(\tfrac{1}{3}) = v_1^{(1)} = 0.9599; \qquad v(\tfrac{2}{3}) = v_2^{(1)} = 1.4354.$$

Approximation n = 4. Equation (4.3.4) applied at $z_1 = \frac{1}{4}$, $z_2 = \frac{1}{2}$, $z_3 = \frac{3}{4}$ (Fig. 4.2c), with

$$v_0 = 0; \qquad v_n = v_4 = 1;$$

$$h = \tfrac{1}{4}; \qquad c_{hi} = 2[1 + \tfrac{1}{16}(9z_i + 2)],$$

gives

at $z_1 = \frac{1}{4}$ $-2.5312v_1 + v_2 = -0.6821;$

at $z_2 = \frac{1}{2}$ $v_1 - 2.8125v_2 + v_3 = -1.3396;$ $\qquad$ (4.3.8)

at $z_3 = \frac{3}{4}$ $v_2 - 3.0938v_3 = -3.3156.$

Equations (4.3.8) can be solved by any of the methods given in Chapter I. For example, the solution *by relaxation* of this system was given in Table 1.15 as

$$v_1^{(1)} = 0.7753; \qquad v_2^{(1)} = 1.2802; \qquad v_3^{(1)} = 1.4855, \tag{4.3.9}$$

and is labeled $v_i^{(1)}$ to indicate that it is a first approximation in which the corrections ϵ have been neglected.

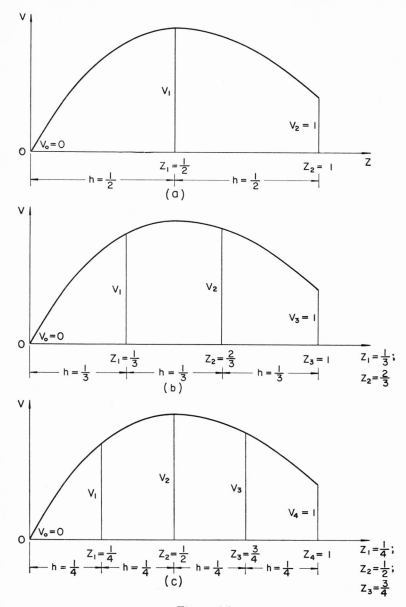

Figure 4.2

Table 4.2

n	1	2	3	4
v_1	0.6646	0.6915	0.7539	0.7699
v_2	1.0682	1.2260	1.2664	1.2767
v_3	1.4169	1.4680	1.4810	1.4843

n	5	6	7	8
v_1	0.7739	0.7750	0.7752	0.7753
v_2	1.2793	1.2800	1.2802	1.2802
v_3	1.4852	1.4854	1.4855	1.4855

The same solution is obtained *by iteration* in Table 4.2, with starting values $v_2^{(0)} = 1$, $v_3^{(0)} = 1$.

Table 4.3 gives the solution of the system (4.3.8), once again, by Cholesky's method.

By increasing the number of pivotal points the graph of $v(z)$ can be obtained to any degree of accuracy at the cost of increased labor.

Table 4.3

	v_1	v_2	v_3	c	1	2	3	v_1	v_2	v_3	k
1	2.5312	−1	0	0.6821	2.5312	0	0	1	−0.3951	0	0.2695
2	−1	2.8125	−1	1.3396	−1	2.4174	0	0	1	−0.4137	0.6656
3	0	−1	3.0938	3.3156	0	−1	2.6801	0	0	1	1.4855

$$v_3 = 1.4855; \qquad v_2 = 0.6656 + 0.4137 \cdot 1.4855 = 1.2802;$$
$$v_1 = 0.2695 + 0.3951 \cdot 1.2802 = 0.7753$$

The accuracy of $v(z)$ may also be increased with small additional labor by the use of Fox's corrections or by extrapolation, as shown in the following sections.

4.4 *Improvement of Solution by Corrections*

[a] GAUSS'S SCHEME

The system of Eqs. (4.3.8) appears solved by Gauss's scheme in the first five columns of Table 4.4. Its roots $v_i^{(1)}$ appear on the first row of the lower part of the table and check (within one unit in the last significant figure) the roots computed by relaxation, iteration, or Cholesky's scheme.

Table 4.4

Rows	v_1	v_2	v_3	c	$c - \epsilon_2'$	$c - \epsilon_2''$	Explanation
1	−2.5312	1	0	−0.6821	−0.7122	−0.7130	I
2	1	−2.8125	1	−1.3396	−1.3697	−1.3705	II
3	0	1	−3.0938	−3.3156	−3.3457	−3.3465	III
4	2.5312	−7.1190	2.5312	−3.3908	−3.4670	−3.4690	2.5312 × (2)
5		−6.1190	2.5312	−4.0729	−4.1792	−4.1820	(1) + (4)
6		6.1190	−18.9310	−20.2882	−20.4723	−20.4772	6.1190 × (3)
7			−16.3998	−24.3611	−24.6515	−24.6592	(5) + (6)

Approx.	v_1 from row 1	v_2 from row 3	v_3 from row 7	for
1	0.7752	1.2801	1.4854	c
2	0.7968	1.3048	1.5032	$c - \epsilon_2'$
3	0.7974	1.3054	1.5036	$c - \epsilon_2''$

The roots $v_i^{(1)}$ are obtained neglecting the corrections ϵ. To evaluate the corrections, the successive central differences of the $v_i^{(1)}$ are evaluated in Table 4.5. For lack of better values, the fourth difference $\delta^4 v$ is assumed constant and equal to $\delta^4 v_2 = -0.3618$, the assumed values of $\delta^4 v_i$ appearing enclosed in parentheses. By means of $\delta^4 v$ and the first term in the expansion of ϵ_2 [Eq. (2.7.16)], an approximate value of the correction ϵ_2 is given by

$$\epsilon_2' \doteq -\frac{\delta^4 v}{12} = 0.0301,$$

which, substituted in Eqs. (4.3.8), gives

at $z = \frac{1}{4}$ $\quad -2.5312v_1 + v_2 = -0.6821 - 0.0301 = -0.7122;$

at $z = \frac{1}{2}$ $\quad v_1 - 2.8125v_2 + v_3 = -1.3396 - 0.0301 = -1.3697;$

at $z = \frac{3}{4}$ $\quad v_2 - 3.0938v_3 = -3.3156 - 0.0301 = -3.3457.$ $\quad$ (4.4.1)

Table 4.5

i	v_i	$\delta v_{i+\frac{1}{2}}$	$\delta^2 v_i$	$\delta^3 v_{i+\frac{1}{2}}$	$\delta^4 v_i$	ϵ_2'
0	0					
		0.7752				
1	0.7752		−0.2703		(−0.3618)	(0.0301)
		0.5049		−0.0293		
2	1.2801		−0.2996		−0.3618	0.0301
		+0.2053		−0.3911		
3	1.4854		−0.6907		(−0.3618)	(0.0301)
		−0.4855				
4	1.0000					

The system (4.4.1) has the same coefficients as system (4.3.8) but different constants. It may therefore be conveniently solved by adding a new column of constants to the Gauss's scheme of Table 4.4. Its roots $v_i^{(2)}$ appear in the second row of the lower part of Table 4.4.

Differencing the $v_i^{(2)}$ we obtain, similarly, an improved value ϵ_2'' of the correction ϵ_2 and a new set of values for the constants in the right-hand members of Table 4.4. Solving these equations, we obtain the approximations $v_i^{(3)}$ of v, and the process is continued until the corrections become stable. In the present problem this takes place in the third approximation and leads to the final values appearing in the third row of the lower part of Table 4.4.

Fox's corrections may also be used in connection with the approximation $n = 2$ of the same problem (page 164), by expressing the correction in terms of v^{iv} [Eq. (2.7.10)]:

$$\epsilon_2 \doteq -\frac{h^4 v^{iv}}{12}. \tag{a}$$

v^{iv} is obtained by two differentiations of Eq. (4.3.3):

$$v^{iv} = 2(9z + 2)v'' + 36v' - 2(9z + 20)e^z,$$

and, using again Eq. (4.3.3);

$$v^{iv} = 2(9z + 2)[2(9z + 2)v - 2(9z + 2)e^z] + 36v' - 2(9z + 20)e^z.$$

In this expression the derivative v' is replaced by the corresponding averaged central difference

$$hv_1' \doteq \mu\delta v_1 = \frac{v_2 - v_0}{2} = 0.5.$$

Applying Eq. (a) at $z = \frac{1}{2}$ with $hv_1' = 0.5$, we obtain

$$\epsilon_2^{(1)} = -\frac{h^4 v^{iv}}{12} = 0.619$$

and hence a corrected equation (4.3.7):

$$-5.25v_1 + 1 = -5.359 - 0.619 = -5.978,$$

from which $v_1^{(2)} = 1.329$. Repeating the process we find, successively,

$$\epsilon_2^{(2)} = 0.515; \qquad v_1^{(3)} = 1.309;$$

$$\epsilon_2^{(3)} = 0.533; \qquad v_1^{(4)} = 1.313;$$

$$\epsilon_2^{(4)} = 0.529; \qquad v_1^{(5)} = 1.312.$$

The same method of approximating the correction by derivatives could have been used in the solution for $n = 4$.

[b] RELAXATION

Relaxation becomes particularly efficient when Fox's corrections are used to improve the results obtained by rough finite difference formulas. For instance, it was found above that a first correction $\epsilon_2^{(1)} = 0.0301$ had to be subtracted from all constants of the system (4.3.8) to obtain the corrected system (4.4.1). Hence the constants k of the corrected system (4.4.1), *ready for iteration*, equal the constants $k^{(1)}$ of the uncorrected system (4.3.8) ready for iteration [system (c), Sec. 1.13] *increased* by $\delta k_i^{(1)} = \epsilon_2^{(1)}/a_{ii}$.

$$\delta k_1^{(1)} = \frac{0.0301}{2.5312} = 0.0119;$$

$$\delta k_2^{(1)} = \frac{0.0301}{2.8125} = 0.0107;$$

$$\delta k_3^{(1)} = \frac{0.0301}{3.0938} = 0.0097.$$

Therefore, if the roots of the uncorrected system from Table 1.15 are used as starting values, the residuals R_i equal the δk_i, and the corrected roots may be computed by relaxation of these residuals. As shown in Table 4.6, block relaxation may be used in the first step with rounded-off

Table 4.6

	7753	~~110~~	12802	~~107~~	14855	~~97~~
	200	~~-1~~	200	~~51~~	200	~~-39~~
	19	~~19~~	50	~~1~~	-23	~~-23~~
	-1		-2	~~-9~~		-1
				~~-2~~		
$v_i^{(2)}$	7972	-1	13050	1	15032	0

coefficients [system (d), Sec. 1.13] and with $\delta = 200$. The final residuals are computed with the complete coefficients of system (c), Sec. 1.13.

The second corrections $\epsilon_i^{(2)}$, obtained by means of the values $v_i^{(2)}$, lead to new increments $\delta k_i = \epsilon_i^{(2)}/a_{ii}$:

$$\delta k_1^{(2)} = 0.0122; \qquad \delta k_2^{(2)} = 0.0110; \qquad \delta k_3^{(2)} = 0.0100,$$

which differ by three units in the last place from the previous $\delta k_i^{(1)}$. Hence, using as initial values the $v_i^{(2)}$ of Table 4.6 and these differences of 0.0003 as residuals, we obtain the third approximations $v_i^{(3)}$ with a small amount of additional labor, as shown in Table 4.7.

Table 4.7

	7972	$\not{3}$	13050	$\not{3}$	15032	$\not{3}$
	4	$\not{4}$	3	$\not{1}$	4	$\not{4}$
	1		3	$\not{3}$		1
$v_i^{(3)}$	7976	0	13056	0	15036	1

A more accurate graph of the temperature function $v(z)$ may be obtained by subdividing its interval of definition (0,1) into six subintervals of width $h = \frac{1}{6}$. The set of linear equations for the pivotal values v_i becomes in this case, by Eq. (4.3.4), the system of Table 4.8. This system is relaxed in Table 4.9 with initial values obtained by linear

Table 4.8

v_1	v_2	v_3	v_4	v_5	k	Block Coefficients
-1	0.4557				0.1047	-0.5443
0.4390	-1	0.4390			0.1702	-0.1220
	0.4235	-1	0.4235		0.2521	-0.1530
		0.4091	-1	0.4091	0.3541	-0.1818
			0.3956	-1	0.8760	-0.6044

interpolation from the roots corresponding to $h = \frac{1}{4}$. The residuals are checked after obtaining three, four, and five figures of the roots; the corrections are evaluated by differences.* The second approximations of the roots are then computed and differenced again to obtain the corrections to the corrections and hence the third approximation of the roots.

* The sixth difference was assumed constant in this example.

Table 4.9

	v_1	v_2		v_3		v_4		v_5	Explanations
	0.56	0	1.00	−1	1.31	−2	1.43	0 1.33	1	Initial values and residuals
						0	6	5 12 / −1 2		
	0.560	0	1.000	−0	1.310	−3	1.490	−7 1.450	18	Roots to one unit in the second decimal place and check of residuals
	−6	−5	−10 / −3 / −0 / 0	−6	1 / −3 / −0 / 0	−8	−7 / 1 / −1 / −2	−3	0 16 / −3 / 0 1	−1 / −2 0	
	−4	0	−4	0	−4	−1	−4	−4	0	Block relaxation
	0.5500	18	0.9800	15	1.2980	−28	1.4830	2 1.4620	7	Roots to one unit in the third decimal place and check of residuals
	13	5	5 2	10	4 / 16 / 0	−28	0 / −4 / 0	−10 −10 / 0	2	
	5	2	5	−1	5	−1	5	−1 5	0	Block relaxation
	0.55180	17	0.98150	−25	1.29570	−10	1.48250	−2 1.46250	−2	Check of residuals
	−13	24	24 / 0 / −5	−13	−28 / −12 / 0 / −8	−13	−8 / −15 / 0	−13	0 / −5 / −3	−13	6	6 0		Block relaxation
	−8		−8 / 0 / −2	−6	0 / −4 / 0 / −2	−4	−2	−1 / 0 / −2		−5 / 0	−5	−2	
	−5	1	−5	−1	−5	−1	−5	−1 −5	1	Block relaxation
	0.55178	1	0.98110	−1	1.29535	−1	1.48227	2 1.46238	1	Check of residuals
$v_i^{(1)}$	0.5518	5	0.9811	7	1.2954	24	1.4823	58 1.4624	98	First approximation of the roots to one unit in the fourth decimal place and first corrections
	115 / −58	−58 / 0 / −15	115 / −32	−7 / −32 / 0	115	0 / −8 / 6 / 13	115 / 32 / 16	32 / 0 / 16 / 8	115 / 38 / 6 / 3	28 / 35 / 0 / 0	Block relaxation
	−15	0		−7 / −1	13	0 / 3 / 2 / 0		7 / 0 / 1 / 2	8 / 7 / 0 / 1	0 / 3 / 0 / 1	
				0	3	0	1	2		
	0.55600	7	0.98940	0	1.30860	−5	1.49950	18 1.47870	2	Check of residuals
	18	−3 / −1	18 / 4	1 / 0	18	−8 / −2 / 0	18 / 15	15 / 0 / −1	18 / −3	−0 / −8 / 0	Block relaxation
	−1	0		0			−1	0		
	0.55617	0	0.98962	−1	1.30878	0	1.49982	0 1.47885	2	Check of residuals
								1 2	0	
	0.55617	0	0.98962	−1	1.30878	0	1.49982	1 1.47887	0	Check of residuals
$v_i^{(2)}$	0.5562	2	0.9896	1	1.3088	1	1.4998	2 1.4789	1	Second approximation of roots and second corrections
	7	−1	7	0	7	0	7	1 7	0	Block relaxation
$v_i^{(3)}$	0.5569		0.9903		1.3095	1	5005	1.4796		

4.5 Improvement of Solution by Extrapolation

In the previous sections the temperature functions $v(z)$ in the boundary value problem (4.3.3) was obtained by means of central differences. In particular, h^2v'' was approximated by δ^2v, and this entails an error of order h^2 in v. Hence the h^2- and (h^2,h^4)-extrapolations [Sec. 2.13], can be used to improve, for example, the value of $v(\tfrac{1}{2})$.

Table 4.10 gives the first approximation values of $v(\tfrac{1}{2})$ obtained by means of $n = 2$, 4, and 6 subintervals; the values of the h^2-extrapolation for $n_2/n_1 = 4/2$ and $n_2/n_1 = 6/4$, and the values of the (h^2,h^4)-extrapolation for $n_3/n_2/n_1 = 6/4/2$. The extrapolation coefficients were taken from Table 2.12 and Table 2.13, respectively.

Table 4.10

n	Uncorrected $v(\tfrac{1}{2})$	n	h^2-extr.	n	(h^2,h^4)-extr.	Corrected $v(\tfrac{1}{2})$	n	h^4-extr.
2	1.2110	2,4	1.3033	2,4,6	1.3081	1.3120	2,4	1.3050
4	1.2802	4,6	1.3076			1.3054	4,6	1.3105
6	1.2954					1.3095		

For example, the h^2-extrapolation

$$v(\tfrac{1}{2})\Big]_{2,4} = 1.3333 \cdot 1.2802 - 0.3333 \cdot 1.2110 = 1.3033$$

is only 0.16 per cent off the value $v_2^{(3)} = 1.3054$ obtained by four subintervals and two corrections (Table 4.4). Similarly, the value

$$v(\tfrac{1}{2})\Big]_{4,6} = 1.8 \cdot 1.2954 - 0.8 \cdot 1.2802 = 1.3076$$

is only 0.08 per cent off the value $v_3^{(3)} = 1.3095$ obtained by six subintervals with two corrections (Table 4.9), presumably the best value obtainable without extrapolation.

Table 4.10 contains also the values of $v(\tfrac{1}{2})$, obtained by two, four, and six subintervals, improved by means of Fox's corrections. Since the inclusion of a correction $-\delta^4v/12$ is equivalent to taking into account the first *two* terms in the difference expansion for h^2D^2 [Eq. (2.7.15)], the error in the second derivative of the *corrected* solution is of order h^4, and h^4-extrapolations may be applied to the corrected values of $v(\tfrac{1}{2})$. The results of the h^4-extrapolation applied to the corrected values appear in

Table 4.10 for $n_2/n_1 = 4/2$ and $n_2/n_1 = 6/4$. Thus, with the coefficients of Table 2.14, we have

$$v(\tfrac{1}{2})\Big]_{2,4} = 1.0667 \cdot 1.3054 - 0.0667 \cdot 1.3120 = 1.3050;$$

$$v(\tfrac{1}{2})\Big]_{4,6} = 1.2462 \cdot 1.3095 - 0.2462 \cdot 1.3054 = 1.3105.$$

It is seen from this example that h^2-type extrapolations can be used to good advantage to save the labor of differencing involved in computing the corrections.

In connection with the finite difference solution of boundary value problems, it is well to note that better approximations for the derivatives of a function may be obtained either by increasing the number of terms in the finite difference expansions or by decreasing the spacing h. The first procedure involves more complicated formulas and a smaller number of pivotal points, the second a larger number of pivotal points and simpler formulas. The choice between these two methods rests essentially with the type of problem to be handled, the available computational device, and the mental make-up of the computer, but only a decrease in h can *guarantee* an approach to the correct solution.

4.6 Solution of Higher-order Problems by Central Differences

As an example of solution by central differences of a boundary value problem involving higher-order derivatives, consider the deflections of a

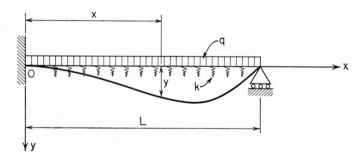

Figure 4.3

beam on an elastic foundation under a uniform load q. The beam has a flexural rigidity EI and is built in at the left end ($x = 0$) and simply supported at the right end ($x = L$) (Fig. 4.3).

The boundary value problem governing the beam deflections y is given by*

$$y^{iv} + \frac{k}{EI} y = \frac{q}{EI};$$

$$y(0) = y'(0) = y(L) = y''(L) = 0,$$

(4.6.1)

where k is the *foundation modulus* (force per unit deflection per unit length of beam).

To solve the problem by central differences of order h^2, the equation is first transformed to nondimensional form by the change of variable:

$$z = \frac{x}{L}; \qquad \frac{d}{dx} = \frac{1}{L} \frac{d}{dz}; \qquad x = 0, \quad z = 0; \qquad x = L, \quad z = 1,$$

and becomes

$$\frac{d^4 y}{dz^4} + \frac{kL^4}{EI} y = \frac{qL^4}{EI}$$

The interval of definition $(0,1)$ of z is then divided into n equal parts of length $h = 1/n$, and the equation is multiplied through by $h^4 = 1/n^4$:

$$\frac{h^4 d^4 y}{dz^4} + \frac{kL^4}{n^4 EI} y = \frac{qL^4}{n^4 EI}.$$

Approximating $h^4 d^4 y/dz^4$ by $\delta^4 y_i$, we obtain

$$\delta^4 y_i + \frac{kL^4}{n^4 EI} y_i = \frac{qL^4}{n^4 EI}$$

or, by means of Eqs. (2.7.16),

$$y_{ll} - 4y_l + 6y_i - 4y_r + y_{rr} + \frac{kL^4}{n^4 EI} y_i = \frac{qL^4}{n^4 EI}.$$

Letting finally

$$\frac{kL^4}{EI} = K,$$

(4.6.2)

the difference equation representing Eq. (4.6.1) takes the form

$$y_{ll} - 4y_l + \left[\frac{K}{n^4} + 6 \right] y_i - 4y_r + y_{rr} = \frac{qL^4}{n^4 EI}.$$

(4.6.3)

For $k = 2{,}604$ psi, $E = 30 \cdot 10^6$ psi, $I = 3 \cdot 10^3$ in.^{4}, $L = 120$ in., $q = 43{,}400$ lbs/in., the constant K takes the value 6, the quantity $qL^4/EI = 100$, and Eq. (4.6.3) becomes

$$y_{ll} - 4y_l + 6 \left(\frac{n^4 + 1}{n^4} \right) y_i - 4y_r + y_{rr} = \frac{100}{n^4}.$$

(a)

* See for example, *Differential Equations*, Sec. 10.8.

The boundary conditions of Eq. (4.6.1) are transformed into central difference conditions by Eqs. (4.1.1):

$$y_0 = 0; \quad y_{-1} = y_1; \quad y_n = 0; \quad y_{n+1} = -y_{n-1}. \tag{b}$$

The difference problem of Eqs. (a) and (b) can now be solved starting with large values of h, that is, small values of n, and the accuracy of y may be increased to any degree of accuracy by increasing n in steps of one.

Approximation n = 2. With $n = 2$ (Fig. 4.4a), Eq. (a) applied at $z = \frac{1}{2}$ gives

$$y_1 - 4 \cdot 0 + 6 \frac{2^4 + 1}{2^4} y_1 - 4 \cdot 0 - y_1 = \frac{100}{2^4},$$

from which $\qquad y(\frac{1}{2}) = y_1 = 0.98.$

Approximation n = 3. With $n = 3$, (Fig. 4.4b) Eq. (a) gives

at $\qquad z = \frac{1}{3} \qquad y_1 + 6 \frac{3^4 + 1}{3^4} y_1 - 4y_2 = \frac{100}{3^4};$

at $\qquad z = \frac{2}{3} \qquad -4y_1 + 6 \frac{3^4 + 1}{3^4} y_2 - y_2 = \frac{100}{3^4},$

from which $\qquad y(\frac{1}{3}) = y_1 = 0.56; \qquad y(\frac{2}{3}) = y_2 = 0.69.$

Approximation n = 4. With $n = 4$, (Fig. 4.4c) Eq. (a) gives

at $\qquad z = \frac{1}{4} \qquad y_1 + 6 \frac{4^4 + 1}{4^4} y_1 - 4y_2 + y_3 = \frac{100}{4^4};$

at $\qquad z = \frac{1}{2} \qquad -4y_1 + 6 \frac{4^4 + 1}{4^4} y_2 - 4y_3 = \frac{100}{4^4};$

at $\qquad z = \frac{3}{4} \qquad y_1 - 4y_2 + 6 \frac{4^4 + 1}{4^4} y_3 - y_3 = \frac{100}{4^4},$

from which

$$y(\tfrac{1}{4}) = y_1 = 0.34; \quad y(\tfrac{1}{2}) = y_2 = 0.64; \quad y(\tfrac{3}{4}) = y_3 = 0.51.$$

The value of y at $z = \frac{1}{2}$ may be improved by h^2-extrapolation using the $n = 2$ and $n = 4$ solutions:

$$y(\tfrac{1}{2}) \Big]_{2,4} = 1.333 \cdot 0.64 - 0.333 \cdot 0.98 = 0.53,$$

and has an error of 3.9 per cent when compared with the value obtained by a rigorous solution of the same problem.

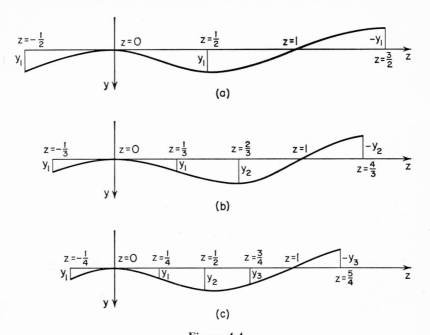

Figure 4.4

4.7 Solution of Characteristic Value Problems

A method of solution of such problems, based upon the use of finite differences and extrapolations, will be given in this section.*

Consider, for example, the Euler buckling problem of a beam, simply supported at the right end $(x = L)$ and built in at the left end $(x = 0)$, acted upon by compressive axial forces P (Fig. 4.5). The deflections y of the axis x of the beam are governed† by the characteristic value problem

$$y^{iv} + \frac{P}{EI} y'' = 0;$$

$$y(0) = y'(0) = y(L) = y''(L) = 0,$$

(4.7.1)

where EI is the flexural rigidity of the beam.

The corresponding difference problem is obtained by substituting in the differential equation and the boundary conditions the central difference operators of Fig. 2.8a or Eqs. (2.7.16) for the derivatives.

* See Sec. 3.12 for a method based on forward integration processes.
† See, for example, *Differential Equations*, Sec. 2.11.

To this purpose, introduce first the change of variable:

$$z = \frac{x}{L}; \qquad \frac{d}{dx} = \frac{1}{L}\frac{d}{dz}; \qquad x = 0, \quad z = 0; \qquad x = L, \quad z = 1,$$

and reduce Eq. (4.7.1) to the nondimensional form

$$y^{iv} + \frac{PL^2}{EI} y'' = 0, \tag{a}$$

where the derivatives are now taken with respect to z. Dividing the interval of definition $(0,1)$ of z in n equal parts of length $h = 1/n$ and multiplying Eq. (a) by h^4, the equation becomes

$$h^4 y^{iv} + \frac{PL^2}{n^2 EI} (h^2 y'') = 0.$$

Substitution of $\delta^4 y_i$ for $h^4 y^{iv}$, and of $\delta^2 y_i$ for $h^2 y''$ gives the difference equation

$$\delta^4 y_i + k_n \delta^2 y_i = 0, \tag{b}$$

where
$$k_n = \frac{PL^2}{n^2 EI} = \frac{1}{n^2} K_n. \tag{4.7.2}$$

Using Eqs. (2.7.16) for $\delta^4 y_i$ and $\delta^2 y_i$, the finite difference equation becomes

$$y_{ll} - 4y_l + 6y_i - 4y_r + y_{rr} + k_n(y_l - 2y_i + y_r) = 0$$

and can finally be written in the form

$$y_{ll} + (k_n - 4)y_l + (6 - 2k_n)y_i + (k_n - 4)y_r + y_{rr} = 0. \tag{4.7.3}$$

Equation (4.7.3) holds at the $n - 1$ internal pivotal points $i = 1, 2, \ldots, n - 1$.

Conditions (4.7.1) must be satisfied at the ends of the beam; introduction in these conditions of the central difference Eqs. (2.7.16) trans-

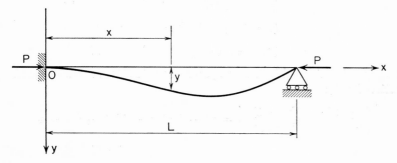

Figure 4.5

forms them into the difference Eqs. (4.1.1):

$$y_0 = 0; \quad y_{-1} = y_1; \quad y_n = 0; \quad y_{n+1} = -y_{n-1}, \tag{4.7.4}$$

where y_{-1} and y_{n+1} are the deflections at the pivotal points of the beam axis prolonged by h beyond the supports. The set of $n - 1$ linear algebraic, *homogeneous* equations (4.7.3) has the trivial solution $y_i = 0$, corresponding to the straight configuration of equilibrium of the beam, but it may have a nonzero solution if and only if the determinant Δ of its coefficients (which is a function of k_n) is identically zero.* The determinantal equation

$$\Delta(k_n) = 0 \tag{4.7.5}$$

is an algebraic equation of, say, order p in k_n, whose roots are approximations to the first p characteristic values k and hence to the first p critical loads P. Since the first critical value is the only value of practical importance, the determinantal equation will be solved for its smallest root k.

It is convenient to start the solution with small values of n and to increase the value of n gradually, that is, to reduce the spacing h of the pivotal points as $1/n$.

Approximation $n = 2$. With $n = 2$ (Fig. 4.4a), Eq. (4.7.3) gives

$$y_1 + (k_2 - 4) \cdot 0 + (6 - 2k_2)y_1 + (k_2 - 4) \cdot 0 - y_1 = 0,$$

or
$$(6 - 2k_2)y_1 = 0.$$

If y_1 is to be different from zero, $6 - 2k_2$ must vanish, $k_2 = 3$, and

$$K_2 = 2^2 k_2 = 12.$$

Approximation $n = 3$. With $n = 3$ (Fig. 4.4b), Eq. (4.7.3) gives

at $\quad\quad z = \frac{1}{3} \quad\quad y_1 + (6 - 2k_3)y_1 + (k_3 - 4)y_2 = 0;$

at $\quad\quad z = \frac{2}{3} \quad\quad (k_3 - 4)y_1 + (6 - 2k_3)y_2 - y_2 = 0;$

or $\quad\quad\quad\quad\quad (7 - 2k_3)y_1 + (k_3 - 4)y_2 = 0;$

$$(k_3 - 4)y_1 + (5 - 2k_3)y_2 = 0.$$

The determinant of this linear system equated to zero is a quadratic equation for k_3:

$$\begin{vmatrix} (7 - 2k_3) & (k_3 - 4) \\ (k_3 - 4) & (5 - 2k_3) \end{vmatrix} = (7 - 2k_3)(5 - 2k_3) - (k_3 - 4)^2$$

$$= 3k_3^2 - 16k_3 + 19 = 0,$$

* See Sec. 1.16.

whose smallest root equals 1.78475. Hence

$$K_3 = 3^2 k_3 = 16.063$$

Approximation $n = 4$. With $n = 4$ (Fig. 4.4c), Eq. (4.7.3) gives

at $\qquad z = \frac{1}{4} \qquad y_1 + (6 - 2k_4)y_1 + (k_4 - 4)y_2 + y_3 = 0;$

at $\qquad z = \frac{1}{2} \qquad (k_4 - 4)y_1 + (6 - 2k_4)y_2 + (k_4 - 4)y_3 = 0;$

at $\qquad z = \frac{3}{4} \qquad y_1 + (k_4 - 4)y_2 + (6 - 2k_4)y_3 - y_3 = 0.$

The smallest root of the corresponding determinantal equation is $k_4 = 1.11075$, from which

$$K_4 = 4^2 \cdot 1.11075 = 17.772.$$

It may be proved* that the error in the characteristic value K of an equation with constant coefficients, obtained by central differences, is also of order h^2. Hence h^2- and (h^2, h^4)-extrapolations evaluated by means of the coefficients of Sec. 2.13 may be used to improve the results of the computations. Table 4.11 contains the values K_n, their extrapolations,

Table 4.11

n	K_n	$e(\%)$
2	12.000	-40.5
3	16.063	-20.4
4	17.772	-12.0
n	h^2-extr.	$e(\%)$
2,3	19.313	-4.3
3,4	19.969	-1.1
n	(h^2, h^4)-extr.	$e(\%)$
2,3,4	20.189	0.01

and the percentage errors computed by means of the true value of $K = 20.187$.

The increase in accuracy, easily obtained by extrapolation, could be achieved only by consideration of a large number of pivotal points and solution of a high-degree determinantal equation.

* See M. G. Salvadori, "Numerical Computation of Buckling Loads by Finite Differences," *Trans. ASCE*, **117** (1952).

4.8 The Use of Unevenly Spaced Pivotal Points

The finite difference operators used in the previous sections were all based upon the use of evenly spaced pivotal points, but many physical problems are better solved by means of unevenly spaced pivotal points.

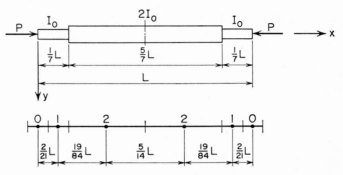

Figure 4.6

As an example of application of formulas with unequal spacing, consider the buckling of a "stepped" beam, simply supported at the ends $x = 0$ and $x = L$, acted upon by compressive axial forces P, whose moment of inertia varies as indicated in Fig. 4.6.

To solve the corresponding boundary value problem*

$$y'' + \frac{P}{EI} y = 0; \qquad y(0) = y(L) = 0, \qquad (4.8.1)$$

the central portion of the beam is divided into two equal parts with pivotal points (2) at the quarter points, and the end portions have one pivotal point (0) at the ends and another (1) at two-thirds of their length from the ends. In this division, the central portion consists of two "lumps" of length $\frac{1}{2}(\frac{5}{7}L) = (\frac{5}{14})L$ with moment of inertia $2I_0$, and each end portion consists of two "lumps" of length $\frac{2}{3}(\frac{1}{7}L) = (\frac{2}{21})L$ with moment of inertia I_0, one-half of one of these lumps being actually beyond the beam ends.

Since the spacing h between the pivotal points varies from point to point, the second derivative appearing in Eq. (4.8.1) may be approximated by Eq. (2.2.3):

$$h^2 y'' = \frac{2}{\alpha(\alpha + 1)} [\alpha y_l - (1 + \alpha)y_i + y_r], \qquad (a)$$

in which $\qquad h = x_i - x_l; \qquad \alpha = \frac{x_r - x_i}{x_i - x_l}. \qquad (b)$

* See, for example, *Differential Equations*, Sec. 2.11.

Equations (b) give in the present problem

at $\qquad$ (1) $\qquad h_1 = \frac{2}{21}L; \qquad \alpha_1 = \frac{\frac{19}{84}}{\frac{2}{21}} = 2.375;$

at $\qquad$ (2) $\qquad h_2 = \frac{19}{84}L; \qquad \alpha_2 = \frac{\frac{5}{14}}{\frac{19}{84}} = 1.579.$

Hence, multiplying Eq. (4.8.1) by h_i^2 and substituting Eq. (a) for $h^2 y''$, the difference equations become

at (1) $\qquad \dfrac{2}{2.375(1 + 2.375)} [2.375 \cdot 0 - (1 + 2.375)y_1 + y_2]$

$$+ \frac{P}{EI_0} (\tfrac{2}{21}L)^2 y_1 = 0,$$

at (2) $\qquad \dfrac{2}{1.579(1 + 1.579)} [1.579 y_1 - (1 + 1.579)y_2]$

$$+ \frac{P}{E(2I_0)} (\tfrac{19}{84}L)^2 y_2 = 0$$

or $\qquad\qquad (0.03635K - 3.375)y_1 + y_2 = 0;$

$$1.579 y_1 + (0.05208K - 1.579)y_2 = 0,$$

where $\qquad\qquad\qquad K = \dfrac{PL^2}{EI_0}.$ $\qquad\qquad\qquad$ (c)

The corresponding determinantal equation

$$\begin{vmatrix} 0.03635K - 3.375 & 1 \\ 1.579 & 0.05208K - 1.579 \end{vmatrix} = 0$$

has a smaller root $K = 19.01$, from which

$$P_{cr} = 19.01 \frac{EI_0}{L^2}.$$

The value of P_{cr} obtained by the energy method, with an assumed sine deflection, which is known to be an upper bound for the buckling load, equals 19.04.*

PROBLEMS

4.1 Express the initial conditions of Eq. (4.1.2) in terms of:

(a) Forward differences with errors of order h.

(b) Forward differences with errors of order h^2.

* For another numerical method of evaluation of buckling loads, based on the iterative process of Vianello-Stodola, see N. M. Newmark, "Numerical Procedure for Computing Deflections, Moments and Buckling Loads," *Trans. ASCE*, **108** (1943).

Ans. (a) $y_0 = 0$; $y_1 = y_0$; $y_2 = 2y_1 - y_0$; $y_3 = 3y_2 - 3y_1 + y_0$; $y_4 = 4y_3 - 6y_2 + 4y_1 - y_0$. (b) $y_0 = 0$; $y_2 = 4y_1 - 3y_0$; $y_3 = 4y_2 - 5y_1 + 2y_0$; $y_4 = (\frac{14}{3})y_3 - 8y_2 + 6y_1 - (\frac{5}{3})y_0$; $y_5 = (\frac{11}{2})y_4 - 12y_3 + 13y_2 - 7y_1 + (\frac{3}{2})y_0$.

4.2 Evaluate by forward integration and linear interpolation the pivotal values of the integrals of the following boundary value problems, using operators with errors of order h^2 and the number of subintervals indicated.

(a) $y'' + \dfrac{1}{x}y = 0$; $y(1) = 1$, $y(2) = 2$; $n = 2, 4$.

(b) $y'' + (\sin x)y = 0$; $y(0) = 0$, $y(1) = 1$; $n = 2, 4$.
(c) $y'' + y'y = 0$; $y(0) = 0$, $y(1) = 1$; $n = 4, 6$.

Ans. (a) $n = 4$; $y_{-1} = 0.586$; $y_1 = 1.351$; $y_2 = 1.635$; $y_3 = 1.850$.

4.3 Evaluate by Taylor series the first three nonzero terms of the series expansion in the solution of the following problems, carrying θ'_0 and y'_0 as unknowns to be determined by the second boundary condition.

(a) $\theta'' + \sin\theta = 0$; $\theta(0) = 0$, $\theta(1) = 1$.
(b) $y'' + y^2 = x^2 + 1$; $y(0) = 0$, $y(1) = 0$.

Ans. (b) $y = \begin{cases} -0.5574x + 0.5x^2 + 0.0574x^4 \\ 12.56x + 0.5x^2 - 13.06x^4. \end{cases}$

4.4 Determine the values of y at the pivotal points of the interval $(0,1)$, if y satisfies the boundary value problem

$$y'' + 4y = 4x^2 + 2;   y(0) = 0, y(1) = 1.$$

Use $n = 2$ and $n = 4$. Compare with the rigorous solution of the problem ($y = x^2$), and state why the numerical solution coincides with the rigorous solution *whatever n*, when y'' is approximated by $\delta^2 y/h^2$.

4.5 (a) Solve the following boundary value problem by central difference formulas with errors of order h^2, using two and four subintervals.

$$y'' - 4y' + 4y = e^{3x};   y(0) = 0, y(1) = -2.$$

Solve the system of simultaneous equations by Gauss's scheme.

(b) Apply the first term of Fox's correction to the values of y in the $n = 2$ approximation.

(c) Repeat (b) for $n = 4$.

(d) Using the uncorrected values of y for $n = 2, 4$, obtain by extrapolation improved values of y at $x = 0.5$.

(e) Repeat (d) for the corrected values of y (from parts b and c).

Ans. (a) $y_2^{(1)}(0.50) = -1.121$; $y_4^{(1)}(0.25) = -0.3473$; $y_4^{(1)}(0.50) = -0.9508$; $y_4^{(1)}(0.75) = -1.7257$. (b) $y_2^{(2)}(0.50) = -0.7840$.
(c) $y_4^{(2)}(0.25) = -0.3294$; $y_4^{(2)}(0.50) = -0.9167$; $y_4^{(2)}(0.75) = -1.6884$. (d) $y_{2,4}^{(1)}(0.50) = -0.8941$. (e) $y_{2,4}^{(2)}(0.50) = -0.9256$.

4.6 (a) Solve the following boundary value problem by central difference formulas with errors of order h^2, using two and four subintervals.

$$y'' - 8y' + 8y = e^x; \qquad y(0) = 0, \quad y(3) = 4.$$

Solve the system of simultaneous equations by Cholesky's method.

(b) Apply the first term of Fox's correction to the values of y in the $n = 2$ approximation.

(c) Repeat (b) for $n = 4$.

(d) Using the uncorrected values of y for $n = 2, 4$, obtain by extrapolation improved values of y at $x = 1.5$.

(e) Repeat (d) for the corrected values of y.

4.7 Solve the heat-flow problem of Sec. 4.3 assuming $L = 100$ cm, $R = 1$ cm, $k = 1$ cal/sec °C cm²/cm, $k_1 = 6 \cdot 10^{-4}$, $u_0 = 0$, $u_n = 1$, and $U(x)$ to be given by the following table:

$z = x/L$	0	0.25	0.50	0.75	1.00
$F(z) = U(x)/u_n$	1.00	1.10	1.35	1.15	1.00

Ans. $v_0 = 0$; $v_1 = 0.658$; $v_2 = 0.984$; $v_3 = 1.035$.

4.8 The circular stepped plate of radius a in Fig. 4.7, built in along its edge, deflects under a uniform load q.

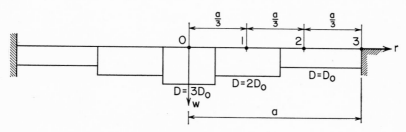

Figure 4.7

(a) Determine its slope $\phi(r)$ by means of the equation*

$$\phi'' + \frac{1}{r}\phi' - \frac{1}{r^2}\phi = \frac{-qr}{2D}$$

and the boundary conditions

$$\phi(0) = 0; \qquad \phi(a) = 0,$$

where r is the radial distance and D is the flexural rigidity of the plate.

* See, for instance, S. Timoshenko and S. Woinowsky-Krieger, *Theory of Plates and Shells*, McGraw-Hill Book Company, Inc., New York, 1959, pp. 51 ff.

(b) Determine its center deflection by numerical integration using the trapezoidal rule.

4.9 Solve Problem 4.8 for the case of a simply supported plate, whose boundary conditions are

$$\phi(0) = 0; \qquad \phi' + \frac{\nu}{r}\,\phi \bigg]_{r=a} = 0,$$

assuming the value $\nu = 0.3$ for Poisson's ratio.

Ans. $\phi(a/3) = 0.046qa^3/D_0$; $\phi(2a/3) = 0.085qa^3/D_0$; $\phi(a) = 0.096qa^3/D_0$;
$w_0 = 0.60qa^4/D_0$.

4.10 Determine the values of y at the pivotal points of the interval $(0,1)$, if y satisfies the boundary value problem

$$y''' + 2y = 12x^2 + 2; \qquad y(0) = 0, \quad y(1) = y'(1) = 0.$$

(a) Use $n = 2$ and approximate y' by averaged central differences, y''' by the unsymmetrical expression of Eq. (2.2.2).
(b) Use $n = 3$ and approximate y''' at $x = \frac{1}{3}$ by Eq. (2.2.2), at $x = \frac{2}{3}$ by averaged central differences.

Ans.   (a) $y_1 = \frac{5}{34} = 0.147$.   (b) $y_1 = 0.186$, $y_2 = 0.149$.

4.11 Determine the values of y at the pivotal points of the interval $(0,1)$, if y satisfies the boundary value problem

$$y^{iv} + 81y = 81x^2; \qquad y(0) = y(1) = y''(0) = y''(1) = 0.$$

Use $n = 3$ and symmetrical approximations for the derivatives.

4.12 Determine the values of y at the pivotal points of the interval $(0,1)$, if y satisfies the boundary value problem

$$y^{iv} + 81y = f(x); \qquad y(0) = y'(0) = y''(1) = y'''(1) = 0.$$

Use $n = 3$ and symmetrical approximations for the derivatives.

(a) Assume $f(x) = 729x^2$.
(b) Solve the same problem when the function $f(x)$ at the right-hand member of the differential equation is given by the following table:

x	1/3	2/3	1
$f(x)$	81	162	243

Ans.   (a) $y_1 = 1.1539$; $y_2 = 3.9231$; $y_3 = 7.4615$.
(b) $y_1 = 0.6154$; $y_2 = 1.6923$; $y_3 = 2.8462$.

4.13 (a) Evaluate the deflection at the pivotal points of the beam of Fig. 4.8, using four subintervals and lumping the distributed load at the pivotal points. Use central difference expressions with errors of order h^2.

   (b) Evaluate the bending moments at the pivotal points $(M = -EIy'')$.

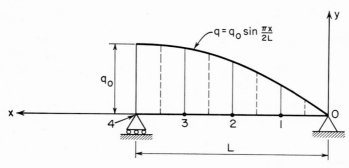

Figure 4.8

4.14 (a) Evaluate the deflection at the pivotal points of the beam of Fig. 4.9, using four subintervals and lumping the distributed load at the pivotal points. Use central difference expressions with errors of order h^2.

   (b) Evaluate the bending moment at the built-in end $(M = -EIy'')$.

Ans. $y_3 = -0.000857qL^4EI$; $y_2 = -0.001025qL^4/EI$;
   $y_1 = -0.00142qL^4/EI$; $M_4 = -0.01828qL^2$.

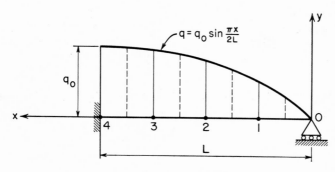

Figure 4.9

4.15 (a) Evaluate the deflection at the pivotal points of the beam of Fig. 4.10 using four subintervals and lumping the distributed load at the pivotal points. Use central differential expressions with errors of order h^2.

   (b) Evaluate the bending moments at the pivotal points $(M = -EIy'')$.

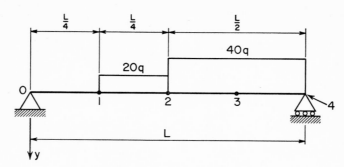

Figure 4.10

4.16 Evaluate the deflections at the pivotal points of a uniformly loaded simply supported beam whose moment of inertia varies linearly from I_0 at its left end to $5I_0$ at its right end. Use central difference expressions with errors of order h^2 and four subintervals.

Ans. $y_1 = 0.003621qL^4/EI_0;$ $y_2 = 0.004883qL^4/EI_0;$ $y_3 = 0.003377qL^4/EI_0.$

4.17 (a) Evaluate the deflections at the pivotal points of a beam on an elastic foundation (see Sec. 4.6) uniformly loaded and simply supported at both ends with $k = 16$. Use central difference formulas with errors of order h^2 with $n = 2, 4$. Extrapolate the value of the deflection at the center.

(b) Evaluate the bending moment at the mid-span section by two and four subintervals and extrapolate $(M = -EIy'')$.

4.18 A simply supported beam of constant moment of inertia I and length L buckles under the action of two equal longitudinal compressive loads P. Evaluate the lowest critical value of P using $n = 2, 3,$ and 4 subintervals and extrapolation. *Hint:* The characteristic value problem is defined by the following equations:

$$y'' + \frac{P}{EI}y = 0; \qquad y(0) = y(L) = 0.*$$

Ans. $K = \dfrac{PL^2}{EI};$ $K_2 = 8;$ $K_3 = 9;$ $K_4 = 9.3726;$ $K_{2,3} = 9.8;$ $K_{3,4} = 9.85164;$

$K_{2,3,4} = 9.86881.$

4.19 A simply supported slender beam of length L, whose moment of inertia is given by

$$I(x) = I_0(1 + 2x/L); \qquad 0 \leq x \leq L/2;$$

$$I(x) = I_0(3 - 2x/L); \qquad L/2 \leq x \leq L.$$

buckles under the action of two longitudinal compressive loads P. Determine the lowest critical value of P, using $n = 2, 3,$ and 4 subintervals and extrapolations of the h^2- and (h^2,h^4)-type. (See Problem 4.18.)

* See Sec. 4.8.

4.20 A cantilever beam of narrow rectangular cross section is built in at $x = 0$ and loaded by a transverse load P at $x = L$. Determine the lowest critical value of P for which the beam buckles laterally using $n = 2, 3,$ and 4 subintervals and an (h^2, h^4)-extrapolation. *Hint:* The rotation β satisfies the following characteristic value problem:

$$\beta'' + \frac{P^2 L^2}{BC}(1 - x/L)^2 \beta = 0; \qquad \beta(0) = 0; \qquad \beta'(L) = 0.*$$

Ans. $P_2 = 4 \sqrt{BC/L^4}; P_3 = 3.933 \sqrt{BC/L^4}; P_4 = 3.959 \sqrt{BC/L^4};$

$P_{2,3,4} = 4.030 \sqrt{BC/L^4}; P = 4.013 \sqrt{BC/L^4}.$

4.21 A beam of narrow rectangular cross section is simply supported at $x = \pm L/2$, while the rotation of its ends around the axis of the beam is prevented. The beam buckles laterally under the action of a vertical load P at $x = 0$. Determine the lowest critical value of P in terms of B, the smallest flexural rigidity of the beam in its principal plane; C, the torsional rigidity; L, the length of the beam. Use $n = 2, 3,$ and 4 subintervals and extrapolation for $P_{2,4}$. *Hint:* The rotation β satisfies the following characteristic value problem:

$$\beta'' + \frac{P^2 L^2}{4BC}\left(\frac{1}{2} - \frac{x}{L}\right)^2 \beta = 0; \qquad \beta\left(\frac{L}{2}\right) = \beta\left(-\frac{L}{2}\right) = 0.†$$

4.22 A circular plate of radius R and flexural rigidity D, clamped at the edge, buckles under a uniform compression N per unit of length. Determine the lowest critical value of N, using $n = 2$ and 3 subintervals and extrapolation. The slope ϕ of the plate satisfies the following characteristic value problem:

$$\phi'' + \frac{1}{r}\phi' + \left(\frac{N}{D} - \frac{1}{r^2}\right)\phi = 0; \qquad \phi(0) = \phi(R) = 0.‡$$

Ans. $N_2 = 12.00D/R^2; N_3 = 13.50D/R^2; N_{2,3} = 14.70D/R^2;$
$N = 14.68D/R^2.$

4.23 The modes and frequencies of a shear beam with a linearly varying spring constant are governed by the following characteristic value problem:§

$$\frac{d^2 x}{dz^2} + \frac{1}{z}\frac{dx}{dz} + \frac{K^2}{z}x = 0; \qquad x(1) = 0, \qquad \frac{dx}{dz}\bigg]_{0.5} = 0,$$

where $K^2 = \omega^2 L^2 m_0/\alpha^2 k_0$; m_0 and k_0, the unit mass and unit spring constant, are equal to $m\big]_{z=0}$ and $k\big]_{z=0}$; $L =$ the length of the beam; and $\alpha =$ the comple-

---

* See, for example, S. Timoshenko, *Theory of Elastic Stability*, pp. 245 ff; see also Problem 4.21.

† See, for example, S. Timoshenko, *Theory of Elastic Stability*, pp. 250 ff.

‡ See, for example, S. Timoshenko, *Theory of Elastic Stability*, pp. 367 ff.

§ See, for instance, M. G. Salvadori, "Earthquake Stresses in Shear Buildings," *Trans. ASCE,* **118** (1953).

mentary slope of the spring-constant line. Evaluate the lowest three values of ω^2, using $n = 1, 2, 3$, and 4 subintervals and extrapolation.

4.24 A slender strut of length L, moment of inertia I, and weight per unit of length q, built in at $x = 0$ and free at $x = L$, buckles under its own weight. Determine the critical value of q using $n = 1, 2$ and extrapolation. The deflection y of the strut is governed by the following characteristic value problem:*

$$y^{\mathrm{iv}} + \frac{qL}{EI}\left(1 - \frac{x}{L}\right)y'' - \frac{qL}{EI}\frac{1}{L}y' = 0;$$

$$y(0) = y'(0) = y''(L) = y'''(L) = 0.$$

Let $k_n = q_n L^3/EI$.

Ans. $k_1 = 4.0000$; $k_2 = 6.7624$; $k_{1,2} = 7.6832$; $k = 7.83$.

4.25 Evaluate the lowest natural frequency of the free oscillations of a simply supported beam of length L, using $n = 2, 3$, and 4 subintervals and extrapolation. *Hint:* The differential equation of motion of the beam is $EI\partial^4 y/\partial x^4 + \rho A\partial^2 y/\partial t^2 = 0$,† where EI = flexural rigidity, ρ = density, A = cross section of beam. Substitute $y(x,t) = X(x) \sin \omega t$ in this equation and state that the beam is simply supported at the ends.

$$X(0) = X(L) = 0; \qquad X''(0) = X''(L) = 0.$$

Let $w = \omega L^2/\sqrt{EI/\rho A}$.

Ans. $w_2 = 8$; $w_3 = 9$; $w_4 = 9.3726$; $w_{2,3} = 9.8$; $w_{3,4} = 9.8516$;
$w_{2,3,4} = 9.8688$.

4.26 Evaluate the lowest natural frequency of the free oscillations of a beam of length L, built in at $x = 0$ and free at $x = L$, using $n = 2$ subintervals. *Hint:* See Problem 4.25.

4.27 Determine the values of y at the pivotal points of the interval $(0,1)$, if y satisfies the boundary value problem $y'' + 2y = f(x)$; $y(0) = y(1) = 0$, and $f(x)$ is given by the following table:

x	0	0.15	0.40	0.75	1.00
$f(x)$	0	16	30	20	0

Use unsymmetrical approximations of y'' with errors of order h.

Ans. $y_1 = -1.8021$; $y_2 = -3.8260$; $y_3 = -2.7060$.

---

* See, for example, S. Timoshenko, *Theory of Elastic Stability*, pp. 115 ff.
† See, for example, S. Timoshenko, *Vibration Problems in Engineering*, 2d ed., D. Van Nostrand Company, Inc., New York, 1937, pp. 332 ff.

4.28 Evaluate the buckling load P of the simply supported beam of Fig. 4.11, using unequal differences of order h and the indicated subdivisions. (See Problem 4.18.)

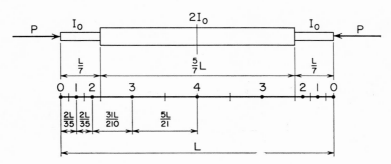

Figure 4.11

4.29 The circular stepped plate of Fig. 4.12, built in along its edge, deflects under a uniform load q.

(a) Determine its slope $\phi(r)$ by means of unsymmetrical approximations ϕ'' with errors of order h. (See Problem 4.8.)

(b) Determine its center deflection by numerical integration.

Ans. $\phi(0.45a) = 0.0163qa^3/D_0$; $\phi(0.8a) = 0.0177qa^3/D_0$;
   $w_0 = 0.0114qa^4/D_0$.

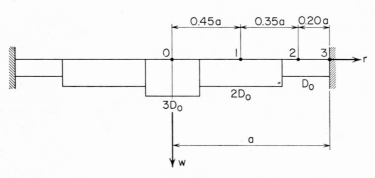

Figure 4.12

4.30 Solve Problem 4.29 for the case of a simply supported plate. (See Problem 4.9.)

V

The Numerical Solution of Partial Differential Equations

5.1 Classification of Partial Differential Equations of the Second Order

Processes of numerical integration have found their widest application in the solution of partial differential equations. However, the numerical integration of the resulting partial difference equations leads to essential questions of convergence and stability of the solution, since basic differences in its fundamental nature are encountered depending on the type of differential equation to be solved.

Since the second-order partial differential equation is of particular interest in the fields of wave propagation, heat conduction, elasticity, vibrations, boundary layer theory, etc., the present chapter will deal, to a great extent, with this type of equation, although several problems involving higher-order equations will also be considered.

Let a second-order partial differential equation in the function u of the two independent variables x, y be of the form

$$A(x,y)\, \frac{\partial^2 u}{\partial x^2} + B(x,y)\, \frac{\partial^2 u}{\partial x \partial y} + C(x,y)\, \frac{\partial^2 u}{\partial y^2} + f\left(x,y,u,\frac{\partial u}{\partial x}, \frac{\partial u}{\partial y}\right) = 0 \quad (5.1.1)$$

This equation is linear in the second-order terms, but the term

$$f\left(x,y,u, \frac{\partial u}{\partial x}, \frac{\partial u}{\partial y}\right)$$

may be linear or nonlinear. In the former case, Eq. (5.1.1) is said to be *linear*, in the latter case to be *quasi-linear*.

Equation (5.1.1) is classified as *elliptic, parabolic,* or *hyperbolic* at the points of a region R depending on whether

$$B^2 - 4AC < 0 \quad \text{(elliptic equation),}$$

$$B^2 - 4AC = 0 \quad \text{(parabolic equation),} \qquad (5.1.2)$$

$$B^2 - 4AC > 0^* \quad \text{(hyperbolic equation).}$$

Since the coefficients A, B, and C, in general, are functions of the independent variables, Eq. (5.1.1) may have different classifications in the different regions of the domain in which the problem is defined.

[a] ELLIPTIC EQUATIONS

A differential equation is elliptic in a region R if $B^2 - 4AC < 0$ at all points of the region. The boundary conditions of this type of equation specify either the function u, or its normal derivative, or a linear combination of the function and its normal derivative at every point of the *closed* boundary of the region R within which the solution $u(x,y)$ is to be determined (Fig. 5.1a). Specified boundary conditions at each point of the closed boundary define uniquely the solution of the boundary value problem (defined by the partial differential equation and the accompanying boundary conditions) in the interior of the domain.

The numerical solution of elliptic partial differential equations by finite differences leads, in general, to a system of simultaneous, linear, algebraic equations in the values of the function at the pivotal points of the region of definition of the problem. This system of equations can be solved by the techniques illustrated in Chapter I.

Laplace's equation:

$$\nabla^2 u \equiv \frac{\partial^2 u}{\partial x^2} + \frac{\partial^2 u}{\partial y^2} = 0, \qquad (5.1.3)$$

---

* The significance of the classification is intimately connected with the theory of *characteristics*. A partial differential equation is classified in terms of its characteristics, i.e., of the loci of possible discontinuities in the derivatives of a solution (see, for example, S. H. Crandall, *Engineering Analysis*, McGraw-Hill Book Company, Inc., New York, 1956, pp. 352 ff.). We call the equation *hyperbolic* at a point if there are two real characteristic directions, *parabolic* if there is only one real characteristic direction, and *elliptic* if there are no real characteristic directions at that point.

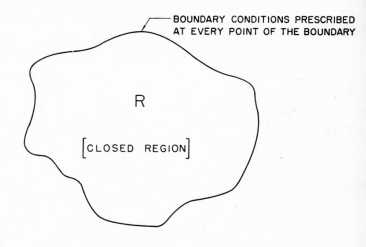

(a)   ELLIPTIC   PROBLEM

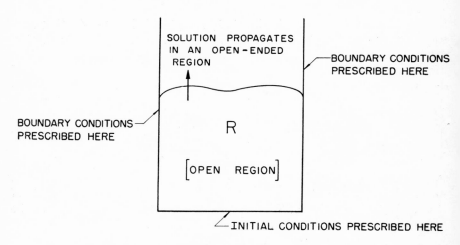

(b)   PARABOLIC   OR   HYPERBOLIC   PROBLEM

Figure 5.1

and Poisson's equation:

$$\nabla^2 u = \frac{\partial^2 u}{\partial x^2} + \frac{\partial^2 u}{\partial y^2} = f(x,y), \tag{5.1.4}$$

are important examples of this type of equation. Their numerical solution by finite differences will be discussed in Secs. 5.4, 5.5, 5.6, and 5.8.

[b] Parabolic equations

A differential equation is parabolic in a region R if $B^2 - 4AC = 0$ at all points of the region. The initial value of the function u at some time t_0 and the value of either the function, or its normal derivative, or a linear combination of the function and its normal derivative on the boundary are the required boundary conditions.

In problems of this type, the solution is not defined in a closed domain but is propagated in an open domain, starting with prescribed conditions on an open boundary (Fig. 5.1b). The one-dimensional heat-flow equation

$$K \frac{\partial^2 u}{\partial x^2} = \frac{\partial u}{\partial t} \tag{5.1.5}$$

is an important equation of the parabolic type. The numerical solution of problems of this type by finite differences is illustrated in Sec. 5.16.

[c] Hyperbolic equations

A differential equation is hyperbolic in a region R if $B^2 - 4AC > 0$ at all points of the region. The initial values of the function u and of its first derivative with respect to time and either the value of the function, or its normal derivative, or a linear combination of the function and its normal derivative on the boundary of the region of definition are the required boundary conditions.

An important equation of the hyperbolic type is the one-dimensional wave equation:

$$c^2 \frac{\partial^2 u}{\partial x^2} = \frac{\partial^2 u}{\partial t^2}. \tag{5.1.6}$$

The numerical solution of problems of this type by finite differences is illustrated in Sec. 5.18.

5.2 Partial Difference Operators in Cartesian Coordinates

The transformation of a partial differential equation into the corresponding partial difference equation is obtained, essentially, by the same methods and expansions developed in previous chapters for ordinary differential equations, since partial derivatives are evaluated by the same limiting process used for ordinary derivatives, keeping all but one variable constant. Thus, indicating by D_x, D_y, ... the partial derivatives of a function $z = f(x,y,...)$ with respect to x, y, ..., respectively, the central difference expansions for D_x, D_y, ... may be obtained directly from Eqs. (2.7.16).

For example, calling h the constant spacing of the pivotal points in the x direction and $\delta_x^n z_i$ the nth central difference of z at i taken in the x direction,

$$2hD_x z_i = z_r - z_l + 2\epsilon_{1x} \qquad \left[\epsilon_{1x} = \mu\left(-\frac{\delta_x^3}{6} + \frac{\delta_x^5}{30} - \dots\right)z_i\right], \quad (5.2.1)$$

$$h^2 D_x^2 z_i = z_r - 2z_i + z_l + \epsilon_{2x} \qquad \left[\epsilon_{2x} = \left(-\frac{\delta_x^4}{12} + \frac{\delta_x^6}{90} - \dots\right)z_i\right], \quad (5.2.2)$$

$$2h^3 D_x^3 z_i = z_{rr} - 2z_r + 2z_l - z_{ll} + 2\epsilon_{3x}$$

$$\left[\epsilon_{3x} = \mu\left(-\frac{\delta_x^5}{4} + \frac{7\delta_x^7}{120} - \dots\right)z_i\right], \quad (5.2.3)$$

$$h^4 D_x^4 z_i = z_{rr} - 4z_r + 6z_i - 4z_l + z_{ll} + \epsilon_{4x}$$

$$\left[\epsilon_{4x} = \left(-\frac{\delta_x^6}{6} + \frac{7\delta_x^8}{240} - \dots\right)z_i\right]. \quad (5.2.4)$$

Similarly, calling k the constant spacing of the pivotal points in the y direction and $\delta_y^n z_i$ the nth central difference of z at i taken in the y direc-

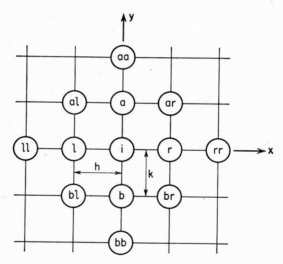

Figure 5.2

tion, and indicating the pivotal points adjoining z_i vertically by z_{aa}, z_a, z_b, and z_{bb}, as shown in Fig. 5.2 (the subscripts a and b stand for "above" and "below"), the partial derivatives with respect to y are given by

$$2kD_y z_i = z_a - z_b + 2\epsilon_{1y} \qquad \left[\epsilon_{1y} = \mu\left(-\frac{\delta_y^3}{6} + \frac{\delta_y^5}{30} - \dots\right)z_i\right], \quad (5.2.5)$$

$$k^2 D_y^2 z_i = z_a - 2z_i + z_b + \epsilon_{2y} \qquad \left[\epsilon_{2y} = \left(-\frac{\delta_y^4}{12} + \frac{\delta_y^6}{90} - \dots\right)z_i\right], \quad (5.2.6)$$

$$2k^3 D_y^3 z_i = z_{aa} - 2z_a + 2z_b - z_{bb} + 2\epsilon_{3y}$$

$$\left[\epsilon_{3y} = \mu \left(-\frac{\delta_y^5}{4} + \frac{7\delta_y^7}{120} - \cdots \right) z_i \right], \quad (5.2.7)$$

$$k^4 D_y^4 z_i = z_{aa} - 4z_a + 6z_i - 4z_b + z_{bb} + \epsilon_{4y}$$

$$\left[\epsilon_{4y} = \left(-\frac{\delta_y^6}{6} + \frac{7\delta_y^8}{240} - \cdots \right) z_i \right]. \quad (5.2.8)$$

The expression for the second mixed derivative of z with respect to x and y, D_{xy}, is obtained by applying the operator giving D_x to the operator giving D_y, that is, by the "product" $D_x D_y$:

$$D_{xy} z_i = \frac{1}{2k} \left[\frac{1}{2h} (z_r - z_l)_a - \frac{1}{2h} (z_r - z_l)_b \right] + \frac{1}{4hk} \epsilon_{1,xy},$$

or

$$4hk D_{xy} z_i = z_{ar} - z_{al} - z_{br} + z_{bl} + \epsilon_{1,xy} \quad [\epsilon_{1,xy} = (\epsilon_{1x})_a - (\epsilon_{1x})_b]. \quad (5.2.9)$$

Similarly, the fourth mixed derivative $\partial^4 z / \partial x^2 \partial y^2 \equiv D_{xxyy}$ is the operational product of D_x^2 and D_y^2, or

$$h^2 k^2 D_{xxyy} z_i = (z_r - 2z_i + z_l)_a - 2(z_r - 2z_i + z_l)_i$$

$$+ (z_r - 2z_i + z_l)_b + \epsilon_{2,xy}$$

$$= (z_{ar} + z_{al} + z_{br} + z_{bl}) - 2(z_a + z_b + z_r + z_l) + 4z_i$$

$$+ \epsilon_{2,xy} \quad [\epsilon_{2,xy} = (\epsilon_{2,x})_a - 2(\epsilon_{2x})_i + (\epsilon_{2x})_b]. \quad (5.2.10)$$

The *Laplacian (or harmonic) operator* ∇^2*

$$\nabla^2 \equiv \frac{\partial^2}{\partial x^2} + \frac{\partial^2}{\partial y^2} = D_x^2 + D_y^2$$

becomes by Eqs. (5.2.2), (5.2.6) for a *rectangular lattice of* mesh sizes h, k

$$h^2 k^2 \nabla^2 z_i = k^2 (z_r - 2z_i + z_l) + h^2 (z_a - 2z_i + z_b) + k^2 \epsilon_{2x} + h^2 \epsilon_{2y} \quad (5.2.11)$$

and for the particular case of equal spacing of the pivotal points in the x and y directions, that is, for a *square lattice* of mesh size h,

$$h^2 \nabla^2 z_i = z_a + z_b + z_r + z_l - 4z_i + \epsilon_{2x} + \epsilon_{2y}, \quad (5.2.12)$$

where ϵ_{2x} and ϵ_{2y} are given by Eqs. (5.2.2) and (5.2.6), respectively. The *biharmonic operator*

$$\nabla^4 \equiv \nabla^2 (\nabla^2) = \frac{\partial^4}{\partial x^4} + \frac{2\partial^4}{\partial x^2 \partial y^2} + \frac{\partial^4}{\partial y^4} \dagger$$

---

* The operator ∇^2 should not be confused with the second backward difference.
† The operator ∇^4 should not be confused with the fourth backward difference.

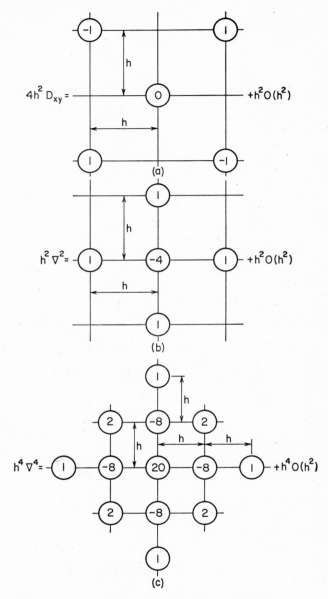

Fig. 5.3. Central difference partial operators.

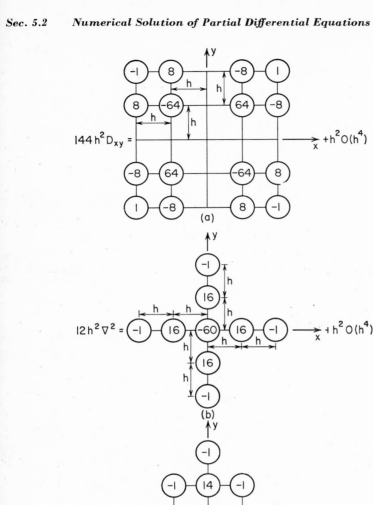

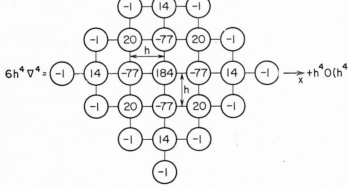

Fig. 5.4.   Second-order operators.

becomes, for a square lattice

$$h^4\nabla^4 z_i = h^4\nabla^2(\nabla^2 z_i) = h^2[\nabla^2 z_a + \nabla^2 z_b + \nabla^2 z_r + \nabla^2 z_l - 4\nabla^2 z_i]$$
$$= (z_{aa} + z_{bb} + z_{rr} + z_{ll}) + 2(z_{al} + z_{ar} + z_{br} + z_{bl})$$
$$- 8(z_a + z_b + z_r + z_l) + 20z_i + \epsilon, \quad (5.2.13)$$

where ϵ is obtained by means of ϵ_{4x}, ϵ_{4y}, and $\epsilon_{4,xy}$.

The partial operators D_{xy}, ∇^2, and ∇^4 for square lattices are conveniently represented by the "molecules" of Fig. 5.3a, b, and c, respectively.

By means of the central difference operators of Fig. 2.8b, we obtain similarly the operators of the "molecules" in Fig. 5.4 with errors of order h^4, which may be used to obtain more refined solutions.

Lateral operators, based on forward or backward differences, are obtained by the same approach.

Three-dimensional operators are obtained in a perfectly analogous manner, and have been used in the solution of heat-flow and elasticity problems.

5.3 Numerical Double Integration

[a] THE TRAPEZOIDAL RULE

The double integral

$$V = \int_a^b \int_c^d f(x,y) \, dx \, dy \tag{5.3.1}$$

extended to a rectangle $x = a$, $x = b$, $y = c$, $y = d$, can be evaluated numerically by two successive integrations in the x and y directions, using the trapezoidal rule of Sec. 2.8a.

For this purpose, divide the rectangle (a,b), (c,d) into a number $m \cdot n$ of rectangles of sides $h = (b - a)/m$, $k = (d - c)/n$, and consider the values f_{ij} of f at the pivotal points (Fig. 5.5)

$$x_i = a + ih \quad (i = 0,1,2,\ldots,m);$$
$$y_j = c + jk \quad (j = 0,1,2,\ldots,n).$$

The value A_1 of the integral extended over one rectangle of sides h,k with its lower left corner at i,j becomes by the trapezoidal rule [Eq. (2.11.3)]:

$$A_1 = \int_{y_j}^{y_{j+1}} dy \int_{x_i}^{x_{i+1}} f(x,y) \, dx \doteq \int_{y_j}^{y_{j+1}} \left\{ \frac{h}{2} [f_i(y) + f_{i+1}(y)] \right\} dy$$
$$\doteq \frac{h}{2} \left[\frac{k}{2} (f_{i,j} + f_{i,j+1}) + \frac{k}{2} (f_{i+1,j} + f_{i+1,j+1}) \right]$$
$$= \frac{hk}{4} [f_{ij} + f_{i,j+1} + f_{i+1,j} + f_{i+1,j+1}]. \tag{5.3.2}$$

Adding the values of A_1 corresponding to each rectangle of the domain and noting that each internal pivotal value is counted four times and each boundary pivotal value is counted twice, with the exception of the corner values, which are counted only once, the value of V may be conveniently represented by the operator or "molecule" of Fig. 5.6.

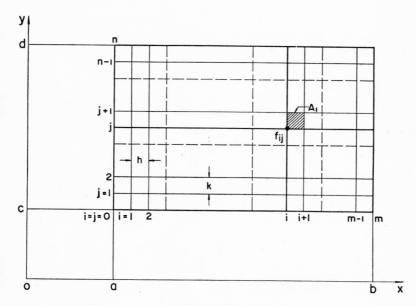

Figure 5.5

To evaluate the error in the operator for double integration by the trapezoidal rule, it must be remembered that the error in the formula for single integration by the trapezoidal rule is of order h^2 [Eq. (2.11.11)]. Hence the area of each section of the volume V, obtained by means of a plane parallel to xz at $y = y_j$, has an error of order h^2:

$$A(y_j) = \int_a^b f(x, y_j) \, dx = A_j + K_j h^2. \tag{a}$$

By means of Eq. (a) and the trapezoidal rule applied in the y direction, the double integral V becomes

$$V = k(\tfrac{1}{2}A_0 + A_1 + \ldots + A_{n-1} + \tfrac{1}{2}A_n)$$
$$+ k(\tfrac{1}{2}K_0 + K_1 + \ldots + K_{n-1} + \tfrac{1}{2}K_n)h^2 + K'k^2,$$

where the last term is the error due to the integration along the y-axis. Substituting $(d - c)/n$ for k in the second term of this equation and setting

$$\bar{K} = \frac{(d - c)}{n} \left(\frac{1}{2} K_0 + K_1 + K_2 + \ldots + K_{n-1} + \frac{1}{2} K_n \right),$$

we see that the error in the double integral is of the type

$$\epsilon_t = \bar{K}h^2 + K'k^2$$

or, calling α the ratio k/h,

$$\epsilon_t = (\bar{K} + \alpha^2 K')h^2. \tag{5.3.3}$$

Equation (5.3.3) shows that the error in the trapezoidal rule for double integration is of order h^2 and that therefore the h^2-extrapolation formula (Sec. 2.13) may be used to improve the results of the numerical integration.

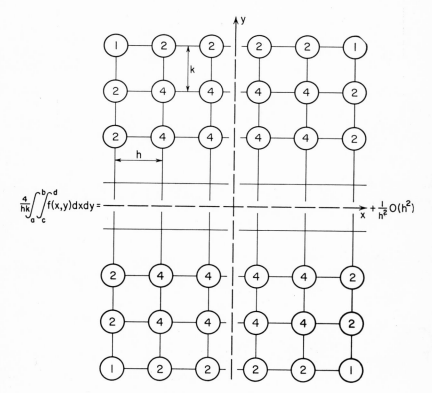

Fig. 5.6.   Trapezoidal rule.

The trapezoidal rule will be now applied to the evaluation of the integral

$$V = \int_1^2 \int_1^2 \frac{dx\, dy}{x + y}$$

$$= \int_1^2 \left[\ln (x + y) \right]_1^2 dx = \int_1^2 [\ln (x + 2) - \ln (x + 1)]\, dx$$

$$= \left[(x + 2)[\ln (x + 2) - 1] - (x + 1)[\ln (x + 1) - 1] \right]_1^2$$

$$= \ln \tfrac{1024}{729} = \ln 1.4046639 = 0.339798. \tag{b}$$

With $n = 2$ and $h = k = 0.5$, the values of $f(x,y) = \dfrac{1}{x + y}$ at the pivotal points of the field of integration become

and the approximate value of V given by the operator of Fig. 5.6, using four significant figures, is

$$V_{t,2} = \frac{0.5 \cdot 0.5}{4} \{(0.3333 + 0.5 + 0.3333 + 0.25)$$

$$+ 2(0.4 + 0.4 + 0.2857 + 0.2857) + 4(0.3333)\} = 0.3433$$

with an error of -1.0 per cent. With $n = 4$ and $h = k = 0.25$, we obtain similarly

$$V_{t,4} = 0.3406,$$

with an error of -0.24 per cent. Using the h^2-extrapolation, with the coefficients $\alpha_2 = 1.3333$, $\alpha_1 = 0.3333$ from Table 2.12 corresponding to the ratio $n_2/n_1 = 2$, we obtain the value

$$V_t\Big]_{2,4} = 1.3333 \cdot 0.3406 - 0.3333 \cdot 0.3433 = 0.3397,$$

with an error of $+0.03$ per cent.

[b] SIMPSON'S $\frac{1}{3}$ RULE

By means of two successive applications of Simpson's $\frac{1}{3}$ rule [Eq. (2.11.4)] in the x and y directions, the value of the double integral V

extended to four adjacent rectangles of sides h,k meeting at x_i,y_j becomes

$$B_4 = \int_{y_{j-1}}^{y_{j+1}} dy \int_{x_{i-1}}^{x_{i+1}} f(x,y)\, dx \doteq \int_{y_{j-1}}^{y_{j+1}} \frac{h}{3}\, [f_{i-1}(y) + 4f_i(y) + f_{i+1}(y)]\, dy$$

$$\doteq \frac{hk}{9}\, [f_{i-1,j-1} + f_{i+1,j-1} + f_{i-1,j+1} + f_{i+1,j+1}$$

$$+ 4(f_{i,j+1} + f_{i,j-1} + f_{i-1,j} + f_{i+1,j}) + 16f_{ij}]. \quad (5.3.4)$$

The operator B_4 appears in the "molecule" of Fig. 5.7.

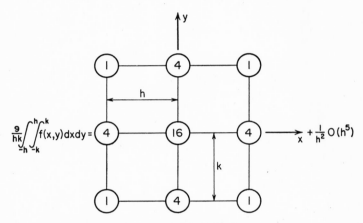

Fig. 5.7.   Simpson's $\frac{1}{3}$ rule for four squares.

Adding the values B_4 corresponding to each rectangle of the domain, we obtain the operator or "molecule" of Fig. 5.8.

By a process similar to the one used in part [a] of this section, it is easy to prove that the error in Simpson's $\frac{1}{3}$ rule for double integration is of order h^4 and that therefore h^4-extrapolations (Sec. 2.13) may be used in connection with the two-dimensional Simpson's rule.

The evaluation of the integral (b) of this section by Simpson's $\frac{1}{3}$ rule gives, for $n = 2$,

$$V_{s,2} = \frac{0.5 \cdot 0.5}{9}\, [0.5 + 0.333333 + 0.25 + 0.333333$$

$$+ 4(0.4 + 0.4 + 0.285714 + 0.285714) + 16 \cdot 0.333333] = 0.339881,$$

with an error of -0.0024 per cent.

Any of the formulas for simple integration of Secs. 2.10 and 2.11 may be similarly used to obtain multiple integration formulas.

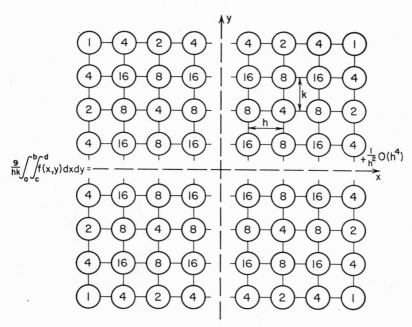

Fig. 5.8.   Simpson's $\frac{1}{3}$ rule.

[c] INTEGRALS WITH AN UPPER VARIABLE LIMIT

The evaluation of the integral

$$V = \int_c^d dy \int_a^{\phi(y)} f(x,y) \, dx, \tag{5.3.5}$$

in which $\phi(y)$ is a single-valued function of y, may be obtained by performing the first integration between a and $x_j = \phi(y_j)$ by the trapezoidal rule with m subintervals (Fig. 5.9):

$$A_j = \int_a^{\phi(y_j)} f(x,y_j) \, dx$$
$$\doteq h_m[\tfrac{1}{2}f_0(y_j) + f_1(y_j) + f_2(y_j) + \ldots + f_{m-1}(y_j) + \tfrac{1}{2}f_m(y_j)], \tag{5.3.6}$$

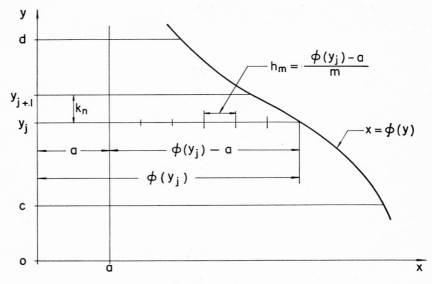

Figure 5.9

and by integrating the A_j again by the trapezoidal rule with n subintervals:

$$V = \int_c^d A_j \, dy$$

$$\doteq k_n[\tfrac{1}{2}A_0 + A_1 + A_2 + \ldots + A_{n-1} + \tfrac{1}{2}A_n]. \qquad (5.3.7)$$

In Eq. (5.3.6) the equal spacing h_m is so chosen that $m h_m = x_j - a$
$= \phi(y_j) - a$, i.e., so that

$$h_m = \frac{\phi(y_j) - a}{m}, \qquad (5.3.8)$$

while in Eq. (5.3.7)

$$k_n = \frac{d - c}{n}. \qquad (5.3.9)$$

For example, given

$$V = \int_0^4 dy \int_0^{y^2} (x + y) \, dx = \tfrac{1}{2} \int_0^4 (x + y)^2 \bigg]_0^{y^2} dy$$

$$= \tfrac{1}{2} \int_0^4 (y^4 + 2y^3) \, dy = 166.4,$$

with $n = 4$, and hence $k_n = 1$, and with $m = 1$, and hence the h_m indi-

Table 5.1

x_i \ y_j	0	1	4	9	16	h_m	$2A_j$	m_j	$2m_jA_j$
0	0					0	0	1/2	0
1	1	2				1	$1(1+2)$	1	3
2	2	3	6			4	$4(2+6)$	1	32
3	3	4	7	12		9	$9(3+12)$	1	135
4	4	5	8	13	20	16	$16(4+20)$	1/2	192

$$V = \Sigma\, m_jA_j = 181; \qquad \Sigma\, 2m_jA_j = 362.$$

cated in Table 5.1, we obtain $V = 181.0$, with an error of -8.77 per cent (Fig. 5.10). With $k_n = 0.5$, $V = 170.75$, with an error of -2.61 per cent.

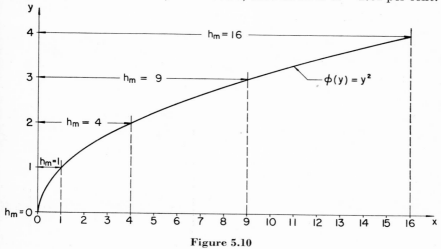

Figure 5.10

Whenever it is convenient to subdivide the intervals $\phi(y_j) - a$ and $d - c$ into an even number of strips, the integration may be carried out by Simpson's $\frac{1}{3}$ rule. When both the upper and lower limits of the x-integration are functions of y,

$$V = \int_c^d dy \int_{\phi_1(y)}^{\phi_2(y)} f(x,y)\, dx, \tag{5.3.10}$$

the procedure remains unchanged except for the evaluation of h_m, which becomes

$$h_m = \frac{\phi_2(y_j) - \phi_1(y_j)}{m}. \tag{5.3.11}$$

Table 5.2

j	h_m	$2A_j$	m_j	$2m_jA_j$
0	0	0	1/2	0
1	0	0	1	0
2	2	$2(4 + 6)$	1	20
3	6	$6(6 + 12)$	1	108
4	12	$12(8 + 20)$	1/2	168

$$V = 148 \ (e = -11\%); \qquad \Sigma \, 2m_jA_j = 296.$$

Table 5.2 and Fig. 5.11 illustrate the evaluation of

$$V = \int_0^4 dy \int_y^{y^2} (x + y) \, dx = \frac{1}{2} \int_0^4 (y^4 + 2y^3 - 3y^2) \, dy = 134.4$$

with $k_n = 1$ and $m = 1$.

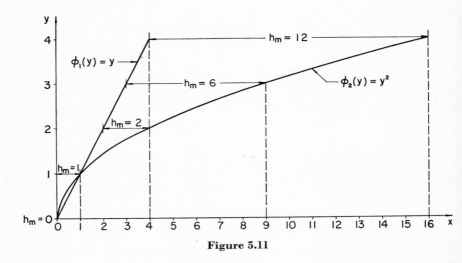

Figure 5.11

5.4 The Solution of Laplace's Equation by Iteration

A large variety of two-dimensional physical problems are governed by the so-called *Laplacian equation*

$$\nabla^2 u = \frac{\partial^2 u}{\partial x^2} + \frac{\partial^2 u}{\partial y^2} = 0 \tag{5.4.1}$$

with appropriate boundary conditions; among these are steady-state heat problems. It may be proved,* in fact, that the temperature $u(x,y)$ in a two-dimensional body (insulated thin plate, or infinitely long cylinder) satisfies Eq. (5.4.1), whenever u is independent of time.

As an example of solution of the Laplacian equation by numerical methods, consider the problem of determining the steady-state temperature u at the pivotal points of a square lattice of mesh size h in a thin square plate of sides L, completely insulated. Substituting in Eq. (5.4.1)

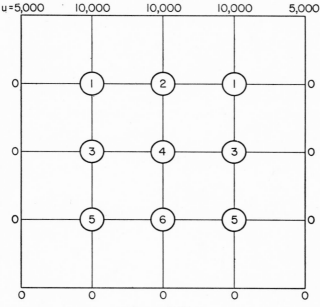

Figure 5.12

for $\nabla^2 u$ the operator of Fig. 5.3b and using the symbols of Fig. 5.2 to indicate the pivotal points, Eq. (5.4.1) becomes the *Laplacian difference equation:*

$$u_a + u_b + u_r + u_l - 4u_i = 0. \qquad (5.4.2)$$

For $h = L/4$, with the temperature on the plate boundary given by Fig. 5.12 and pivotal points numbered as in the same figure, Eq. (5.4.2) leads to the system of six linear equations:

Point	u_1	u_2	u_3	u_4	u_5	u_6	c
1	-4	1	1				$-10,000$
2	2	-4		1			$-10,000$
3	1		-4	1	1		0
4		1	2	-4		1	0
5			1		-4	1	0
6				1	2	-4	0

(a)

* See, for example, *Differential Equations*, page 243.

whose roots, evaluated by Gauss's scheme, are

$$u_1 = 4286; \qquad u_2 = 5268; \qquad u_3 = 1875;$$
$$u_4 = 2500; \qquad u_5 = \ \ 714; \qquad u_6 = \ \ 982. \tag{b}$$

Laplacian equations are also conveniently solved by iteration (Sec. 1.12). Solving Eq. (5.4.2) for u_i,

$$u_i = \tfrac{1}{4}(u_a + u_b + u_r + u_l), \tag{5.4.3}$$

it is seen that the temperature at i is the average of the four temperatures at the adjoining corners of the lattice. Starting with any tentative values for u at the pivotal points and averaging successively the temperatures at four adjoining corners, iterated values for u_i are obtained in a very simple manner.

Table 5.3

n	u_1	u_2	u_3	u_4	u_5	u_6
0	4375	5312	1875	2500	625	938
1	4296	5273	1855	2480	698	969
2	4282	5261	1865	2490	708	976
3	4281	5263	1869	2494	711	979
4	4283	5265	1872	2497	712	980
...	...	...	...	...	...	...
9	4286	5268	1875	2500	714	982

In order to have rapid convergence of the iteration process, which is known as *Liebmann's procedure* in this particular case, it is important to start with good initial values. These are usually obtained by means of a lattice with larger mesh size. Thus with $h = L/2$, the initial value at the center of the plate becomes by Eq. (5.4.3)

$$u_4^{(0)} = \tfrac{1}{4}(10{,}000 + 0 + 0 + 0) = 2{,}500.$$

The initial values at points 1 and 5 may now be obtained by averaging the four values *diagonally* adjoining these points, since the diagonals of a square lattice constitute another square lattice, and the operator ∇^2 is invariant with respect to a rotation of the coordinate axes. Thus,

$$u_1^{(0)} = \tfrac{1}{4}(10{,}000 + 2{,}500 + 0 + 5{,}000) = 4{,}375;$$
$$u_5^{(0)} = \tfrac{1}{4}(0 + 2{,}500 + 0 + 0) = 625.$$

The initial values at points 2, 3, and 6 are obtained by averaging the four adjoining values of the original lattice:

$$u_2^{(0)} = \tfrac{1}{4}(4{,}375 + 10{,}000 + 4{,}375 + 2{,}500) = 5{,}312;$$
$$u_3^{(0)} = \tfrac{1}{4}(0 + 4{,}375 + 2{,}500 + 625) = 1{,}875;$$
$$u_6^{(0)} = \tfrac{1}{4}(625 + 2{,}500 + 625 + 0) = 938.$$

Table 5.3 gives the successive values of the u_i obtained by Liebmann's averaging process, which check the solution by Gauss's scheme to the last figure.

5.5 Solution of Laplace's Equation by Relaxation

The solution of Laplace's equation $\nabla^2 u = 0$, which is of great importance in field theory (electromagnetism, heat conduction, elasticity, etc.), may be also conveniently obtained by relaxation (Sec. 1.13).

Table 5.4

The residual R_i in the Laplacian difference operator (5.4.2) due to approximate values for the u_i,

$$u_a + u_b + u_r + u_l - 4u_i = R_i,$$

shows that a change δu_i in the pivotal value u_i will decrease R_i by $4\delta u_i$ and increase the four adjoining R by δu_i. Thus the ∇^2 operator of Fig.

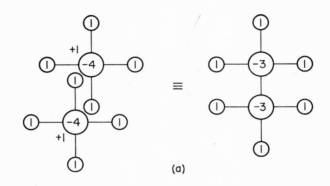

(a)

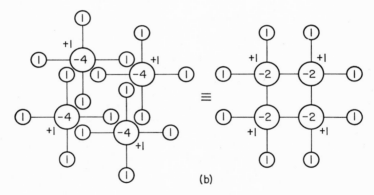

(b)

Figure 5.13

5.3b represents also the residual changes at a, b, r, l, i due to a unit change in u_i, and is called the *relaxation pattern*. The relaxation operations thus involve equal integral multipliers at each pivotal point and may be performed without the use of a calculating machine.

Table 5.4 shows the relaxation of the six equations (a) of Sec. 5.4, starting with the initial values of the first row of Table 5.3. The largest residual is systematically reduced to zero at every step, and since the temperature is symmetrical about the middle axis of the plate, only six pivotal points have been used. Note that, because of symmetry (Fig. 5.12), a change δu at 1, 3, and 5 will increase the residuals at 2, 4, and 6, respectively, by $2\delta u$. In this type of problem, relaxation is often the simplest and fastest method of solution.

Block relaxation (see Sec. 1.13) may be efficiently used in the solution of the Laplacian equation. In order to obtain the relaxation pattern

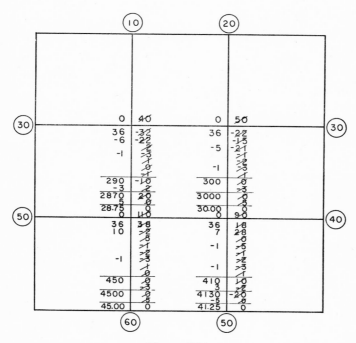

Figure 5.14

due to a unit change in two adjoining pivotal values, the relaxation patterns due to each change are superimposed as in Fig. 5.13a. Similarly Figure 5.13b gives the relaxation pattern for four unit changes at four adjoining corners of the mesh. It is seen from these figures that block relaxation patterns have coefficients equal to 1 at all points exterior to the block and coefficients equal to minus the number of lines connecting the interior point with the exterior points at all interior points.

In Figure 5.14 the relaxation of the Laplacian equation for a function u with the given boundary values is obtained starting with zero initial values for the u_i. The total initial residual is $40 + 50 + 90 + 110 = 290$. Using unit block relaxation on the four interior points, the total relaxa-

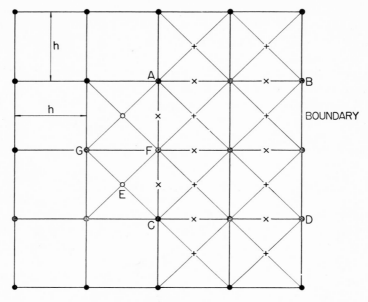

Figure 5.15

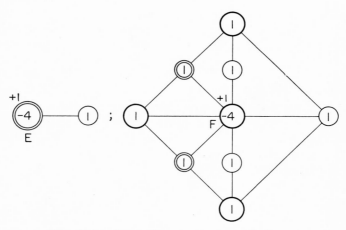

Fig. 5.16.   Relaxation patterns for graded nets.

tion coefficient from Fig. 5.13b is $4(-2) = -8$. Hence an initial block change $(-290)/(-8) \doteq 36$ is introduced at the four interior points. From then on the maximum residual is relaxed at each step, and two additional figures are obtained after two separate checks of the residuals.

Once relaxation has been obtained on a given net, one may want to refine the solution in a region of the domain. This may be done by using a mesh size equal to $h/2$ in that region of the domain and obtaining initial values by diagonal operators. Thus in Fig. 5.15, once the "black circle" values are obtained, the "white circle" auxiliary values and the "cross" values are computed by diagonal operators, the $\times$ values are evaluated by regular cross operators, and the solution is obtained on the new *graded net* with mesh sizes h everywhere and mesh size $h/2$ in the area *ABCD*. In so doing, it is only necessary to notice that a change δu at points like *E* and *F* will introduce residual changes at points of both nets, so that the relaxation patterns at *E* and *F* are those given in Fig. 5.16.

5.6 Solution of Poisson's Equation by Relaxation

Another fundamental equation of mathematical physics, the *Poissonian equation*,

$$\nabla^2 z = \frac{\partial^2 z}{\partial x^2} + \frac{\partial^2 z}{\partial y^2} = f(x,y),$$

which governs phenomena in electricity, magnetism, elasticity, etc., can also be conveniently solved by relaxation. It is applied here to a problem in elasticity.

Consider a perfectly flexible thin membrane evenly stretched over a horizontal square hole of side L and slightly deflected (up or down) by a constant pressure p (Fig. 5.17). Let S be the *constant* tension per unit of length in the membrane and z its ordinates above the plane of the hole, taken as the x,y-plane. The forces acting on an element $dx\,dy$ of the membrane are (1) the pressure $p\,dx\,dy$, (2) the resultant of the tension S applied to the sides dy, (3) the resultant of the tension S applied to the sides dx. The weight of the membrane is considered negligible.

Assuming the slope of the membrane to be everywhere very small (Fig. 5.18), the resultant in the vertical direction of the tension S applied to the sides dy of the element equals

$$-S\,dy\,\frac{\partial z}{\partial x} + S\,dy\left(\frac{\partial z}{\partial x} + \frac{\partial}{\partial x}\frac{\partial z}{\partial x}\,dx\right) = S\,\frac{\partial^2 z}{\partial x^2}\,dx\,dy.$$

Similarly, the resultant of the tension S on the sides dx of the element equals

$$-S\,dx\,\frac{\partial z}{\partial y} + S\,dx\left(\frac{\partial z}{\partial y} + \frac{\partial}{\partial y}\frac{\partial z}{\partial y}\,dy\right) = S\,\frac{\partial^2 z}{\partial y^2}\,dx\,dy.$$

Hence the differential equation of equilibrium of the membrane in the

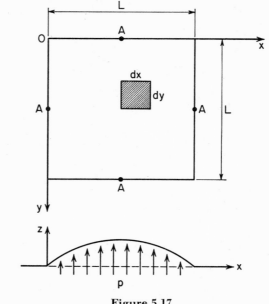

Figure 5.17

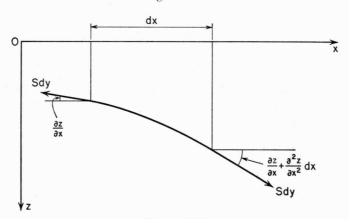

Figure 5.18

z direction reduces, after division by $S\,dx\,dy$, to

$$\frac{\partial^2 z}{\partial x^2} + \frac{\partial^2 z}{\partial y^2} + \frac{p}{S} = 0, \tag{5.6.1}$$

a Poissonian equation with $f(x,y) = -p/S = $ constant. The boundary conditions require that

$$z = 0 \quad \text{on the boundary.} \tag{5.6.2}$$

To obtain a numerical solution of the membrane problem in nondimensional form, let

$$x = \xi L; \qquad y = \eta L; \qquad z(x,y) = \frac{pL^2}{S} \phi(\xi,\eta) \qquad (5.6.3)$$

in Eqs. (5.6.1) and (5.6.2):

$$\frac{\partial^2 z}{\partial x^2} + \frac{\partial^2 z}{\partial y^2} + \frac{p}{S} = \frac{pL^2}{S} \left[\frac{\partial^2 \phi}{L^2 \partial \xi^2} + \frac{\partial^2 \phi}{L^2 \partial \eta^2} \right] + \frac{p}{S} = 0;$$

$$\frac{pL^2}{S} \phi = 0 \quad \text{on the boundary.}$$

The function ϕ is thus found to be a solution of the boundary value problem

$$\frac{\partial^2 \phi}{\partial \xi^2} + \frac{\partial^2 \phi}{\partial \eta^2} + 1 = 0;$$

$$\phi(0,\eta) = \phi(1,\eta) = \phi(\xi,0) = \phi(\xi,1) = 0. \qquad (5.6.4)$$

To transform the first of Eqs. (5.6.4) into a difference equation using a square lattice of mesh size $h = 1/n$, the equation is multiplied through by $h^2 = 1/n^2$, and the molecule of Fig. 5.3b is substituted for $h^2\nabla^2$. The difference equations,

$$\phi_a + \phi_b + \phi_r + \phi_l - 4\phi_i + \frac{1}{n^2} = 0, \qquad (5.6.5)$$

together with the conditions (5.6.4) on the boundary, are the numerical equations for the membrane problem. Once the values of ϕ have been obtained, the actual membrane deflections may be computed by means of Eq. (5.6.3).

Starting with $n = 2$ (Fig. 5.19a) and remembering that $\phi = 0$ on the boundary, Eq. (5.6.5) gives

$$0 + 0 + 0 + 0 - 4\phi_1 + \tfrac{1}{4} = 0$$

or $\phi_1 = 0.0625$. For $n = 3$ (Fig. 5.19b), Eq. (5.6.5) gives

$$0 + 0 + \phi_1 + \phi_1 - 4\phi_1 + \tfrac{1}{9} = 0$$

or $\phi_1 = 0.0556$.

For $n = 6$, Eq. (5.6.5), multiplied through by 10^4 to avoid the decimal point, gives

$$\phi_a + \phi_b + \phi_r + \phi_l - 4\phi_i + 278 = 0. \qquad (5.6.6)$$

Due to symmetry, only one-eighth of the membrane and six values of ϕ are considered, as shown in Fig. 5.19c. Also because of symmetry, the

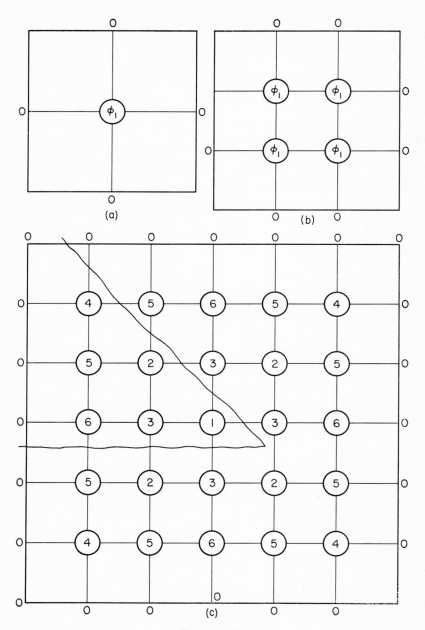

Figure 5.19

Table 5.5

δR_i $\delta\phi_i$	$i = 1$	2	3	4	5	6
$i = 1$	-4	0	$+1$	0	0	0
2	0	-4	$+2$	0	$+1$	0
3	$+4$	$+2$	-4	0	0	$+1$
4	0	0	0	-4	$+1$	0
5	0	$+2$	0	$+2$	-4	$+2$
6	0	0	$+1$	0	$+1$	-4

changes δR in the residuals due to changes $\delta\phi = 1$ in the ϕ have the values indicated in Table 5.5.

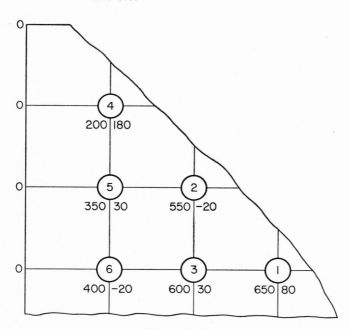

Figure 5.20

The initial values of ϕ are computed by interpolation at sight from the values $10^4\phi_1 = 625$ for $n = 2$ and $10^4\phi_1 = 556$ for $n = 3$; they appear in Fig. 5.20 together with the corresponding residuals.

The relaxation Table 5.6 gives, first, the values of ϕ to two figures evaluated by rounded-off residuals (the largest residual is reduced at each step principally by overrelaxation); two more figures in the ϕ are then computed by relaxing the residuals due to the ϕ values with two figures (again overrelaxation is used principally).

The actual membrane deflections are computed by means of the ϕ values of Table 5.6 and Eq. (5.6.3).

Table 5.6

①			②		③		④		⑤		⑥
65	8̶	55	-2̶ 60	3̶	20	18̶ 35	3̶	40	-2̶		
6	-16̶	3	4̶ 3	5̶	5	-2̶ 3	8̶	2	4̶		
	-4̶		10̶ 1	11̶	1	4̶	-4̶		-4̶		
	0		-2̶	-1̶		0	-2̶		-1̶		
			0	5̶			1̶		0		
71				1	26		2				
	58							42			
			64			38					
710	-2̶	580	-2̶ 640	8̶	260	-2̶ 380	18̶	420	-2̶		
10	38̶	8	14̶ 10	24̶	4	14̶ 8	-14̶	7	14̶		
1.5	-2̶	2	-18̶ 2	-16̶	0.5	-2̶ 2	-16̶	0.5	24̶		
	8̶	0.5	2̶	-8̶		2̶	-2̶		-4̶		
	0		8̶	1̶		0	8̶		9̶		
721.5			2̶	5̶		-3̶	-1̶		2̶		
			0	-3̶	264.5		-0.5		0		
				-1.5			-0.5				
	590.5			-0.5			8̶	427.5			
			652.0	0			0.5				
							390.0				

5.7 Elastic Torsion

It is proved in theory of elasticity* that the tangential stress τ_z in a twisted prismatic bar of constant cross section, whose axis is taken to be the z-axis, may be expressed in terms of the derivatives of a *torsion function* ψ by the equations

$$\tau_{xz} = G\theta \frac{\partial \psi}{\partial y}; \qquad \tau_{yz} = -G\theta \frac{\partial \psi}{\partial x}. \tag{5.7.1}$$

Here τ_{xz} and τ_{yz} are the components of τ_z in the x- and y-directions,

* See, for example, S. Timoshenko and J. N. Goodier, *Theory of Elasticity*, McGraw-Hill Book Company, Inc., New York, 1951, pp. 258 ff.

respectively, G is the shear modulus, θ is the angle of twist per unit length, and the function ψ satisfies the Poissonian equation

$$\nabla^2\psi + 2 = 0 \tag{5.7.2}$$

and the boundary condition

$$\psi = 0 \qquad \text{on the boundary,} \tag{5.7.3}$$

if the bar has a solid cross section.

The torque M_t producing the stresses of Eqs. (5.7.1) is expressed in terms of ψ by the equation

$$M_t = 2G\theta \int\int \psi \, dx \, dy, \tag{5.7.4}$$

where the double integral is extended over the cross section of the bar.

We wish to evaluate numerically the maximum stress in a prismatic bar of square cross section with sides L parallel to the x- and y-axes, when the bar is acted upon by a torque M_t producing stresses within the elastic limit.

To obtain a numerical solution in nondimensional form, take the origin at one of the corners of the cross section and let in Eqs. (5.7.2), (5.7.3)

$$\phi(\xi,\eta) = \frac{1}{L^2}\,\psi(x,y);$$

$$\xi = \frac{x}{L}; \qquad \eta = \frac{y}{L}, \tag{5.7.5}$$

thus obtaining the boundary problem for ϕ

$$\frac{\partial^2\phi}{\partial\xi^2} + \frac{\partial^2\phi}{\partial\eta^2} + 2 = 0;$$

$$\phi(0,\eta) = \phi(1,\eta) = \phi(\xi,0) = \phi(\xi,1) = 0. \tag{5.7.6}$$

Comparison of Eqs. (5.7.6) with Eqs. (5.6.4) proves that the nondimensional torsion function ϕ of this section satisfies the same boundary value problem as the nondimensional membrane deflection ϕ of Sec. 5.6, except for a factor of 2 in the constant of the equation. Since the differential equations in Eqs. (5.6.4) and (5.7.6) are linear, their solutions are proportional to the constant; hence the values of the nondimensional torsion function ϕ of Eqs. (5.7.6) are twice the values of the membrane deflection ϕ of Table 5.6. In other words, the membrane deflection is an *analogue* of the torsion function.

Table 5.7 gives the values of the nondimensional torsion function ϕ, obtained from the membrane relaxation solution for $n = 6$ of Table 5.6.

In terms of ϕ [Eqs. (5.7.5)], the stresses [Eqs. (5.7.1)] and the torque [Eq. (5.7.4)] take the form

$$\tau_{xz} = G\theta L \frac{\partial \phi}{\partial \eta}; \qquad \tau_{yz} = -G\theta L \frac{\partial \phi}{\partial \xi}; \tag{5.7.7}$$

$$M_t = 2G\theta L^4 \int \int \phi \, d\xi \, d\eta \equiv 2G\theta L^4 V, \tag{5.7.8}$$

and show that the stress components are proportional to the *slope* of the ϕ membrane in the x- and y-directions and the torque is proportional to the volume V under the membrane ϕ.

Table 5.7

Point	1	2	3
$10^4 \cdot \phi$	1443	1181	1304
Point	4	5	6
$10^4 \cdot \phi$	529	780	855

In particular, the maximum stress occurs at the middle point A of the cross-section side (Fig. 5.17):

$$|\tau_{\max}| = G\theta L \left| \frac{\partial \phi}{\partial \xi} \right|_A . \tag{5.7.9}$$

The value of the maximum slope $\partial \phi / \partial \xi$ at A may be obtained by the forward difference expansion of the first derivative of Eq. (2.5.4), using the differences of the ϕ values of Table 5.7 and $h = \frac{1}{6}$. Table 5.8 gives

Table 5.8

n	ϕ	$\Delta \phi$	$\Delta^2 \phi$	$\Delta^3 \phi$	$\Delta^4 \phi$	$\Delta^5 \phi$	$\Delta^6 \phi$
0	0	855	−406	96	−64	0	0
1	855	449	−310	+32	−64	0	
2	1304	+139	−278	−32	−64		
3	1443	−139	−310	−96			
4	1304	−449	−406				
5	855	−855					
6	0						

the successive forward differences of ϕ along the middle axis of the cross section, by means of which Eq. (2.5.4) yields

$$\frac{\partial \phi}{\partial \xi}\Bigg]_A = \frac{1}{\frac{1}{6}} [855 - \tfrac{1}{2}(-406) + \tfrac{1}{3}(96) - \tfrac{1}{4}(-64)] = 6636.$$

Hence by Eq. (5.7.9), and remembering the factor 10^4 used in Table 5.7,

$$|\tau_{\max}| = 0.6636G\theta L.$$

This value differs by 1.7 per cent from the value $0.675G\theta L$ obtained by Timoshenko using a power series expansion for ϕ.*

The corresponding value of the torque M_t is obtained by evaluating the double integral of Eq. (5.7.8) by means of Simpson's rule, applying the operator B_4 of Fig. 5.7 once at 1, four times at 4, and four times at 6 (Fig. 5.19c), or using the operator of Fig. 5.8:

$$\int\int \phi \, d\xi \, d\eta = \frac{1}{9 \cdot 36} \{4 \cdot 1181 + 4 \cdot 4 \cdot 1304 + 16 \cdot 1443$$

$$+ \; 4[0 + 0 + 0 + 1181 + 4(0 + 0 + 780 + 780) + 16 \cdot 529]$$

$$+ \; 4[0 + 0 + 1181 + 1181 + 4(0 + 780 + 780 + 1304) + 16 \cdot 855]\}$$

$$= 685.8.$$

Hence, $M_t = 2 \cdot 685.8 \cdot 10^{-4}G\theta L^4 = 0.1372G\theta L^4.$ (a)

This value is 2.42 per cent smaller than the value $0.1406G\theta L^4$ computed by Timoshenko by means of a power series.*

5.8 Solution of a Problem in Plastic Torsion by Relaxation

The numerical solution of the torsion problem for stresses *beyond the elastic limit*, that is, in the plastic range, is easily obtained by means of the membrane analogy of the previous section.

To this purpose, notice first of all that the solution of the elastic torsion problem by finite differences and relaxation is analogous to the substitution of an elastic net for the continuous membrane. The net is loaded at the nodes, which correspond to the pivotal points, and the residual equation corresponding to Eq. (5.7.6),

$$R_i = (\phi_a + \phi_b + \phi_r + \phi_l - 4\phi_i) + \frac{2}{n^2} \qquad (5.8.1)$$

contains a term in parentheses proportional to the resultant of the tensions in the four wires meeting at the ith node and the term $2/n^2$, which is proportional to the applied load. The residual thus represents the *unbalanced* force at the ith node, which must vanish for equilibrium.

Let us now assume that the material of the bar under torsion behaves

---

* S. Timoshenko and J. N. Goodier, *Theory of Elasticity*, McGraw-Hill Book Company, Inc., New York, 1951, p. 277.

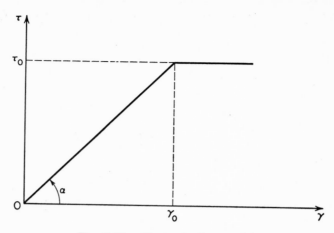

Fig. 5.21. Elasto-plastic material.

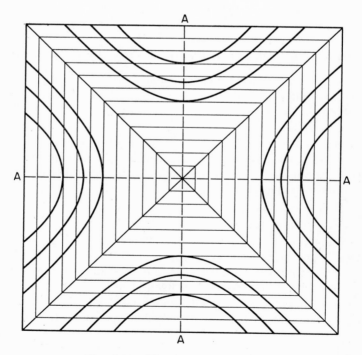

Fig. 5.22. Plastic regions in torsion.

elastically up to a value τ_0 of the shear stress τ and plastically from then on: an increase in the strain γ beyond the maximum elastic strain γ_0, that is, in the twist θ beyond its limiting elastic value θ_0 will not increase the shear stress beyond τ_0 (Fig. 5.21). Calling M_0 the value of the torque producing a stress τ_0 at the middle points A of the edge (Fig. 5.22)

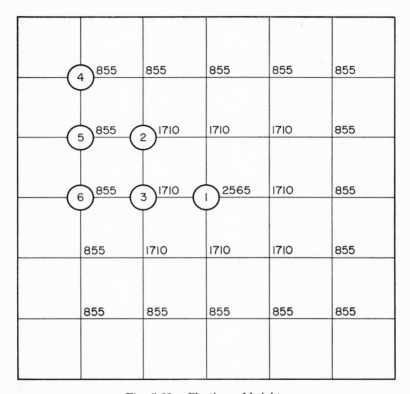

Fig. 5.23.   Plastic roof heights.

where the stress is maximum, an increase of the torque beyond M_0 will cause the penetration of the plastic stress τ_0 into the section, so that in certain plastic regions around the points A the stress will be everywhere equal to τ_0. It is easy to visualize these regions with the help of the membrane analogy. As the torque M increases, the analogue of M, that is, the membrane volume V, increases due to an increase in the pressure p. The membrane is blown up and its slope increases. Imagine a glass "roof" of constant slope m, corresponding to the maximum stress τ_0, set over the membrane. As the membrane is blown up, it will touch the roof, starting at the points A; as the pressure is increased, the contact between the membrane and the roof will be extended to larger and larger "plastic" regions as shown in Fig. 5.22. At the limit, when the whole section is in the plastic range, the membrane touches the roof everywhere and has the shape of a pyramid.

It is now clear that, while in the elastic region the external load p is equilibrated by the tension S in the membrane, in the plastic regions

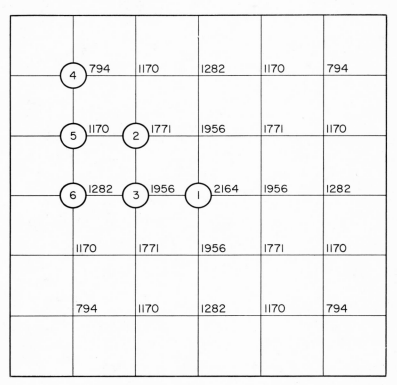

Fig. 5.24.   Elastic heights ($\theta_1 = 1.5\theta_0$).

any unbalanced force is automatically equilibrated by the reaction of the roof. This observation of Southwell gives a simple means of solving the elasto-plastic torsion problem.

Let us assume that the nondimensional deflections ϕ of the "membrane" determined in Table 5.7 correspond to the value θ_0 of the twist and that therefore the "slope" of the ϕ surface at A corresponds to the plastic stress τ_0. Approximating slopes by first differences, the constant slope of the plastic roof must be taken equal to the height 855 of the membrane at the pivotal point 6 divided by $h = \frac{1}{6}$ (Fig. 5.19c). The heights of the points on the roof are then equal to 855 for the points 4, 5, and 6, to $855 \cdot 2 = 1710$ for the points 2 and 3, and to $855 \cdot 3 = 2565$ for point 1 (Fig. 5.23).

On the other hand, since by Eq. (5.7.9) τ is proportional to θ, if the twist reached a value, say $1.5\theta_0$, and the material still behaved elastically, the heights of the membrane would be 1.5 times the elastic heights computed in Table 5.7 and would have the values given in Fig. 5.24. Whenever the ordinates in Fig. 5.24 are higher than those in Fig. 5.23, the roof will prevent the displacement of the membrane; hence the membrane must be brought *down* to the level of the roof at points 2, 3, 5, and 6 by means of the negative displacements of Table 5.9. The residuals due to these displacements are evaluated by means of Eq. (5.8.1) and appear in Table 5.10. Remembering that residuals represent unbalanced forces and noting that positive residuals represent *upward* unbalanced forces equilibrated by the roof, the positive residuals are neglected and the *negative* residuals only are relaxed at each step. This relaxation is performed in Table 5.11, which gives the new heights of the membrane to three figures. The height at point 6, corresponding to the plastic stress τ_0, is 855, and the plastic region extends to points between 6 and 3 and between 4 and 5.

Table 5.9

Point	2	3	5	6
Displacement	$1710 - 1771$ $= -61$	$1710 - 1956$ $= -246$	$855 - 1170$ $= -315$	$855 - 1282$ $= -427$

Table 5.10
Lowering of Membrane to Roof

Table 5.11
Relaxation of Negative Residuals ($\theta_1 = 1.5\theta_0$)

	4				
794	-630				
-157.5					
636.5	0				

	5		2		
855	$+772$	1710	-878		
0		-282			
855	$+332.5$	1428	0		

	6		3		1
855	$+832$	1710	$+435$	2164	-984
0		-125		-371	
855	707	1585	0	1793	0

Table 5.12 gives the same calculations for $\theta = 1.75\theta_0$. Here the plastic region extends again between points 6 and 3 and between points 4 and 5, but its boundary is nearer points 6 and 4 than for the case $\theta = 1.5\theta_0$. Fig. 5.25 gives the plastic regions corresponding to $\theta = 1.5\theta_0$ and $\theta = 1.75\theta_0$.

Table 5.12
Relaxation of Negative Residuals ($\theta_2 = 1.75\theta_0$)

	4				
855	-736.8				
-184.2					
670.8	0				

	5		2		
855	$+971$	1710	-736		
0		-186			
855	600.8	1524	0		

	6		3		1
855	$+972$	1710	$+933$	2525	-2288
0		-4		-576	
855	968	1706	1	1949	0

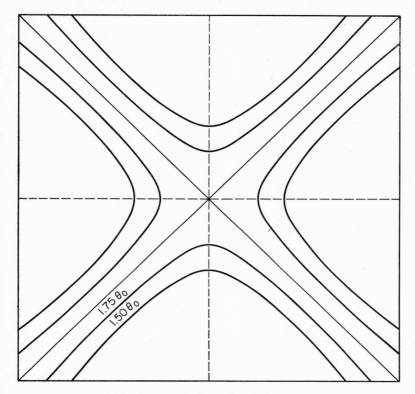

Fig. 5.25.   Plastic regions in torsion.

It is now possible to compute by Simpson's rule (Sec. 5.3b) the integral V of the elastoplastic ϕ function. For $\theta_1 = 1.5\theta_0$ we obtain $V_1 = 779.1$; for $\theta_2 = 1.75\theta_0$ the volume is $V_2 = 810.3$.

In order to obtain the corresponding values of the plastic torque M_1 and M_2, substitute in Eq. (5.7.8) the value of $G\theta L$ given by Eq. (5.7.9):

$$M_t = 2G\theta L^4 V = \frac{2\tau_{\max}}{\left|\dfrac{\partial \phi}{\partial \xi}\right|_{\max}} L^3 V, \tag{5.8.2}$$

and notice that since

$$\tau_{\max} = \tau_0 \qquad \text{and} \qquad \left|\frac{\partial \phi}{\partial \xi}\right|_{\max} = m$$

for both the plastic and the elastic cases, the ratio

$$\tau_{\max} \Big/ \left|\frac{\partial \phi}{\partial \xi}\right|_{\max} = \tau_0/m = \text{const.}$$

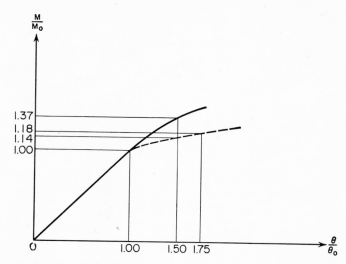

Fig. 5.26. Torque vs. twist in plastic torsion of square section.

Thus the elastic and the plastic torques are proportional to V and

$$\frac{M_1}{M_0} = \frac{V_1}{V_0} = \frac{779.1}{685.8} = 1.136 \qquad \text{for } \frac{\theta_1}{\theta_0} = 1.5$$

$$\frac{M_2}{M_0} = \frac{V_2}{V_0} = \frac{810.3}{685.8} = 1.182 \qquad \text{for } \frac{\theta_2}{\theta_0} = 1.75$$

Fig. 5.26 gives the graph of M/M_0 versus θ/θ_0 for

$$\left|\frac{\partial \phi}{\partial \xi}\right|_{\max} = \frac{855}{1/6} = 5130 \quad \text{(broken line)}$$

and for

$$\left|\frac{\partial \phi}{\partial \xi}\right|_{\max} = \frac{1106}{1/6} = 6636 \quad \text{(continuous line)},$$

that is, for the more accurate value of the slope at A obtained by Table 5.8. It is seen that the relation between torque and twist is nonlinear in the plastic range and that the numerical approximation of the boundary slope influences considerably the results.

5.9 Membrane Vibrations

The technique used in the preceding section to solve torsion problems may be used to solve two-dimensional vibration problems.

The differential equation for the free vibrations of a membrane is obtained by adding to the equilibrium equation (5.6.1) the inertia forces

$-m \dfrac{\partial^2 z}{\partial t^2}$, where m is the membrane mass per unit of area, and by setting the external pressure p equal to zero:

$$\frac{\partial^2 z}{\partial x^2} + \frac{\partial^2 z}{\partial y^2} - \frac{m}{S} \frac{\partial^2 z}{\partial t^2} = 0. \tag{5.9.1}$$

To find the natural frequencies ω of a membrane, the function $z(x,y,t)$ is assumed to represent a harmonic vibration:

$$z(x,y,t) = Z(x,y) \sin \omega t \tag{a}$$

and is substituted in Eq. (5.9.1), which becomes, after division by $\sin \omega t$,

$$\frac{\partial^2 Z}{\partial x^2} + \frac{\partial^2 Z}{\partial y^2} + \frac{m\omega^2}{S} Z = 0. \tag{5.9.2}$$

To solve the problem in nondimensional form for the case of a square membrane of side L supported on a flat boundary, the usual transformation

$$x = \xi L; \qquad y = \eta L \tag{b}$$

is introduced in Eq. (5.9.2), which thus becomes

$$\frac{\partial^2 Z}{\partial \xi^2} + \frac{\partial^2 Z}{\partial \eta^2} + KZ = 0, \tag{5.9.3}$$

with

$$K = \frac{mL^2}{S} \omega^2, \tag{5.9.4}$$

and Eq. (5.9.3) is then transformed into a finite difference equation by the operator of Fig. 5.3b with $h^2 = 1/n^2$:

$$Z_a + Z_b + Z_r + Z_l + \left(\frac{K}{n^2} - 4 \right) Z_i = 0. \tag{5.9.5}$$

The conditions on the boundary require that

$$Z = 0 \quad \text{on the boundary.} \tag{5.9.6}$$

For $n = 2$ and 3 (Fig. 5.27a, b), Eq. (5.9.5) gives

$$n = 2; \qquad \left(\frac{K_2}{4} - 4 \right) Z_1 = 0; \quad K_2 = 16 \quad (e = +19\%)$$

$$n = 3; \qquad Z_1 + 0 + Z_1 + 0 + \left(\frac{K_3}{9} - 4 \right) Z_1 = 0; \quad K_3 = 18$$

$$(e = +9\%)$$

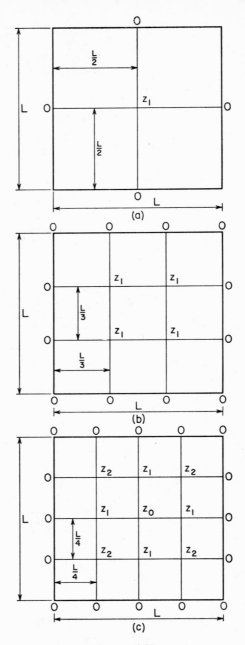

Figure 5.27

The determinantal equation for $n = 4$ (Fig. 5.27c) is

$$\begin{vmatrix} \dfrac{K_4}{16} - 4 & 2 & 0 \\[2mm] 2 & \dfrac{K_4}{16} - 4 & 1 \\[2mm] 0 & 4 & \dfrac{K_4}{16} - 4 \end{vmatrix} = 0$$

and its smallest root is

$$K_4 = 18.75 \quad (e = +5\%).$$

The extrapolated values of K are

$$K_{2,3} = 19.60 \quad (+0.7\%); \qquad K_{3,4} = 19.71 \quad (+0.15\%);$$
$$K_{2,3,4} = 19.75 \quad (-0.051\%).$$

The true value of K is 19.739.

5.10 *Pivotal Points Near Curved Boundaries*

In all the problems of the preceding sections the pivotal points inside the rectangular domains and on their boundaries fell on the corners of a rectangular lattice and were evenly spaced in the x- and the y-directions. When a two-dimensional domain covered by a rectangular lattice is bounded by curves, instead, some or all of its pivotal boundary points do not fall on the corners of the lattice, and special formulas must be used at pivotal points adjoining the boundaries.

Consider, for example, the steady-state temperature problem of the plate of Fig. 5.28, a square plate of sides L with two corners rounded off by arcs of circle of radius $L/2$. The temperature u in the plate satisfies the Laplacian equation $\nabla^2 u = 0$ (Sec. 5.4). This equation can be transformed into a difference equation by the operator of Fig. 5.3b at points (1), (2), and (3), but point (4) is not evenly spaced from the adjoining pivotal points and must be dealt with by means of a special equation.

The difference equation $\nabla^2 u = 0$ at the upper point (4) may be obtained, for example, by means of Eq. (2.2.3), which in the present case becomes

$$\frac{\partial^2 u}{\partial x^2} = \frac{1}{h^2} \frac{2}{\alpha(\alpha + 1)} [\alpha u_l - (1 + \alpha) u_i + u_r] + 0(h); \tag{a}$$

$$\alpha = \frac{x_r - x_i}{h} = \frac{x_5 - x_4}{L/4}, \tag{b}$$

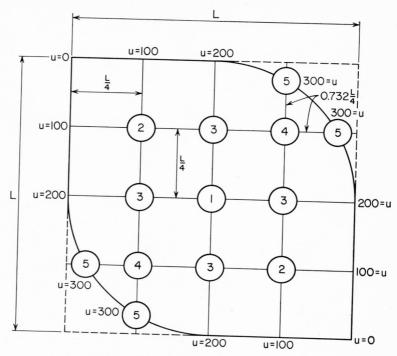

Figure 5.28

and by the corresponding equation in the y direction;

$$\frac{\partial^2 u}{\partial y^2} = \frac{1}{h^2} \frac{2}{\beta(\beta + 1)} [\beta u_b - (1 + \beta)u_i + u_a] + 0(h); \qquad (c)$$

$$\beta = \frac{y_a - y_i}{h} = \frac{y_5 - y_4}{L/4}. \qquad (d)$$

Adding up Eqs. (a) and (c), the operator $\nabla^2 u$ is obtained in the form

$$\frac{h^2}{2} \alpha(1 + \alpha)\beta(1 + \beta)\nabla^2 u = \beta(1 + \beta)[\alpha u_l - (1 + \alpha)u_i + u_r]$$
$$+ \alpha(1 + \alpha)[\beta u_b - (1 + \beta)u_i + u_a], \quad (5.10.1)$$

which is also given in the molecule of Fig. 5.29.

In the problem of Fig. 5.28, $\alpha = \beta$ and the operator of Fig. 5.29 becomes, after division by $\alpha(1 + \alpha)$, the operator of Fig. 5.30.

If this operator is applied at point (4) with $\alpha = \sqrt{3} - 1 = 0.732$, and the operator of Fig. 5.3b is applied at the points (1), (2), and (3),

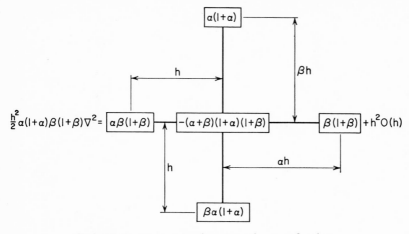

Fig. 5.29. ∇^2 operator for unevenly spaced points.

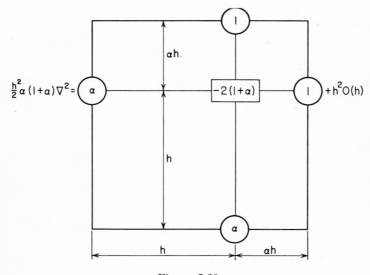

Figure 5.30

one obtains the system of linear equations for the u_i of Table 5.13, whose roots are

$$u_1 = 203.7; \qquad u_2 = 151.9; \qquad u_3 = 203.7; \qquad u_4 = 259.3.$$

The operator in Fig. 5.30 has an error of order h, while the operator of Fig. 5.3b has an error of order h^2. To have consistent errors throughout the domain one may express $\nabla^2 u$ by means of the operator of Eq.

Table 5.13

Point	u_1	u_2	u_3	u_4	c
1	-4	0	4	0	0
2	0	-4	2	0	-200
3	1	1	-4	1	-200
4	0	0	1.464	-3.464	-600

(2.3.6), but in the present example this does not change the first four figures of the u_i (see Problem 5.32).

The type of difference formulas used in this section are also applied in problems involving so-called *graded nets* (see Sec. 5.5). These lattices, with different values of the mesh size in different regions of the domain, are used whenever the function to be determined varies rapidly in a given region, since a smaller mesh size gives better accuracy at points where it is needed. While the detailed technique of graded nets goes beyond the scope of this book, the reader may consult Southwell's books and papers on this particular subject.*

5.11 An Improved Poissonian Operator in Cartesian Coordinates

The difference Laplacian operator

$$Hz_i \equiv z_a + z_b + z_r + z_l - 4z_i \doteq h^2\nabla^2 z_i \tag{5.11.1}$$

of Fig. 5.3b is affected by an error of order h^2. An error of the same order affects the *diagonal Laplacian operator* in the ξ, η coordinates:

$$Xz_i \equiv z_{ar} + z_{bl} + z_{al} + z_{br} - 4z_i \doteq (\sqrt{2}\,h)^2\nabla^2 z_i \tag{5.11.2}$$

of Fig. 5.31. It will now be shown that a linear combination of Hz_i and Xz_i may be formed with an error of order h^4.

To this purpose, consider the Poissonian equation

$$\nabla^2 z = f(x,y), \tag{5.11.3}$$

and substitute for $h^2\nabla^2 z$ the Hz operator together with the first term of its error expansion:

$$h^2\nabla^2 z \doteq Hz - \frac{h^4}{12}(z_{xxxx} + z_{yyyy}) \doteq h^2 f, \tag{a}$$

where subscripts indicate partial derivatives. Adding and subtracting $(2h^4/12)z_{xxyy}$ to the second member of Eq. (a), and noticing that, by Eq. (5.11.3),

$$\nabla^4 z = \nabla^2 f, \tag{b}$$

* See, for example, R. V. Southwell, *Relaxation Methods in Theoretical Physics,* Oxford University Press, London, 1946, p. 50.

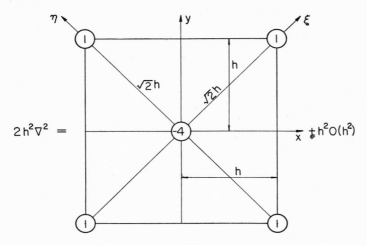

Fig. 5.31.   *X* operator.

we obtain

$$h^2\nabla^2 z \doteq Hz - \frac{h^4}{12}\nabla^2 f + \frac{h^4}{6} z_{xxyy} \doteq h^2 f. \tag{c}$$

Consider now the diagonal Laplacian operator Xz and the first term of its error expansion:

$$Xz = 2h^2(z_{\xi\xi} + z_{\eta\eta}) + \frac{4h^4}{12}(z_{\xi\xi\xi\xi} + z_{\eta\eta\eta\eta})$$

$$= 2h^2(z_{\xi\xi} + z_{\eta\eta}) + \frac{4h^4}{12}(z_{\xi\xi\xi\xi} + 2z_{\xi\xi\eta\eta} + z_{\eta\eta\eta\eta}) - \frac{8h^4}{12} z_{\xi\xi\eta\eta}. \tag{d}$$

Since the ∇^2 and ∇^4 operators are invariant with respect to a rotation of the axes, ∇^2 and ∇^4 are identical whether taken with respect to x, y or to ξ, η, and Eq. (5.11.3) may be written, by Eqs. (b) and (d),

$$2h^2\nabla^2 z \doteq Xz - \frac{h^4}{3}\nabla^2 f + \frac{2}{3} h^4 z_{\xi\xi\eta\eta} \doteq 2h^2 f. \tag{e}$$

Introducing the linear transformation changing ξ, η into x, y:

$$x = \frac{\sqrt{2}}{2}(\xi - \eta); \qquad y = \frac{\sqrt{2}}{2}(\xi + \eta), \tag{f}$$

the derivatives of z with respect to ξ and η become

$$z_\xi = z_x x_\xi + z_y y_\xi = \frac{\sqrt{2}}{2}(z_x + z_y);$$

$$z_\eta = z_x x_\eta + z_y y_\eta = \frac{\sqrt{2}}{2}(z_y - z_x);$$

$$z_{\xi\xi} = \tfrac{1}{2}(z_{xx} + 2z_{xy} + z_{yy});$$

$$z_{\eta\eta} = \tfrac{1}{2}(z_{yy} - 2z_{xy} + z_{xx});$$

$$z_{\xi\xi\eta\eta} = \tfrac{1}{4}[(z_{xxxx} - 2z_{xxxy} + z_{xxyy}) + 2(z_{xxxy} - 2z_{xxyy} + z_{xyyy})$$
$$+ (z_{xxyy} - 2z_{xyyy} + z_{yyyy})] = \tfrac{1}{4}[z_{xxxx} - 2z_{xxyy} + z_{yyyy}]$$
$$= \tfrac{1}{4}\nabla^4 z - z_{xxyy} = \tfrac{1}{4}\nabla^2 f - z_{xxyy}. \tag{g}$$

Substitution of Eq. (g) into Eq. (e) finally gives

$$2h^2\nabla^2 z \doteq \boldsymbol{X}z - \frac{h^4}{6}\nabla^2 f - \frac{4}{6}h^4 z_{xxyy} \doteq 2h^2 f \tag{h}$$

Adding Eq. (c) multiplied by 4 to Eq. (h), the error term in h^4 is eliminated and the operator $\nabla^2 z$ is expressed in terms of a nine-point formula
with an error of order h^4:

$$6h^2\nabla^2 z \doteq (4\boldsymbol{H} + \boldsymbol{X})z = 6h^2 f + \frac{h^4}{2}\nabla^2 f. \tag{5.11.4}$$

The operator

$$\boldsymbol{N} \equiv 4\boldsymbol{H} + \boldsymbol{X} \tag{5.11.5}$$

is represented in Fig. 5.32. Whenever $\nabla^2 f = 0$, Eq. (5.11.4) simplifies to

$$h^2\nabla^2 z = \tfrac{1}{6}\boldsymbol{N}z_i = h^2 f \quad (\nabla^2 f = 0). \tag{5.11.6}$$

Whenever $f = 0$, the Laplacian difference operator with error of order
h^4 becomes

$$z_i = \tfrac{1}{20}[4(z_a + z_b + z_r + z_l) + (z_{ar} + z_{br} + z_{al} + z_{bl})]. \tag{5.11.7}$$

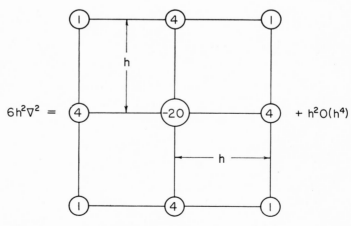

Fig. 5.32.   *N* operator.

Table 5.14 gives the solution of the Laplacian equation problem of Sec. 5.4 by Eq. (5.11.7), and should be compared with Table 5.3 to appreciate both the faster convergence of the N-operator and the effect of the mesh-size lumping error on the solutions by different operators.

Table 5.14

n	u_1	u_2	u_3	u_4	u_5	u_6
0	4375	5312	1875	2500	625	938
1	4312	5412	1805	2486	673	947
2	4318	5405	1813	2495	677	951
3	4318	5408	1817	2498	679	953
4	4320	5409	1818	2500	679	953
5	4320	5410	1818	2500	679	953
6	4320	5410	1818	2500	679	953

5.12 The Laplacian Operator in Skew Coordinates

Difference operators in Cartesian coordinates are well adapted to the solution of problems involving rectangular domains. When the domain to be considered is a parallelogram, it may be often more accurate and simpler to use coordinates parallel to the sides of the parallelogram, or *skew coordinates*.

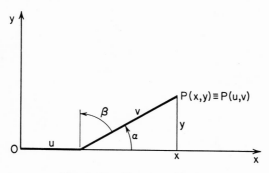

Fig. 5.33.   Skew coordinates.

A point of Cartesian coordinates (x,y) (Fig. 5.33) is located in the plane by skew coordinates (u,v) given by the transformation

$$x = u + v \cos \alpha; \qquad y = v \sin \alpha, \qquad (5.12.1)$$

where α is the complement of the *angle of skew* β.

Indicating partial derivatives by subscripts, the partial derivatives of x and y with respect to u and v are given by

$$x_u = 1; \qquad x_v = \cos \alpha; \qquad y_u = 0; \qquad y_v = \sin \alpha. \qquad \text{(a)}$$

Consider now a function $z(u,v)$ in which u, v are related to x, y by means of Eqs. (5.12.1). The first derivative of z with respect to u and v

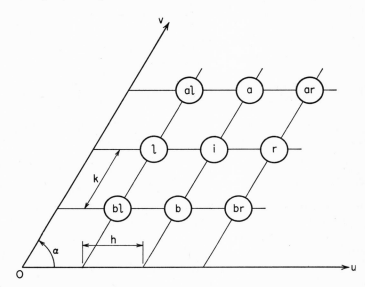

Fig. 5.34.   Lattice in skew coordinates.

are obtained by the rule for the differentiation of composite functions:

$$z_u = z_x x_u + z_y y_u = z_x$$
$$z_v = z_x x_v + z_y y_v = z_x \cos \alpha + z_y \sin \alpha.$$

The second derivatives of z with respect to u and v are obtained by "squaring" the operators z_u and z_v and by means of their "product":

$$z_{uu} = z_{xx} \qquad \text{(b)}$$
$$z_{vv} = z_{xx} \cos^2 \alpha + 2z_{xy} \sin \alpha \cos \alpha + z_{yy} \sin^2 \alpha \qquad \text{(c)}$$
$$z_{uv} = z_{xx} \cos \alpha + z_{xy} \sin \alpha. \qquad \text{(d)}$$

Substituting Eqs. (b) and (d) in Eq. (c),

$$z_{vv} = z_{uu} \cos^2 \alpha + 2 \cos \alpha(z_{uv} - z_{uu} \cos \alpha) + z_{yy} \sin^2 \alpha,$$

z_{yy} is obtained in terms of z_{uu}, z_{vv}, z_{uv}:

$$z_{yy} = \frac{1}{\sin^2 \alpha} (z_{vv} - 2z_{uv} \cos \alpha + z_{uu} \cos^2 \alpha),$$

and the *Laplacian operator in skew coordinates* becomes, by Eq. (b)

$$(\sin^2 \alpha)\nabla^2 z = z_{uu} - 2z_{uv} \cos \alpha + z_{vv}. \tag{5.12.2}$$

For $\alpha = \pi/2$, Eq. (5.12.2) reduces to $\nabla^2 z = z_{xx} + z_{yy}$.

The ∇^2 operator in skew coordinates is transformed into the corresponding difference operator by substituting for the derivatives z_{uu}, z_{uv},

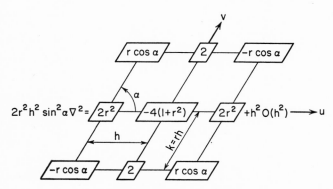

Fig. 5.35. ∇^2 in skew coordinates.

z_{vv} their expressions given by Fig. 2.8a. With the symbols of Fig. 5.34,

$$h^2 z_{uu} = z_r - 2z_i + z_l; \qquad k^2 z_{vv} = z_a - 2z_i + z_b;$$

$$4hk z_{uv} = z_{ar} - z_{br} - z_{al} + z_{bl},$$

and the ∇^2 operator takes the form of the molecule in Fig. 5.35, in which $r = k/h$.

The operator of Fig. 5.35 may be used, for example, to determine the center deflection w of a skew plate of sides $a = b$ with an angle of skew of 30° ($\alpha = 60°$), simply supported all around its boundary and uniformly loaded. The corresponding problem may be shown* to reduce to the integration of the two equations

$$\nabla^2 M = -q; \qquad \nabla^2 w = -M/D \tag{e}$$

with the conditions

$$M = 0; \qquad w = 0 \qquad \text{on the boundary.} \tag{f}$$

With $a = b$, $r = 1$, $n = 2$, $\alpha = 60°$, the operator of Fig. 5.35 becomes the operator of Fig. 5.36, and with $h = a/2$, gives at the center of the

---

* See, for example, S. Timoshenko and S. Woinowsky-Krieger, *Theory of Plates and Shells*, Sec. 83.

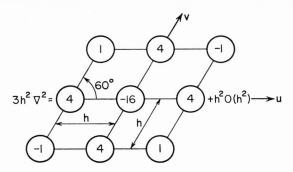

Figure 5.36

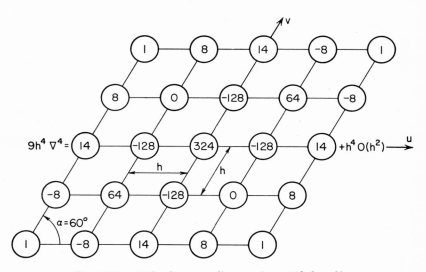

Fig. 5.37. ∇^4 in skew coordinates: ($\alpha = 60°$, $h = k$).

plate, for the first of Eqs. (e),

$$\frac{-16}{3(a/2)^2} M_0 = -q \quad \therefore \quad M_0 = \tfrac{3}{64} qa^2,$$

and for the second of Eqs. (e),

$$\frac{-16}{3(a/2)^2} w_0 = -\frac{3}{64}\frac{qa^2}{D} \quad \therefore \quad w_0 \Big]_2 = 0.00220 \frac{qa^4}{D}.$$

Using $n = 4$, and solving the corresponding system of four simultaneous equations, it is found that $w_0]_4 = 0.00241qa^4/D$, and an h^2-extrapolation gives

$$w_0\bigg]_{2,4} = 0.00248 \, \frac{qa^4}{D}.$$

It is simple to obtain the operator ∇^4 in skew coordinates in each numerical case, once ∇^2 is known. For example, using the ∇^2 of Fig. 5.36,

$$9h^4\nabla^4 z_i = (\nabla^2 z_{al} - \nabla^2 z_{ar} - \nabla^2 z_{bl} + \nabla^2 z_{br}) + 4(\nabla^2 z_a + \nabla^2 z_b + \nabla^2 z_r + \nabla^2 z_l)$$
$$- 16\nabla^2 z_i,$$

and ∇^4 becomes the operator of Fig. 5.37.

5.13 The Laplacian Operator in Polar Coordinates

Polar coordinates (Fig. 5.38) are used in connection with circular domains and are obtained from Cartesian coordinates through the

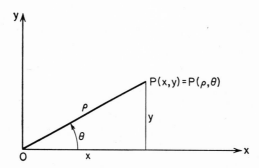

Fig. 5.38.   Polar coordinates.

transformations

$$x = \rho \cos \theta; \qquad y = \rho \sin \theta;$$

$$\rho = +(x^2 + y^2)^{\frac{1}{2}}; \qquad \theta = \tan^{-1} \frac{y}{x}. \tag{5.13.1}$$

The partial derivatives of ρ and θ with respect to x and y are, by Eqs. (5.13.1),

$$\rho_x = \frac{1}{2} \frac{2x}{(x^2 + y^2)^{\frac{1}{2}}} = \frac{x}{\rho} = \cos \theta; \qquad \rho_y = \frac{1}{2} \frac{2y}{(x^2 + y^2)^{\frac{1}{2}}} = \sin \theta;$$

$$\theta_x = -\frac{y/x^2}{1 + (y/x)^2} = -\frac{y}{\rho^2} = -\frac{\sin \theta}{\rho}; \tag{a}$$

$$\theta_y = \frac{1/x}{1 + (y/x)^2} = \frac{x}{\rho^2} = \frac{\cos \theta}{\rho}.$$

Consider a function $z(\rho,\theta)$, in which ρ and θ are functions of x and y through Eqs. (5.13.1). The first partial derivatives of z with respect to x and y, by the rule for the differentiation of composite functions and Eqs. (a), are given by

$$z_x = z_\rho \rho_x + z_\theta \theta_x = z_\rho \cos\theta - z_\theta \frac{\sin\theta}{\rho};$$

$$z_y = z_\rho \rho_y + z_\theta \theta_y = z_\rho \sin\theta + z_\theta \frac{\cos\theta}{\rho}. \qquad \text{(b)}$$

"Squaring" the first of Eqs. (b), we obtain

$$z_{xx} = \left(\frac{\partial}{\partial\rho}\cos\theta - \frac{\partial}{\partial\theta}\frac{\sin\theta}{\rho}\right)\left(z_\rho \cos\theta - z_\theta \frac{\sin\theta}{\rho}\right)$$

$$= z_{\rho\rho}\cos^2\theta + z_\rho \frac{\sin^2\theta}{\rho} + z_{\theta\theta}\frac{\sin^2\theta}{\rho^2} - 2z_{\rho\theta}\frac{\sin\theta\cos\theta}{\rho}$$

$$+ 2z_\theta \frac{\sin\theta\cos\theta}{\rho^2}. \qquad \text{(c)}$$

To obtain z_{yy}, either "square" the second of Eqs. (b) or change θ into $\theta + \pi/2$, i.e., $\cos\theta$ into $\sin\theta$ and $\sin\theta$ into $-\cos\theta$ in Eq. (c), obtaining

$$z_{yy} = z_{\rho\rho}\sin^2\theta + z_\rho \frac{\cos^2\theta}{\rho} + z_{\theta\theta}\frac{\cos^2\theta}{\rho^2} + 2z_{\rho\theta}\frac{\cos\theta\sin\theta}{\rho}$$

$$- 2z_\theta \frac{\cos\theta\sin\theta}{\rho^2}. \qquad \text{(d)}$$

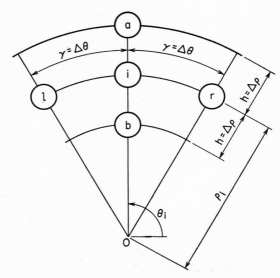

Fig. 5.39. Lattice in polar coordinates.

Adding Eqs. (c) and (d), the Laplacian in polar coordinates becomes

$$\nabla^2 z = z_{\rho\rho} + \frac{1}{\rho} z_\rho + \frac{1}{\rho^2} z_{\theta\theta}. \tag{5.13.2}$$

By means of the operators of Fig. 2.8a and with the symbols of Fig. 5.39, the derivatives of Eq. (5.13.2) are approximated by

$$z_{\rho\rho} = \frac{1}{h^2}(z_a - 2z_i + z_b); \quad z_\rho = \frac{1}{2h}(z_a - z_b); \quad z_{\theta\theta} = \frac{1}{\gamma^2}(z_r - 2z_i + z_l),$$

where

$$h = \Delta\rho; \qquad \gamma = \Delta\theta \tag{5.13.3}$$

and the Laplacian operator takes the form given in Fig. 5.40.

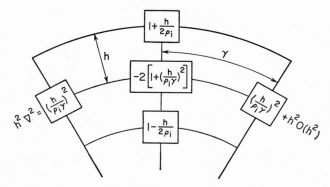

Fig. 5.40. ∇^2 in polar coordinates.

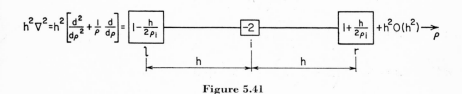

Figure 5.41

When the problem is symmetrical about the origin, and hence z does not depend on θ, the ∇^2 operator becomes the ordinary operator of Fig. 5.41.

The operator of Fig. 5.41 may be used to determine the deflections w at the pivotal points of an annular membrane of internal radius a and external radius $2a$, under uniform pressure p (Fig. 5.42). In this case, due to symmetry, Eq. (5.6.1), governing the deflections of the membrane, reduces to

$$\frac{d^2w}{d\rho^2} + \frac{1}{\rho}\frac{dw}{d\rho} + \frac{p}{S} = 0, \tag{e}$$

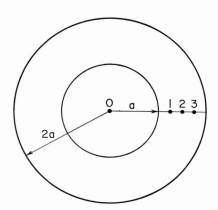

Figure 5.42

and letting

$$\rho = ax; \qquad w = \frac{pa^2}{S} z; \qquad h = \frac{1}{n}, \tag{f}$$

the corresponding difference equation becomes

$$\left(1 - \frac{1}{2nx_i}\right) z_l - 2z_i + \left(1 + \frac{1}{2nx_i}\right) z_r = -\frac{1}{n^2}. \tag{g}$$

Dividing the width of the membrane into four equal parts of width $\frac{a}{4}$,
Eq. (g) gives

at $\qquad x = \frac{5}{4} \qquad 0 - 2z_1 + \left(1 + \frac{1}{8\left(\frac{5}{4}\right)}\right) z_2 = -\frac{1}{16};$

at $\qquad x = \frac{3}{2} \qquad \left(1 - \frac{1}{8\left(\frac{3}{2}\right)}\right) z_1 - 2z_2 + \left(1 + \frac{1}{8\left(\frac{3}{2}\right)}\right) z_3 = -\frac{1}{16};$

at $\qquad x = \frac{7}{4} \qquad \left(1 - \frac{1}{8\left(\frac{7}{4}\right)}\right) z_2 - 2z_3 + 0 = -\frac{1}{16},$

or $\qquad\qquad\qquad -2z_1 + \frac{11}{10}z_2 \qquad\qquad = -\frac{1}{16};$

$$\frac{11}{12}z_1 - 2z_2 + \frac{13}{12}z_3 = -\frac{1}{16};$$

$$\frac{13}{14}z_2 - 2z_3 = -\frac{1}{16}.$$

The roots of this system are

$$z_1 = 0.100; \qquad z_2 = 0.126; \qquad z_3 = 0.090,$$

and the corresponding membrane deflections are

$$w_1 = 0.100pa^2/S; \qquad w_2 = 0.126pa^2/S; \qquad w_3 = 0.090pa^2/S.$$

5.14 The Laplacian Operator in Triangular Coordinates

One of the non-Cartesian lattices most commonly used to cover domains of irregular shape is the *triangular lattice* (Fig. 5.43). The Laplacian may be expressed in terms of the pivotal values of a triangular

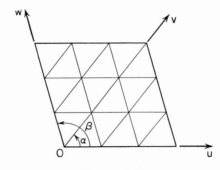

Figure 5.43

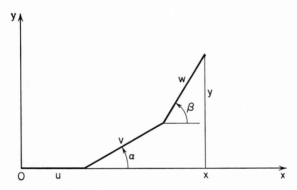

Fig. 5.44. Triangular coordinates.

lattice by the use of *triangular coordinates*, which locate a point in a plane by means of three coordinates u, v, and w (Fig. 5.44). A constant ratio v/u, w/u, or w/v is maintained among the three coordinates, so that only two coordinates are essential.

Assuming the direction u coincident with the x-axis, and calling α and β the angles between v and u, and w and u, the transformation from Cartesian to triangular coordinates becomes

$$x = u + v \cos \alpha + w \cos \beta;$$
$$y = v \sin \alpha + w \sin \beta.$$

$$(5.14.1)$$

The partial derivatives of x and y with respect to u, v, and w are therefore

$$x_u = 1; \qquad x_v = \cos \alpha; \qquad x_w = \cos \beta;$$
$$y_u = 0; \qquad y_v = \sin \alpha; \qquad y_w = \sin \beta. \tag{a}$$

A function $z(x,y)$ may be considered a function of u, v, w through the intermediate functions x, y defined by Eqs. (5.14.1), and its derivatives may be computed by the rule for the differentiation of composite functions. Thus by Eqs. (a),

$$z_u = z_x x_u + z_y y_u = z_x;$$
$$z_v = z_x x_v + z_y y_v = z_x \cos \alpha + z_y \sin \alpha;$$
$$z_w = z_x x_w + z_y y_w = z_x \cos \beta + z_y \sin \beta,$$

and "squaring" these operators,

$$z_{uu} = z_{xx}; \tag{b}$$
$$z_{vv} = z_{xx} \cos^2 \alpha + 2z_{xy} \sin \alpha \cos \alpha + z_{yy} \sin^2 \alpha; \tag{c}$$
$$z_{ww} = z_{xx} \cos^2 \beta + 2z_{xy} \sin \beta \cos \beta + z_{yy} \sin^2 \beta. \tag{d}$$

Substituting Eq. (b) in Eqs. (c) and (d), and eliminating z_{xy} between these last two equations, z_{yy} becomes

$$z_{yy} = \frac{z_{uu} \, 2 \cos \alpha \cos \beta \sin (\beta - \alpha) - z_{vv} \sin 2\beta + z_{ww} \sin 2\alpha}{2 \sin \alpha \sin \beta \sin (\beta - \alpha)},$$

and hence, by Eq. (b),

$$\nabla^2 z = z_{xx} + z_{yy} = z_{uu} + z_{yy}$$
$$= \frac{z_{uu} \sin 2(\beta - \alpha) - z_{vv} \sin 2\beta + z_{ww} \sin 2\alpha}{2 \sin \alpha \sin \beta \sin (\beta - \alpha)}. \tag{5.14.2}$$

For the commonly used *equilateral triangular lattice*, with

$$\alpha = 60°; \qquad \beta = 120°; \qquad \beta - \alpha = 60°;$$

$$\sin \alpha = \sin \beta = \sin (\beta - \alpha) = \sin 2\alpha = \sin 2(\beta - \alpha) = \frac{\sqrt{3}}{2};$$

$$\sin 2\beta = -\frac{\sqrt{3}}{2},$$

Eq. (5.14.2) reduces to

$$\nabla^2 z = \tfrac{2}{3}(z_{uu} + z_{vv} + z_{ww}). \tag{5.14.3}$$

The corresponding ∇^2 difference operator in *equilateral triangular (hexago-*

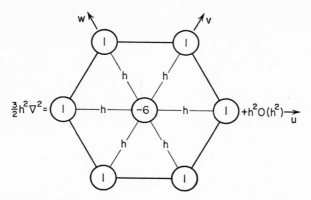

Fig. 5.45. ∇^2 in equilateral triangular (hexagonal) coordinates.

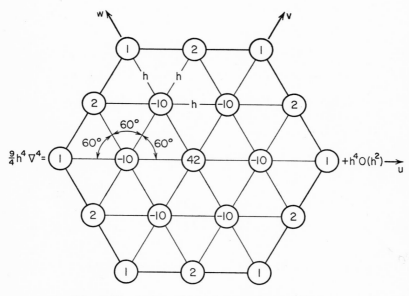

Fig. 5.46. ∇^4 in equilateral triangular coordinates.

nal) coordinates obtained by means of the operator h^2D^2 of Fig. 2.8a applied in the u-, v-, and w-directions appears in Fig. 5.45.

"Squaring" the operator of Fig. 5.45, we obtain the ∇^4 *operator in equilateral triangular coordinates*, given in Fig. 5.46.

The operator of Fig. 5.45 may be used, for example, to determine the values of the harmonic function z, whose values on a hexagonal boundary are given in Fig. 5.47. A harmonic function satisfies, by definition, the Laplacian equation $\nabla^2 z = 0$. Hence the values of z at the pivotal points of the hexagonal domain satisfy the system of equations

at   (1) $2z_2 + 4z_3 - 6z_1 = 0;$

at   (2) $z_1 + 2z_3 - 6z_2 + 200 + 200 + 300 = 0;$

at   (3) $z_1 + z_2 + z_3 - 6z_3 + 50 + 100 + 200 = 0,$

whose roots are

$$z_1 = 156; \qquad z_2 = 189; \qquad z_3 = 139.$$

The z_i could be interpreted as the values of the temperature inside a hexagonal plate, whose boundaries are kept at the temperatures of

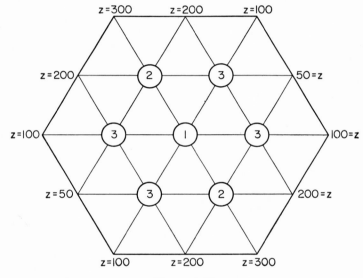

Figure 5.47

Fig. 5.47, or as the ordinates of a pressureless membrane, whose ordinates on the boundary are given by Fig. 5.47.

The skew plate considered in Sec. 5.12, having an angle of skew of 30° ($\alpha = 60°$), may also be covered by an equilateral triangular lattice. For $n = 4$, for example, the operator of Fig. 5.45 must be applied at the four points of Fig. 5.48 in order to solve the two Poissonian equations (e) of Sec. 5.12. Solution of the corresponding systems* gives a

* See F. L. Ehasz, "Structural Skew Plates," *Trans. ASCE*, **111**, 1011 (1946).

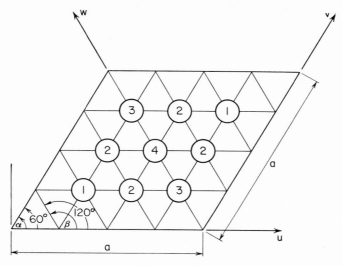

Figure 5.48

central deflection

$$w_0 \Big]_4 = 0.00283 \frac{qa^4}{D},$$

while the deflections obtained with $n = 8$ and $n = 10$ are, respectively,

$$w_0 \Big]_8 = 0.00262 \frac{qa^4}{D}; \qquad w_0 \Big]_{10} = 0.00260 \frac{qa^4}{D}.$$

The extrapolated values of the deflection are

$$w_0 \Big]_{4,8} = 0.00255 \frac{qa^4}{D}; \qquad w_0 \Big]_{8,10} = 0.00256 \frac{qa^4}{D};$$

$$w_0 \Big]_{4,8,10} = 0.00256 \frac{qa^4}{D}.$$

Assuming the coefficient 0.00256 to be correct, it is interesting to notice that it was obtained by solving at least 16 simultaneous equations, while the results obtained by skew coordinates with only two and four pivotal points and extrapolation (0.00248) is only 3 per cent off.

These results indicate that each domain should be covered with the lattice of pivotal points best adapted to the solution of the problem, in order to attain the greatest numerical efficiency.

5.15 An Improved Poissonian Operator in Triangular Coordinates

An improved solution of Poisson's equation in triangular coordinates may be obtained by a method analogous to the procedure used in Sec. 5.11.

Consider the sum of the three second differences in the u-, v-, w-directions of a function $z(x,y)$ and the first two terms of their derivative expansions:

$$(\delta_u^2 + \delta_v^2 + \delta_w^2)z \doteq h^2(z_{uu} + z_{vv} + z_{ww}) + \frac{h^4}{12}(z_{uuuu} + z_{vvvv} + z_{wwww}), \quad \text{(a)}$$

which by Eq. (5.14.3) becomes

$$(\delta_u^2 + \delta_v^2 + \delta_w^2)z \doteq \frac{3}{2}h^2\nabla^2 z + \frac{h^4}{12}(z_{uuuu} + z_{vvvv} + z_{wwww}). \quad \text{(b)}$$

By the square of the operator of Eq. (5.14.3),

$$\nabla^4 z = \nabla^2(\nabla^2 z) = \tfrac{4}{9}[z_{uuuu} + z_{vvvv} + z_{wwww} + 2z_{uuvv} + 2z_{vvww} + 2z_{wwuu}],$$

the sum of the fourth nonmixed derivatives becomes

$$z_{uuuu} + z_{vvvv} + z_{wwww} = \tfrac{9}{4}\nabla^4 z - 2(z_{uuvv} + z_{vvww} + z_{wwuu}). \quad \text{(c)}$$

With

$$\alpha = 60°; \qquad \beta = 120°; \qquad \alpha + \beta = 180°;$$

$$\cos \alpha = \frac{1}{2}; \qquad \sin \alpha = \frac{\sqrt{3}}{2}; \qquad \cos \beta = -\frac{1}{2}; \qquad \sin \beta = \frac{\sqrt{3}}{2}, \quad \text{(d)}$$

the mixed derivatives may be obtained in terms of the derivatives in the x-, y-directions as follows:

$$z_u = z_x; \qquad z_v = \frac{1}{2}z_x + \frac{\sqrt{3}}{2}z_y; \qquad z_w = -\frac{1}{2}z_x + \frac{\sqrt{3}}{2}z_y;$$

$$z_{uv} = \frac{1}{2}z_{xx} + \frac{\sqrt{3}}{2}z_{xy}; \qquad z_{vw} = -\frac{1}{4}z_{xx} + \frac{3}{4}z_{yy};$$

$$z_{wu} = -\frac{1}{2}z_{xx} + \frac{\sqrt{3}}{2}z_{xy};$$

$$z_{uuvv} = \frac{1}{4}z_{xxxx} + \frac{3}{4}z_{xxyy} + \frac{3}{4}z_{xxxy};$$

$$z_{vvww} = \frac{1}{16}z_{xxxx} + \frac{9}{16}z_{yyyy} - \frac{3}{8}z_{xxyy};$$

$$z_{wwuu} = \frac{1}{4}z_{xxxx} - \frac{\sqrt{3}}{2}z_{xxxy} + \frac{3}{4}z_{xxyy}.$$

Their sum becomes

$$z_{uuvv} + z_{vvww} + z_{wwuu} = \tfrac{9}{16}(z_{xxxx} + 2z_{xxyy} + z_{yyyy}) = \tfrac{9}{16}\nabla^4 z,$$

by means of which Eq. (c) reduces to

$$z_{uuuu} + z_{vvvv} + z_{wwww} = \tfrac{9}{4}\nabla^4 z - 2\tfrac{9}{16}\nabla^4 z = \tfrac{9}{8}\nabla^4 z. \qquad (e)$$

Introducing Eq. (e) in Eq. (b), one obtains

$$h^2\nabla^2 z \doteq \frac{2}{3}(\delta_u^2 + \delta_v^2 + \delta_w^2)z - \frac{h^4}{16}\nabla^4 z. \qquad (5.15.1)$$

The Poissonian equation to be solved,

$$\nabla^2 z = f, \qquad (5.15.2)$$

gives

$$h^2\nabla^2 z = h^2 f; \qquad \nabla^4 z = \nabla^2 z, \qquad (f)$$

the first of which, by means of Eq. (5.15.1), becomes

$$(\delta_u^2 + \delta_v^2 + \delta_w^2)z = \tfrac{3}{2}h^2 f + \tfrac{3}{32}h^4\nabla^2 f. \qquad (5.15.3)$$

This improved Poissonian difference equation has an error of order h^4 and involves the same pivotal points as the operator of Fig. 5.45. This improvement is, therefore, a generalization of Noumerov's procedure.

In order to evaluate the influence of the correction $\tfrac{3}{32}h^4\nabla^2 f$ in Eq. (5.15.3), consider the problem of the simply supported hexagonal plate of side a under a uniform load q, which is governed by Eqs. (e), (f) of Sec. 5.12. With $h = a$, calling M_0 and w_0 the moment and the deflection at the center of the plate, we obtain without the correction

$$-6M_0 = \frac{3}{2}a^2(-q); \qquad M_0 = 0.250qa^2;$$

$$-6w_0 = \frac{3}{2}a^2\left(-\frac{M_0}{D}\right); \qquad w_0\Big]_1 = 0.0625\frac{qa^4}{D}. \qquad (g)$$

Similarly, with $h = a/2$ and indicating by M_1, w_1 the moment and deflection at the six pivotal points located around the center, one obtains without correction

$$-4M_1 + M_0 = \frac{3}{2}\left(\frac{a}{2}\right)^2(-q); \qquad 6M_1 - 6M_0 = \frac{3}{2}\left(\frac{a}{2}\right)^2(-q),$$

from which

$$M_0 = 0.208qa^2; \qquad M_1 = 0.146qa^2,$$

and hence

$$-4w_1 + w_0 = \frac{3}{2}\left(\frac{a}{2}\right)^2\left(-0.146\frac{qa^2}{D}\right);$$

$$6w_1 - 6w_0 = \frac{3}{2}\left(\frac{a}{2}\right)^2\left(-0.208\frac{qa^2}{D}\right),$$

from which

$$w_0 \Big]_2 = 0.0356 \frac{qa^4}{D}. \tag{h}$$

An h^2-extrapolation between (g) and (h) gives

$$w_0 \Big]_{1,2} = 0.0266 \frac{qa^4}{D}. \tag{i}$$

Introducing the correction, we obtain, instead, with $h = a$,

for $f_0 = -q$ $\nabla^2 f_0 = 0;$ $M_0 = 0.250qa^2;$

for $f_0 = -\dfrac{M_0}{D}$ $\nabla^2 f_0 = \dfrac{2}{3a^2}(-6)\left(-0.250\dfrac{qa^2}{D}\right) = \dfrac{q}{D};$

$$-6w_0' = \frac{3}{2}a^2\left(-0.250\frac{qa^2}{D}\right) + \frac{3}{32}a^4\left(\frac{q}{D}\right) \quad \therefore \quad w_0'\Big]_1 = 0.0469 \frac{qa^4}{D}. \tag{j}$$

Similarly, with $h = a/2$,

$$M_0 = 0.208qa^2; \qquad M_1 = 0.146qa^2;$$

$$\nabla^2 f_0 = \frac{q}{D}; \qquad\qquad \nabla^2 f_1 = \frac{q}{D};$$

$$w_0'\Big]_2 = 0.0323 \frac{qa^4}{D}. \tag{k}$$

An h^4-extrapolation between (j) and (k) gives

$$w_0'\Big]_{1,2} = 0.313 \frac{qa^4}{D}.$$

The percentage difference between w_0 and w_0' is 33 per cent for $h = a$ and 10 per cent for $h = a/2$. The difference between the two extrapolated values is 15 per cent.

5.16 Transient Heat-flow Problems (Parabolic Partial Differential Equations)

[a] ONE-DIMENSIONAL SPACE–TIME PROBLEM: HEAT FLOW IN A BAR

A bar of constant cross section and length L, insulated along its lateral surface, is heated to a temperature $u_0(x)$ and then cooled by insulating the end of the bar at $x = 0$ and by keeping the end at $x = L$ at a temperature of a degrees. The variation of temperature with time is to be determined for all points of the bar, i.e., for $0 < x < L$.

The differential equation satisfied by the temperature $u(x,t)$ at a point x of the bar at a time t may be shown to be*

$$K \frac{\partial^2 u}{\partial x^2} = \frac{\partial u}{\partial t}; \qquad \begin{array}{c} 0 < x < L \\ t > 0 \end{array} \qquad (5.16.1)$$

where K, the thermal diffusivity of the bar, is given by

$$K = \frac{k'}{c\delta}, \qquad (5.16.2)$$

and k' is the thermal conductivity, c the specific heat, and δ the mass density (per unit of volume) of the bar. The temperature must moreover satisfy the boundary conditions

$$u_x(0,t) = 0; \qquad (5.16.4)$$

$$u(L,t) = a, \qquad (5.16.3)$$

and the initial condition

$$u(x,0) = u_0. \qquad (5.16.5)$$

Equations (5.16.1), (5.16.3) to (5.16.5) constitute a boundary value problem in one-dimensional space–time. The problem is of the boundary value type for the space variable and of the initial value type for the time variable.

It is convenient to consider the problem in nondimensional form. Using the transformation

$$\bar{x} = \frac{x}{L}; \qquad \bar{t} = \frac{Kt}{L^2}; \qquad \bar{u} = \frac{u - a}{u_0 - a}, \qquad (5.16.6)$$

the boundary value problem becomes, after dropping the bars in the variables,

$$\frac{\partial^2 u}{\partial x^2} = \frac{\partial u}{\partial t}; \qquad \begin{array}{c} 0 < x < 1 \\ t > 0 \end{array} \qquad (5.16.7)$$

$$u_x(0,t) = 0;$$

$$u(1,t) = 0; \qquad (5.16.8)$$

$$u(x,0) = 1.$$

The integration of this type of problem is best discussed by considering the solution to lie in the space-time plane formed by the two independent variables x and t. Consider the infinite strip of Fig. 5.49, defined by the limits $0 < x < 1$, $t > 0$, and the values of the function defined on the boundaries by the initial and boundary conditions of Eqs. (5.16.8). The problem becomes one in which the solution, starting with the initial

* See, for example, *Differential Equations*, Sec. 11.6.

value 1 at $t = 0$ and governed by the boundary conditions on the boundaries $x = 0$ and $x = 1$, propagates in the direction of the t axis at the various points x in the x,t plane. The problem, therefore, becomes one of determining the propagation of an "open-ended" solution in the x,t plane as against the solution of the elliptic equation, which is defined in a closed domain.

Finite differences are conveniently used to solve problems of this type. Consider a rectangular grid in the x,t plane in which the quantity u_{ij} is defined as the temperature at the point $x = x_i$ at the time $t = t_j$. Let

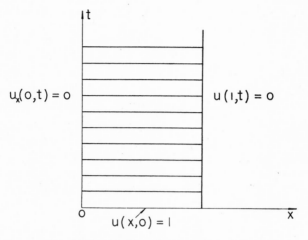

Fig. 5.49. Problem in space-time plane.

the grid spacing be $\Delta x = h$ in space and $\Delta t = k$ in time (Fig. 5.50). Using the central difference operator of order h^2 in the space coordinate and the first forward difference operator $[e = 0(h)]$ in the time coordinate

$$u_{xx} = \frac{u_{i+i,j} - 2u_{i,j} + u_{i-1,j}}{h^2}; \qquad (5.16.9)$$

$$u_t = \frac{u_{i,j+1} - u_{i,j}}{k}, \qquad (5.16.10)$$

Eq. (5.16.7) becomes the following difference equation:

$$u_{i+1,j} - 2u_{i,j} + u_{i-1,j} = \frac{1}{\alpha}[u_{i,j+1} - u_{i,j}], \qquad (5.16.11)$$

where

$$\alpha = \frac{k}{h^2}. \qquad (5.16.12)$$

A recurrence equation which allows the determination of the temperature at the point $x = x_i$ at the time $t = t_{j+1}$ is derived from Eq. (5.16.11) by solving it for the quantity $u_{i,j+1}$:

$$u_{i,j+1} = \alpha u_{i+1,j} + (1 - 2\alpha)u_{i,j} + \alpha(u_{i-1,j}). \qquad (5.16.13)$$

Equation (5.16.13) allows the evaluation of $u_{i,j+1}$ in terms of the temperatures at the points x_i, x_{i+1}, and x_{i-1} at the time t_j.

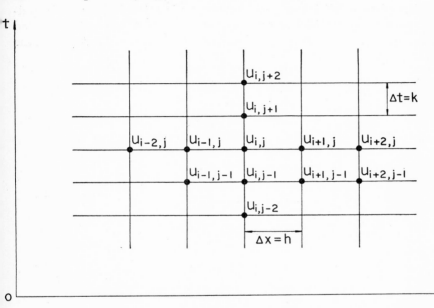

Fig. 5.50.   Finite difference grid.

For the particular case where $\alpha = \frac{1}{2}$, the temperature $u_{i,j}$ is not required for the evaluation of $u_{i,j+1}$ and the recurrence equation simplifies to

$$u_{i,j+1} = \frac{1}{2}[u_{i+1,j} + u_{i-1,j}]. \qquad (5.16.14)$$

Equation (5.16.14) shows that the temperature $u_{i,j+1}$ at a time t_{j+1} may be evaluated by averaging the temperatures at the surrounding points x_{i+1} and x_{i-1} at the previous time t_j.

Let the bar of the present example be covered with a lattice in the space-time plane, such that

$$\underline{\alpha = \tfrac{1}{2};} \qquad k = \tfrac{1}{8}; \qquad h = \tfrac{1}{2}. \qquad (5.16.15)$$

Fig. (5.51) illustrates the prolongation of the solution in the x,t plane. The condition of the insulated boundary at $x = 0$ requires that u_x

vanish there, i.e., that

$$\frac{u_{i+1,j} - u_{i-1,j}}{2h} = 0 \quad \text{at} \quad i = 0, \tag{5.16.16}$$

thus giving the prolongation formula

$$u_{+1,j} = u_{-1,j}. \tag{5.16.17}$$

The boundary condition of zero temperature is entered along the boundary $x = 1$, and the initial value of the temperature, $u(x,0) = 1$, is entered at the points $x = 0$ and $x = \frac{1}{2}$. The discontinuity at the point $(1,0)$ in the

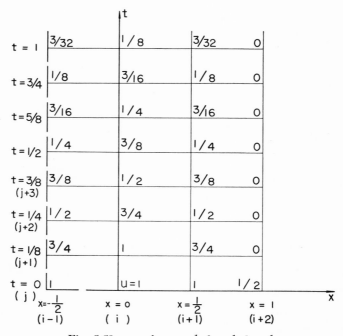

Fig. 5.51. $u_{i,j}$ for $\alpha = \frac{1}{2}$, $h = \frac{1}{2}$, $k = \frac{1}{8}$.

x,t plane between the boundary value of $u = 0$ and the initial value $u = 1$ is arbitrarily set equal to an average temperature $\frac{1}{2}$. The results are shown in Fig. (5.51) up to the time $t = 1$.

Similar results, obtained by the use of a finer grid but maintaining $\alpha = \frac{1}{2}$, i.e., with

$$\alpha = \tfrac{1}{2}; \qquad h = \tfrac{1}{4}; \qquad k = \tfrac{1}{32}, \tag{5.16.18}$$

are shown in Fig. 5.52.

It is of interest to note that h^2-extrapolations can be used in this problem. For a fixed ratio $\alpha = k/h^2$, the time step k is a function of h^2

and hence the error is $O(h^2)$. Therefore, at any point $x = x_i$ in the space-time plane, at which the temperature is known through two different approximations corresponding to the same α, an h^2-extrapolation of the results can be computed. The requirement that the successive approximations of the function under consideration increase or decrease mono-

	x = -1/4	x = 0	x = 1/4	x = 1/2	x = 3/4	x = 1
$t = \frac{1}{2}$	.3404	.3693	.3404	.2611	.1410	0
$\frac{15}{32}$	.3693	.3988	.3693	.2819	.1530	0
$\frac{7}{16}$	.3988	.4326	.3988	.3059	.1650	0
$\frac{13}{32}$	.4326	.4668	.4326	.3301	.1792	0
$\frac{3}{8}$	.4668	.5068	.4668	.3584	.1934	0
$\frac{11}{32}$	.5068	.5469	.5068	.3867	.2099	0
$\frac{5}{16}$	.5469	.5938	.5469	.4199	.2266	0
$\frac{9}{32}$	.5938	.6406	.5938	.4531	.2461	0
$\frac{1}{4}$	.6406	.6953	.6406	.4922	.2656	0
$\frac{7}{32}$	.6953	.7500	.6953	.5313	2891	0
$\frac{3}{16}$	.7500	.8125	.7500	.5781	.3125	0
$\frac{5}{32}$	.8125	.8750	.8125	.6250	.3438	0
$\frac{1}{8}$	.8750	.9375	.8750	.6875	.3750	0
$\frac{3}{32}$	.9375	1.000	.9375	.7500	.4375	0
$\frac{1}{16}$	1.000	1.000	1.000	.8750	.5000	0
$\frac{1}{32}$	1.000	1.000	1.000	1.000	.7500	0
$t = 0$	1.000	1.000	1.000	1.000	1.000	1/2

Fig. 5.52. $u_{i,j}$ for $\alpha = \frac{1}{2}$, $h = \frac{1}{4}$, $k = \frac{1}{32}$.

tonically still holds. As an example of the use of an h^2-extrapolation, consider the temperature at the point $(\frac{1}{2},\frac{1}{2})$ in the space-time plane. From Figs. 5.51, 5.52,

$$\alpha = \tfrac{1}{2}; \qquad h = \tfrac{1}{2}; \qquad u_{(\frac{1}{2},\frac{1}{2})} = 0.2500;$$

$$\alpha = \tfrac{1}{2}; \qquad h = \tfrac{1}{4}; \qquad u_{(\frac{1}{2},\frac{1}{2})} = 0.2611.$$

Using the coefficients for the h^2-extrapolations from Table 2.12, the extrapolated temperature is given by

$$u_{(\frac{1}{4},\frac{1}{4})}\Big]_{2,4} = 1.3333(0.2611) - 0.3333(0.2500) = 0.2648.$$

The important question of the stability of the numerical solution of propagation problems arising from parabolic partial differential equations will be treated in Sec. 5.17. The reader will find in that section a procedure by which values of α may be determined for which the numerical solution will not diverge.

[b] TWO-DIMENSIONAL SPACE–TIME PROBLEM: HEAT FLOW IN A PLATE

A square plate of side L, initially at zero temperature, has two opposite sides suddenly raised to a constant temperature u_0 while the other two are kept at zero temperature (Fig. 5.53). The variation of the temperature with time is to be determined at points inside the plate.

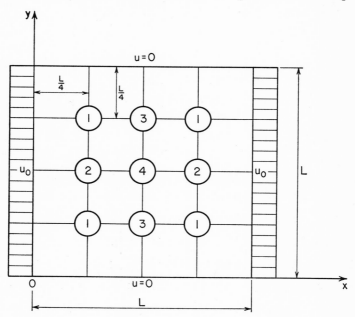

Figure 5.53

The differential equation satisfied by the temperature $u(x,y,t)$, at a point x,y of the plate at a time t, is the two-dimensional counterpart of Eq. (5.16.1) and is given by*

$$K\left(\frac{\partial^2 u}{\partial x^2} + \frac{\partial^2 u}{\partial y^2}\right) = \frac{\partial u}{\partial t}. \qquad (5.16.19)$$

* See, for example, *Differential Equations*, Page 423.

The temperature must moreover satisfy the boundary conditions

$$u(0,y,t) = u(L,y,t) = u_0; \qquad u(x,0,t) = u(x,L,t) = 0, \quad (5.16.20)$$

and the initial condition

$$u(x,y,0) = 0. \tag{5.16.21}$$

The problem may be solved by finite differences, in a manner similar to that used for the one-dimensional space-time problem of this section by following a suggestion of Bender and Schmidt.

The square plate is covered by a square lattice of size $h = L/n$ and a time interval $\Delta t = k$ is used (Fig. 5.53). Denoting by $u_{i,j}$ the temperature at a point i at a time $t = t_j$, and using the central difference operator of Fig. 5.3b for $\nabla^2 u$ and the forward difference operator of Fig. 2.5a for the derivative $\partial u/\partial t$, Eq. (5.16.19) becomes the following equation:

$$u_{a,j} + u_{b,j} + u_{r,j} + u_{l,j} - 4u_{i,j} = \frac{1}{\alpha}(u_{i,j+1} - u_{i,j}), \quad (5.16.22)$$

where

$$\alpha = \frac{Kk}{h^2}. \tag{5.16.23}$$

A recurrence equation which allows the determination of the temperature at the point i at the time t_{j+1} is derived from Eq. (5.16.22) by solving it for $u_{i,j+1}$:

$$u_{i,j+1} = \alpha(u_{a,j} + u_{b,j} + u_{r,j} + u_{l,j}) + (1 - 4\alpha)u_{i,j}. \quad (5.16.24)$$

As in the one-dimensional case, a considerable simplification can be obtained by choosing such a value of k as to make $\alpha = Kk/h^2 = \frac{1}{4}$* that is,

$$k = \frac{h^2}{4K}; \qquad \alpha = \frac{1}{4}. \tag{5.16.25}$$

In this case Eq. (5.16.24) reduces to the form

$$u_{i,j+1} = \frac{1}{4}(u_{a,j} + u_{b,j} + u_{r,j} + u_{l,j}). \quad (5.16.26)$$

The temperature at a point i at a time t_{j+1} becomes the average of the temperatures at the four adjoining pivotal points at the previous time t_j. As shown by Eq. (5.16.25), a refinement in the temperature-time variation, requiring a decrease in the value of k, entails a decrease in h and hence an increase in the number of pivotal points considered, so that a

---

* It may be proved that the finite difference solution of the partial differential equation (5.16.19) does not converge toward the true solution if $k > h^2/4K$. For a discussion of the stability of the numerical solution for the heat-flow equation, the reader is referred to Sec. 5.17.

very fine mesh is needed to obtain accurate temperatures for small values of t.

The square plate of the present example was covered by a lattice of mesh size $h = L/4$, so that the time interval k has the value

$$k = \frac{L^2}{64K}. \tag{a}$$

The initial temperature on the opposite sides $x = 0$, $x = L$ was assumed equal to 10,000; the successive values of the temperature at the pivotal

Table 5.15

② $x = L/4$ $y = L/2$				④ $x = L/2$ $y = L/2$			
$n = t/k$	u	6250	∞	$n = t/k$	u	5000	∞
0	0	6242	19	0	0	4990	19
1	2500	6240	18	1	0	4985	18
2	3750	6235	17	2	1250	4980	17
3	4375	6230	16	3	2500	4970	16
4	5000	6220	15	4	3125	4960	15
5	5312	6210	14	5	3750	4941	14
6	5625	6191	13	6	4062	4921	13
7	5781	6171	12	7	4375	4882	12
8	5937	6132	11	8	4531	4843	11
9	6015	6093	10	9	4687	4765	10
			$n = t/k$				$n = t/k$

① $x = L/4$ $y = L/4$				③ $x = L/2$ $y = L/4$			
$n = t/k$	u	5000	∞	$n = t/k$	u	3750	∞
0	0	4995	19	0	0	3742	19
1	2500	4992	18	1	0	3741	18
2	3125	4990	17	2	1250	3735	17
3	3750	4985	16	3	1875	3730	16
4	4062	4980	15	4	2500	3720	15
5	4375	4970	14	5	2812	3710	14
6	4531	4960	13	6	3125	3691	13
7	4687	4941	12	7	3281	3671	12
8	4765	4921	11	8	3437	3632	11
9	4843	4882	10	9	3515	3593	10
			$n = t/k$				$n = t/k$

points, appearing in Table 5.15 for one-quarter of the plate, were computed by successive averaging, according to Eq. (5.16.26), noticing that the temperature distribution is symmetrical about $x = L/2$ and $y = L/2$. The values of the temperature in Table 5.15 must be read moving downward up to $t = 9k$, and upward from then on. The last value of the temperature, corresponding to $t = \infty$, is the steady-state value and was computed by relaxation, using the methods of Sec. 5.5.

The table illustrates the fact that an accurate determination of the temperature variation immediately after $t = 0$ would require the use of a very fine mesh.

Similar heat conduction problems in three-dimensional space–time can be solved numerically by an extension of the procedures used in the previous two examples. Using a three-dimensional operator for $\nabla^2 u$ and a forward difference operator in time, recurrence formulas for the temperature at a point i at the time t_{j+1} can be developed and used to compute the temperature distribution in the body.

5.17 Stability of the Numerical Solution of the One-dimensional Heat Conduction Equation (Parabolic Equations)

The stability of the numerical solution of partial differential equations of the parabolic type is established by determining the range of values of the ratio α for which the solution does not diverge. For example, in the problem of Sec. 5.16a, one seeks the limiting value of the ratio $\alpha = k/h^2$ for which the temperature in the finite difference solution will eventually decay.

The boundary value problem to be studied is given in difference equation form by

$$u_{i+1,j} - 2u_{i,j} + u_{i-1,j} = \frac{1}{\alpha} [u_{i,j+1} - u_{i,j}]; \qquad (5.17.1)$$

$$u_{-1,j} = u_{1,j};$$

$$u_{N,j} = 0; \qquad (5.17.2)$$

$$u_{i,0} = 1, \qquad (5.17.3)$$

where $N = 1/h$ is the number of subdivisions in the x-direction.

It is convenient for the purpose of simplicity to shift the origin of the x-coordinate to the end of the bar which is kept at zero temperature. Using the transformation

$$x' = 1 - x, \qquad (5.17.4)$$

the original boundary value problem takes the following form:

$$u_{i+1,j} - 2u_{i,j} + u_{i-1,j} = \frac{1}{\alpha} [u_{i,j+1} - u_{i,j}]; \tag{5.17.5}$$

$$u_{0,j} = 0; \tag{5.17.6}$$
$$u_{N-1,j} = u_{N+1,j};$$

$$u_{i,0} = 1. \tag{5.17.7}$$

The difference equation, Eq. (5.17.5), is a linear equation with constant coefficients and can be solved by "separation of the variables."* Letting

$$u_{i,j} = X_i T_j \tag{5.17.8}$$

in Eq. (5.17.5), we obtain the equation

$$\alpha \left[\frac{X_{i+1} - 2X_i + X_{i-1}}{X_i} \right] = \frac{T_{j+1} - T_j}{T_j} = -\lambda, \tag{5.17.9}$$

where λ is an (arbitrary) constant, since each side of Eq. (5.17.9) is a function of only one of the independent variables, x and t. The solutions of the two ordinary difference equations which are obtained from Eq. (5.17.9),

$$X_{i+1} - \left[2 - \frac{\lambda}{\alpha} \right] X_i + X_{i-1} = 0; \tag{5.17.10}$$

$$T_{j+1} - (1 - \lambda) T_j = 0, \tag{5.17.11}$$

are computed by the methods discussed in Sec. 3.13 and are given, respectively, by

$$X_i = C_1 \sin \gamma i + C_2 \cos \gamma i; \tag{5.17.12}$$

$$T_j = (1 - \lambda)^j, \tag{5.17.13}$$

where

$$\cos \gamma = 1 - \frac{\lambda}{2\alpha}. \tag{5.17.14}$$

Inserting X_i and T_j in the conditions of Eq. (5.17.6), we obtain

$$u_{0,j} = 0 \quad \therefore \quad X_0 = 0; \quad C_2 = 0; \tag{5.17.15}$$

$$u_{N-1,j} = u_{N+1,j} \quad \therefore \quad X_{N-1} = X_{N+1}$$
$$\therefore \quad \sin (N - 1)\gamma = \sin (N + 1)\gamma. \tag{5.17.16}$$

---

* See, for example, Kaiser Kunz, *Numerical Analysis*, McGraw-Hill Book Company, Inc., New York, 1957, pp. 328 ff., or S. H. Crandall, *Engineering Analysis*, McGraw-Hill Book Company, Inc., New York, 1956, pp. 380 ff.

The requirement of Eq. (5.17.16) is satisfied if γ takes the discrete values

$$\gamma_n = \frac{2n-1}{N}\frac{\pi}{2} \quad (1 \leq n \leq N). \tag{5.17.17}$$

Solving Eq. (5.17.14) for λ and using Eq. (5.17.17), we obtain

$$(1-\lambda)^j = \left\{1 - 2\alpha\left[1 - \cos\frac{(2n-1)\pi}{2N}\right]\right\}^j. \tag{5.17.18}$$

The most general solution satisfying the difference equation, [Eq. (5.17.5)] and the boundary conditions of Eq. (5.17.6) is obtained by summation of the individual solutions $u_{i,j}$ for each value of γ_n:

$$u_{i,j} = \sum_{n=1}^{N} C_n \left\{1 - 2\alpha\left[1 - \cos\frac{(2n-1)\pi}{2N}\right]\right\}^j \sin\frac{(2n-1)\pi i}{2N}, \tag{5.17.19}$$

where the coefficients C_n are to be determined from the initial condition of Eq. (5.17.7). Noting that the expression

$$G_n = 1 - 2\alpha\left[1 - \cos\frac{(2n-1)\pi}{2N}\right] \tag{5.17.20}$$

appears in each term of the series of Eq. (5.17.19), it is seen that the stability of the solution is controlled by the values of the function G_n, which is always <1.*

If $G_n > 0$, the solution decays steadily. If, however, one is satisfied with a solution in which the terms are alternately positive and negative but in which the series eventually decays, the value of G_n may be as low as -1. For values of G_n less than -1, the series will oscillate with an increasing amplitude.

The limiting value of G_n for stability is thus -1. If the initial conditions of the problem excite the mode n corresponding to G_n, or if the random round-off errors in the numerical solution excite this mode for cases in which theoretically $C_n = 0$, the numerical solution will diverge for values of $G_n < -1$. The limiting value α_n for the stability of the nth term is determined by solving Eq. (5.17.20) for α when $G_n = -1$:

$$\alpha_n = \frac{1}{1 - \cos\dfrac{(2n-1)\pi}{2N}}. \tag{5.17.21}$$

In order to have stability for all values of n between 1 and N, the value of α used in the numerical integration must be smaller than the

---

* It should be noted that the terms of the type appearing in Eq. (5.17.20) play the same role as negative exponentials in the time t in the analytical solution of the heat-flow equation by separation of the variables.

smallest of the α_n, namely, of α_N:

$$\alpha_N = \frac{1}{1 + \cos \dfrac{\pi}{2N}}. \tag{5.17.22}$$

Similarly, to guarantee a *steady* decay of the nth term of the solution, G_n must have the limiting value zero and hence,

$$\bar{\alpha}_n = \frac{1}{2 \left[1 - \cos \dfrac{(2n - 1)\pi}{2N} \right]}. \tag{5.17.23}$$

To guarantee the steady decay of the entire solution α must be smaller than the smallest $\bar{\alpha}_n$, namely, of $\bar{\alpha}_N$:

$$\bar{\alpha}_N = \frac{1}{2 \left(1 + \cos \dfrac{\pi}{2N} \right)} = \tfrac{1}{2}\alpha_N. \tag{5.17.24}$$

Table 5.16 gives the values of α_N and $\bar{\alpha}_N$ as a function of N. The table shows that the value $\alpha = \tfrac{1}{2}$ used in Sec. 5.16a with $N = 2$ and $N = 4$ gives a stable but oscillatory solution.

Table 5.16

N	α_N	$\bar{\alpha}_N$
2	0.5858	0.2929
3	0.5359	0.2680
4	0.5198	0.2599
5	0.5125	0.2563
6	0.5086	0.2543
∞	0.5000	0.2500

The stability of the heat-flow problem in two-dimensional and three-dimensional space–time can be investigated by means of a perfectly analogous approach.

5.18 The Vibrating String Problem (Hyperbolic Partial Differential Equations)

A perfectly flexible elastic string of length L is stretched between two fixed points in a horizontal plane (Fig. 5.54). The string is given an initial vertical displacement, $y(x,0) = f(x)$ and is released from rest at a time $t = 0$, keeping its ends fixed. The deflection $y(x,t)$ of any particle of the string at any time $t > 0$ is to be determined for small oscillations of the string.

The differential equation satisfied by the deflection $y(x,t)$ at a point x on the string at a time t may be shown to be*

$$a^2 \frac{\partial^2 y}{\partial x^2} = \frac{\partial^2 y}{\partial t^2},$$ (5.18.1)

where

$$a = \sqrt{S/\rho}$$ (5.18.2)

is the velocity of propagation of waves in the string, and S (lb) and ρ (lb sec^2/in.^{2}) are, respectively, the tension applied at the ends of the string to keep it taut and the mass per unit length of the string.

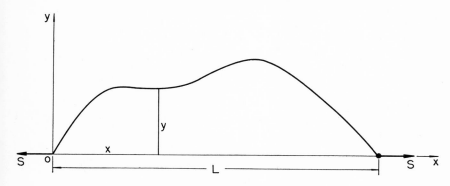

Figure 5.54

The deflection $y(x,t)$ must moreover satisfy the boundary conditions

$$y(0,t) = 0;$$ (5.18.3)

$$y(L,t) = 0,$$ (5.18.4)

and the initial conditions

$$y(x,0) = f(x);$$ (5.18.5)

$$y_t(x,0) = 0.$$ (5.18.6)

The hyperbolic Eq. (5.18.1) together with the boundary and initial conditions of Eqs. (5.18.3) to (5.18.6) constitute a boundary value problem in one-dimensional space-time. The problem is of the boundary value type for the space variable and of the initial value type for the time variable.

As in the case of parabolic and elliptic equations, finite differences may be used to solve hyperbolic problems. Consider a rectangular grid in the x,t plane and indicate by $y_{i,j}$ the deflection at the point $x = x_i$ at a time $t = t_j$. Let the grid spacing be $\Delta x = h$ in space and $\Delta t = k$ in time.

---

* See, for example, *Differential Equations*, Sec. 11.1.

Using central difference operators of order h^2 and k^2 in space and time, respectively,

$$\frac{\partial^2 y}{\partial x^2} = \frac{y_{i+1,j} - 2y_{i,j} + y_{i-1,j}}{h^2};$$ (5.18.7)

$$\frac{\partial^2 y}{\partial t^2} = \frac{y_{i,j+1} - 2y_{i,j} + y_{i,j-1}}{k^2},$$ (5.18.8)

Eq. (5.18.1) reduces to the following difference equation:

$$y_{i+1,j} - 2y_{i,j} + y_{i-1,j} - \frac{1}{\alpha^2}[y_{i,j+1} - 2y_{i,j} + y_{i,j-1}] = 0, \quad (5.18.9)$$

where

$$\alpha^2 = \frac{a^2 k^2}{h^2}. \quad = \frac{\Delta t\ (\Delta t)}{\Delta x \Delta x\ (\Delta x)^2} = \frac{(\Delta t)^3}{(\Delta x)^4}$$ (5.18.10)

A recurrence formula which allows the determination of the displacement at the point $x = x_i$ at the time $t = t_{j+1}$ is derived from Eq. (5.18.9) by solving it for $y_{i,j+1}$:

$$y_{i,j+1} = \alpha^2[y_{i+1,j} + y_{i-1,j}] + 2(1 - \alpha^2)y_{i,j} - y_{i,j-1}. \quad (5.18.11)$$

An obvious simplification of Eq. (5.18.11) is obtained by taking $\alpha = 1$:

$$y_{i,j+1} = [y_{i+1,j} + y_{i-1,j}] - y_{i,j-1}. \quad (5.18.12)$$

Letting the spacing of the pivotal points in the x-direction be

$$h = \frac{L}{N}, \quad (5.18.13)$$

the boundary and initial conditions of Eqs. (5.18.3) to (5.18.6) become, in finite difference form,

$$y_{0,j} = 0; \quad (5.18.14)$$

$$y_{N,j} = 0; \quad (5.18.15)$$

$$y_{i,0} = f(x_i); \quad (5.18.16)$$

$$y_{i,1} = y_{i,-1}. \quad (5.18.17)$$

Substituting Eq. (5.18.17) into Eq. (5.18.12) we obtain the *starting formula*

$$y_{i,1} = \frac{1}{2}[y_{i+1,0} + y_{i-1,0}]. \quad (5.18.18)$$

Equation (5.18.12) together with the starting formulas, Eqs. (5.18.16) and (5.18.18), and the boundary conditions, Eqs. (5.18.14) and (5.18.15), allow the determination of the displacements $y_{i,j}$. For example, knowing $y_{i,j}$ for all pivotal points i at the time steps $j = 0$ and $j = 1$, the quantities $y_{i,2}$ are computed from Eq. (5.18.12), where the two end values $y_{0,2}$ and $y_{N,2}$ are given by Eqs. (5.18.14) and (5.18.15). Thus, in general, starting at any time $t = t_j$ with known values $y_{i,j}$ and $y_{i,j-1}$, the value of $y_{i,j+1}$ can be computed by working forward in time, using the recurrence equation (5.18.12). This procedure represents a solution which propagates outward in time in an open region, defined by $x = 0$, $x = L$, and starts with the initial conditions of the problem (see Fig. 5.1b).

The stability of the finite difference solution of this problem has been considered by Courant, Friedrichs, and Lewy,* who showed that it depends on the ratio α in the following manner:

(a) for $\alpha > 1$, the finite difference approximation is unstable and becomes more violently unstable with increasing values of α.

(b) for $\alpha = 1$, the finite difference approximation is stable. Moreover, it gives results identical with those of the solution of the continuous boundary value problem.†

(c) for $\alpha < 1$, the finite difference approximation is stable, but the accuracy of the solution decreases with decreasing values of α.

It is of interest to note that we obtain a *rigorously correct* solution for $\alpha = 1$, while the solution remains stable but *decreases* in accuracy for smaller values of α. The question of accuracy is intimately connected with the theory of characteristics for hyperbolic equations.‡ It can be shown that, in general, optimal accuracy will be obtained by finite differences, when the characteristics of the finite difference solution coincide with the characteristics of the solution of the hyperbolic partial differential equation. The fact that an exact finite difference solution is obtained for the problem in question comes from the peculiar property of the wave equation of having characteristics $x - at$ and $x + at$, which are straight lines. For more complicated hyperbolic equations, which, in general, have curved characteristics, optimal accuracy is obtained by using a curvilinear system of coordinates, corresponding as nearly as possible to the curvilinear characteristics of the partial differential equation rather than a fixed system of rectangular coordinates of the type used in this problem. In many problems of practical interest, it has been found convenient to use the arcs of the curved characteristics as coordinates in the finite difference network for the hyperbolic system.

* R. Courant, K. Friedrichs, and H. Lewy, "Über die partieller Differenzen-gleichugen der mathematischen Physik," *Math. Ann.* **100**, 32–74 (1928).

† The analytical solution of the problem is given by

$$y(x,t) = \tfrac{1}{2}[f(x + at) + f(x - at)],$$

where f is the function appearing in the initial condition of Eq. (5.18.5).

‡ See, for example, S. H. Crandall, *Engineering Analysis*, McGraw-Hill Book Company, Inc., New York, 1956, pp. 358–365 and p. 396 ff.

5.19 A Boundary Value Problem Involving $\nabla^4 z$

The boundary value problem for the deflections w of a square plate of sides a, built in all around, is given by*

$$\nabla^4 w = \frac{q}{D}; \qquad w = \frac{\partial w}{\partial n} = 0 \qquad \text{on the boundary,} \qquad (5.19.1)$$

where q = load per unit area of plate,

$\quad D = \dfrac{Eh^3}{12(1 - \nu^2)}$ = flexural rigidity of plate,

$\quad h$ = plate thickness,

$\quad E, \nu$ = Young's modulus and Poisson's ratio, respectively, of the plate material,

$\quad n$ = direction of the normal to the boundary.

The problem (5.19.1) is reduced to nondimensional form by the transformation

$$x = \xi a; \qquad y = \eta a; \qquad w(x,y) = \frac{qa^4}{D} z(\xi,\eta), \qquad (a)$$

giving

$$\nabla^4 z = 1; \qquad z = \frac{\partial z}{\partial n} = 0 \qquad \text{on the boundary,} \qquad (5.19.2)$$

where the operator ∇^4 is taken with respect to ξ and η.

The numerical solution of the problem (5.19.2) is obtained by substituting for $\nabla^4 z$ the central difference operator of Fig. 5.3c with a square lattice of mesh size $1/n$.

The boundary conditions, by Eq. (4.1.1), state that the values of z at pivotal points immediately outside the boundary are equal to the values of z at points immediately inside the boundary on the same normal.

Starting with $n = 2$ (Fig. 5.55), Eq. (5.19.2) gives

$$(z_0 + z_0 + z_0 + z_0) + 2 \cdot 0 - 8 \cdot 0 + 20 z_0 = \frac{1}{2^4},$$

from which

$$z_0 \Big]_2 = \frac{1}{2^4 \cdot 24} = \frac{1}{384}.$$

For $n = 4$, Eq. (5.19.2) applied at the points of Fig. 5.56 gives

at   (0) $$20 z_0 - 32 z_1 + 8 z_2 = \frac{1}{4^4};$$

---

* See, for example, S. Timoshenko and S. Woinowsky-Krieger, *Theory of Plates and Shells*, p. 197.

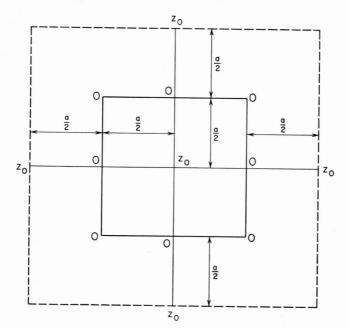

Figure 5.55

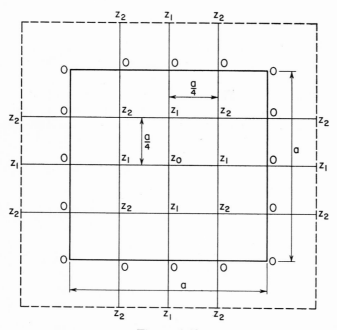

Figure 5.56

at   (1) $$-8z_0 + 26z_1 - 16z_2 = \frac{1}{4^4};$$

at   (2) $$2z_0 - 16z_1 + 24z_2 = \frac{1}{4^4},$$

from which, for example, by Gauss's scheme,

$$z_0 \Big]_4 = \frac{0.461}{4^4}; \qquad z_1 \Big]_4 = \frac{0.309}{4^4}; \qquad z_2 \Big]_4 = \frac{0.209}{4^4}.$$

For $n = 8$, it is similarly found that $z_0 \Big]_8 = 5.857/8^4$.

The deflection at the center of the plate for $\nu = 0.3$ and with $n = 2$, 4, 8 becomes, by Eq. (a),

$$w_0 \Big]_2 = \frac{12(1 - 0.3^2)}{384} \frac{qa^4}{Eh^3} = 0.0284 \frac{qa^4}{Eh^3} \qquad (e = -106\%),$$

$$w_0 \Big]_4 = \frac{12(1 - 0.3^2) \cdot 0.461}{256} \frac{qa^4}{Eh^3} = 0.0197 \frac{qa^4}{Eh^3} \quad (e = -43\%),$$

$$w_0 \Big]_8 = \frac{12(1 - 0.3^2) \cdot 5.857}{4096} \frac{qa^4}{Eh^3} = 0.0156 \frac{qa^4}{Eh^3} \quad (e = -13\%).$$

The percentage errors e are computed from the series solution value ($w_0 = 0.0138 qa^4/Eh^3$) given by Timoshenko.[*] Extrapolations of the h^2-type can be used on the approximate values (see Sec. 2.13) and give

$$w_0 \Big]_{2,4} = 0.0167 \frac{qa^4}{Eh^3} \qquad (e = -21\%);$$

$$w_0 \Big]_{4,8} = 0.0142 \frac{qa^4}{Eh^3} \qquad (e = -2.9\%),$$

$$w_0 \Big]_{2,4,8} = 0.0140 \frac{qa^4}{Eh^3} \qquad (e = -1.4\%).$$

5.20 Two-dimensional Characteristic Value Problems

Consider a square plate of side a, simply supported along two opposite edges and built in along the other two edges. The plate is acted upon by a uniform compressive force N per unit of length, perpendicular to the simply supported edges and acting in the plane of the plate (Fig. 5.57). Choosing the x-axis parallel to the built-in edges, with origin at the center

[*] See S. Timoshenko and S. Woinowsky-Krieger, *Theory of Plates and Shells*, p. 202.

of the plate, it may be proved that the deflection w of the plate at a point (x,y) satisfies the differential equation*

$$\nabla^4 w + \frac{N}{D} \frac{\partial^2 w}{\partial x^2} = 0, \qquad (5.20.1)$$

where D is the flexural rigidity of the plate. We wish to find the lowest value of the compression N for which the plate will buckle, that is, for

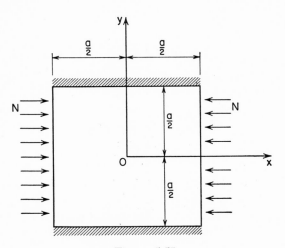

Figure 5.57

which the deflection w will not be identically zero, while satisfying the boundary conditions of simple support:

$$w = 0; \qquad \frac{\partial^2 w}{\partial x^2} = 0 \quad \text{at} \quad x = \pm \frac{a}{2} \qquad (5.20.2)$$

and the conditions for complete lack of rotation:

$$w = 0; \qquad \frac{\partial w}{\partial y} = 0 \quad \text{at} \quad y = \pm \frac{a}{2}. \qquad (5.20.3)$$

Equation (5.20.1) is first reduced to nondimensional form by the transformation

$$\xi = \frac{x}{a}; \qquad \eta = \frac{y}{a}, \qquad (a)$$

and, multiplied through by a^4, becomes

$$\nabla^4 w + \frac{N a^2}{D} \frac{\partial^2 w}{\partial \xi^2} = 0, \qquad (5.20.4)$$

* See, for instance, S. Timoshenko, *Theory of Elastic Stability*, p. 337.

where $\nabla^4 w$ is taken with respect to ξ and η. The plate is then covered with a square lattice of mesh size $1/n$. Multiplying the equation through by $h^4 = 1/n^4$, and using the operator of Fig. 5.3c for $h^4\nabla^4 w$ and the operator of Eq. (5.2.2) for $\partial^2 w/\partial \xi^2$, the difference equation corresponding to Eq. (5.20.4) is obtained in molecular form:

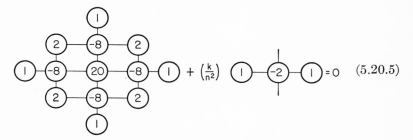

$$(5.20.5)$$

where

$$k = \frac{Na^2}{D}. \tag{5.20.6}$$

The application of Eq. (5.20.5) at the internal pivotal points gives rise to a set of homogeneous linear algebraic equations in the unknown pivotal displacements w_i, whose determinant must be identically zero if the w_i are to be different from zero. The lowest value of N making the determinant of Eqs. (5.20.5) equal to zero is the lowest critical value of the compressive force.

In order to apply Eq. (5.20.5) at the pivotal points immediately inside the boundary, the deflection must be known at fictitious pivotal points immediately *outside* the boundary. These deflections are given in terms of the deflections at the pivotal points immediately inside the boundary by the boundary conditions. In fact, by Eqs. (4.1.1), Eqs. (5.20.2) become

$$w_i = 0; \qquad w_l = -w_r \qquad \text{at } \xi = \pm\tfrac{1}{2}, \tag{5.20.7}$$

while Eqs. (5.20.3) give

$$w_i = 0; \qquad w_a = w_b \qquad \text{at } \eta = \pm\tfrac{1}{2}. \tag{5.20.8}$$

Starting with $n = 3$ and the antisymmetrical deflections of Fig. 5.58,[*] we obtain

$$(-w_1 + w_1 + 0 + 0) + 2(0 + 0 + 0 - w_1) - 8(0 + 0 + w_1 - w_1)$$
$$+ 20w_1 + \frac{k^3}{9}(0 - 2w_1 - w_1) = 0,$$

---

[*] Symmetrical deflections in the x direction give a higher buckling load.

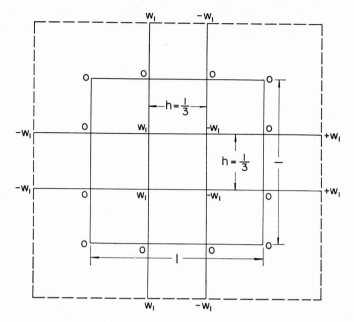

Figure 5.58

or

$$w_1\left(18 - \frac{k_3}{3}\right) = 0,$$

from which

$$k_3 = 54 = 5.471\pi^2. \tag{b}$$

With $n = 4$ and the antisymmetrical deflections of Fig. 5.59, we obtain the four equations of Table 5.17, in which

$$\gamma = \frac{k_4}{16}.$$

Table 5.17

w_1	w_2	w_3	w_4
$20 - 2\gamma$	-16	0	0
-8	$22 - 2\gamma$	0	0
2	$\gamma - 8$	$20 - 2\gamma$	-8
$\gamma - 8$	4	-16	$18 - 2\gamma$

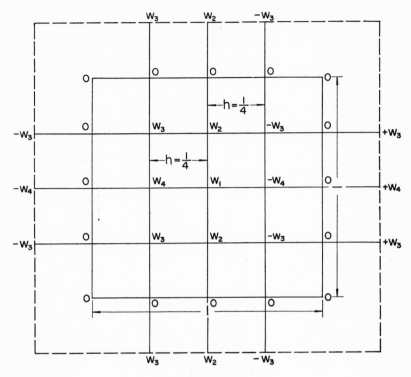

Figure 5.59

Setting the determinant of this set of equations equal to zero,

$$(20 - 2\gamma)[(20 - 2\gamma)(22 - 2\gamma) - 8 \times 16][(20 - 2\gamma)(18 - 2\gamma) - 8 \times 16]$$
$$= 0,$$

we obtain from its third factor the lowest root, $\gamma = 3.821$, and hence,

$$k_4 = 61.136 = 6.193\pi^2. \tag{c}$$

The extrapolated value $k_{3,4} = 7.121\pi^2$ is slightly higher than the minimum value of k given by Timoshenko* (which occurs for a plate with ratio of sides a/b between 0.6 and 0.7 and a symmetrical deflection) and hence cannot differ appreciably from the true value of k.

5.21 The Solution of Partial Differential Equations by Separation of the Variables and Finite Differences

The classical method of the separation of the variables and modern numerical procedures may often be advantageously combined to solve

* See S. Timoshenko, *Theory of Elastic Stability*, p. 345.

partial differential equations. This mixed approach will be illustrated by its application to the buckling problem of the preceding section.

Since two sides of the square plate are simply supported and the minimum buckling load corresponds to an antisymmetrical deformation in the x-direction, it is logical to assume the deflection w in the form

$$w(x,y) = Y(y) \sin \frac{2\pi}{a} x, \tag{5.21.1}$$

where $Y(y)$ is an unknown function of y only. This deflection function w satisfies the boundary conditions on the simply supported boundaries [Eqs. (5.20.2)], and when substituted in the equilibrium equation [Eq. (5.20.1)], reduces it to the ordinary differential equation in Y:

$$Y^{iv} - 8\frac{\pi^2}{a^2} Y'' + \left(\frac{16\pi^4}{a^4} - \frac{N}{D}\frac{4\pi^2}{a^2}\right) Y = 0. \tag{5.21.2}$$

Substitution of Eq. (5.21.1) in the boundary conditions along the built-in edges [Eqs. (5.20.3)] gives the boundary conditions for Y:

$$Y = 0; \qquad Y' = 0 \quad \text{at} \quad y = \pm \frac{a}{2}. \tag{5.21.3}$$

The partial characteristic value problem of Eqs. (5.20.1), (5.20.2), and (5.20.3) has thus been reduced to the ordinary characteristic value problem of Eqs. (5.21.2) and (5.21.3).

To solve this last problem in nondimensional form, we use the transformation $y = a\eta$, obtaining

$$\frac{d^4Y}{d\eta^4} - 8\pi^2 \frac{d^2Y}{d\eta^2} + \left(16\pi^4 - 4\pi^2 \frac{Na^2}{D}\right) Y = 0; \tag{5.21.4}$$

$$Y(\eta) = 0; \qquad \frac{dY}{d\eta} = 0 \quad \text{at} \quad \eta = \pm\tfrac{1}{2}. \tag{5.21.5}$$

Multiplying Eq. (5.21.4) by $h^4 = 1/n^4$ and substituting central difference expressions for the derivatives of Y [Eqs. (2.7.16)], we obtain the difference equation in Y:

$$Y_{bb} - \left(\frac{8\pi^2}{n^2} + 4\right) Y_b + \left(6 + \frac{16\pi^2}{n^2} + \frac{16\pi^4}{n^4} - \frac{4\pi^2 k}{n^4}\right) Y_i - \left(\frac{8\pi^2}{n^2} + 4\right) Y_a$$

$$+ Y_{aa} = 0, \tag{5.21.6}$$

where k is given by Eq. (5.20.6). The boundary conditions require that

$$Y_a = Y_b \quad \text{at} \quad \eta = \pm\tfrac{1}{2}. \tag{5.21.7}$$

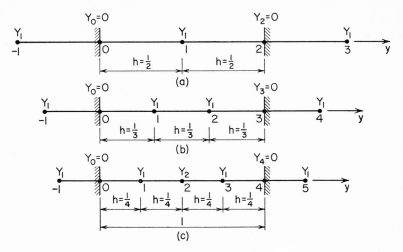

Figure 5.60

Starting with $n = 2$ and the values Y of Fig. 5.60a, in which the y-axis is plotted horizontally for convenience, Eq. (5.21.6) gives

$$Y_1 + 0 + \left(6 + \frac{16\pi^2}{4} + \frac{16\pi^4}{16} - \frac{4\pi^2}{16} k_2\right) Y_1 + 0 + Y_1 = 0,$$

from which
$$k_2 = 5.95\pi^2. \tag{a}$$

With $n = 3$ and the values Y of Fig. 5.60b, Eq. (5.21.6) gives

$$Y_1 + 0 + \left(6 + \frac{16\pi^2}{9} + \frac{16\pi^4}{81} - \frac{4\pi^2}{81} k_3\right) Y_1 - \left(\frac{8\pi^2}{9} + 4\right) Y_1 + 0 = 0,$$

from which
$$k_3 = 6.36\pi^2. \tag{b}$$

With $n = 4$ and the values Y of Fig. 5.60c, we obtain the two equations

$$Y_1 + 0 + \left(6 + \frac{16\pi^2}{16} + \frac{16\pi^4}{256} - \frac{4\pi^2}{256} k_4\right) Y_1 - \left(\frac{8\pi^2}{16} + 4\right) Y_2 + Y_1 = 0;$$

$$0 - \left(\frac{8\pi^2}{16} + 4\right) Y_1 + \left(6 + \frac{16\pi^2}{16} + \frac{16\pi^4}{256} - \frac{4\pi^2}{256} k_4\right) Y_2 - \left(\frac{8\pi^2}{16} + 4\right) Y_1$$
$$+ 0 = 0.$$

The smallest root of the determinant of these equations equals

$$k_4 = 6.70\pi^2. \tag{c}$$

The h^2-extrapolations applied to Eqs. (a), (b), and (c) give the following results:

$$k_{2,3} = 6.69\pi^2; \qquad k_{3,4} = 7.14\pi^2.$$

The solution by separation of the variables gives results of the same order of accuracy as those of the finite difference solution in two dimensions of Sec. 5.20 but requires much less labor, since the evaluation of k_4, for example, involves a determinant of the second order in the one-dimensional solution and a determinant of the fourth order in the two-dimensional solution.

PROBLEMS

5.1 Derive the difference operators corresponding to the following differential operators in terms of forward differences with error of order h^2:

(a) h^2D_{xy}. (b) $h^2\nabla^2$. (c) h^4D_{xxyy}.

Sketch the corresponding molecules.

Ans. See Fig. 5.61.

5.2 Determine the finite difference operators corresponding to the following differential operators, in terms of backward differences with errors of order h^2.

(a) h^2D_{xy}. (b) $h^2\nabla^2$. (c) h^4D_{xxyy}.

Sketch the corresponding molecules.

Ans. See Fig. 5.62.

5.3 (a) Determine the first term of the error in the operators of Problems 5.1(a), (b), (c).

(b) Determine the first term of the error in the operators of Problems 5.2(a), (b).

5.4 Show that the error in Simpson's $\frac{1}{3}$ rule for double integration is of order h^4.

5.5 Evaluate the following integrals to four significant figures by the trapezoidal rule, using square lattices with $n = 2$ and 4 subintervals and extrapolation.

(a) $\displaystyle\int_2^4 dy \int_4^6 \ln xy^2\, dx.$

(b) $\displaystyle\int_0^{\pi/2} dy \int_0^{\pi/2} \sin \sqrt{2xy}\, dx.$

(c) $\displaystyle\int_1^5 dy \int_1^5 \frac{dx}{(x^2 + y^2)^{1/2}}.$

(d) $\displaystyle\int_0^1 dy \int_0^1 e^{-(x^2+y^2)}\, dx.$

Ans. (a) $A_2 = 14.95$; $A_4 = 15.02$; $A_{2,4} = 15.05$. (c) $A_2 = 4.134$; $A_4 = 3.997$; $A_{2,4} = 3.952$.

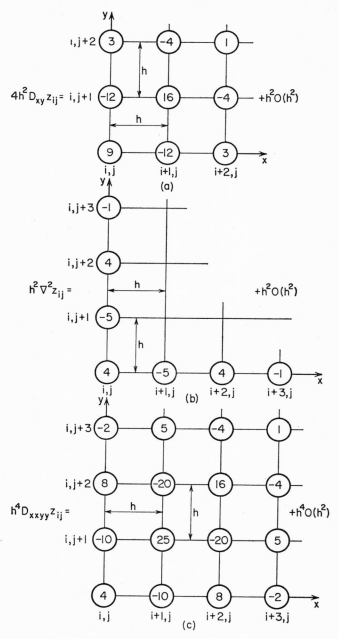

Figure 5.61

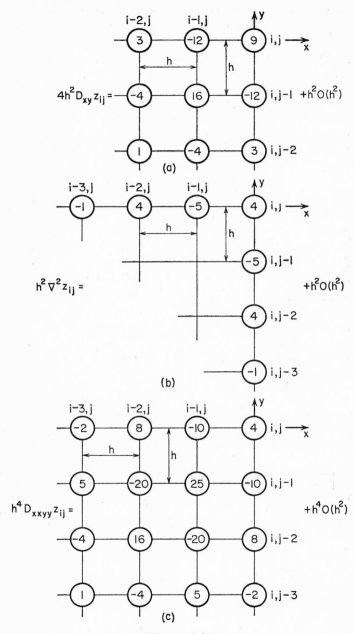

Figure 5.62

5.6 Evaluate the integrals of Problem 5.5 to four significant figures by Simpson's $\frac{1}{3}$ rule, using square lattices with $n = 2$ and 4 subintervals and extrapolation.

Ans.   (b) $A_2 = 1.585$; $A_4 = 1.724$; $A_{2,4} = 1.733$.   (c) $A_2 = 3.962$; $A_4 = 3.963$; $A_{2,4} = 3.963$.

5.7 Evaluate the following integral to four significant figures, using rectangular lattices with $n = 2$ and 4 subintervals and extrapolation

(a) by the trapezoidal rule,
(b) by Simpson's $\frac{1}{3}$ rule.

$$\int_0^1 dy \int_0^{0.5} \sinh\,(x^2 y)\,dx$$

5.8 Evaluate the integral of Eq. (5.3.10) by the trapezoidal rule for

(a) $f(x,y) = x^2 + y^2$; $\phi_1(y) = 1$; $\phi_2(y) = 2y$; $c = 1$; $d = 4$.
(b) $f(x,y) = (x^2 + y^2)^{-\frac{1}{2}}$; $\phi_1(y) = 0$; $\phi_2(y) = y^2$; $c = 1$; $d = 4$.
(c) $f(x,y) = (x^2 + y^2)^{-\frac{1}{2}}$; $\phi_1(y) = y$; $\phi_2(y) = y^2$; $c = 1$; $d = 4$.
(d) $f(x,y) = x + y^2$; $\phi_1(y) = y^2$; $\phi_2(y) = y$; $c = 1$; $d = 4$.

Use $k = 1$, $m = 4$.

Ans.   (a) $I = 295.9$.   (c) $I = 2.119$.

5.9 Solve Problems 5.8 by Simpson's rule for $k = \frac{1}{2}$, $m = 4$.

Ans.   (a) $I = 275.2$.   (c) $I = 2.225$.

5.10 Determine, by Liebmann's procedure, the steady-state temperature at the pivotal points of the rectangular plate of sides a and $b = 2a$ of Fig. 5.63, if the sides have the temperature indicated in the figure. Use the operator of Fig. 5.3b.

Ans.	(1)	(2)	(3)	(4)	(5)	(6)	(7)	(8)
	72	102	132	151	87	104	127	139

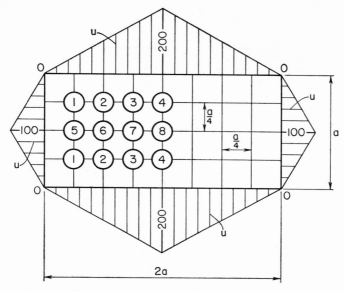

Figure 5.63

5.11 Determine by iteration the values, at the pivotal points of the square of Fig. 5.64, of the harmonic function whose boundary values are given in the figure. Use the operator of Fig. 5.3b, $n = 2$ and 4 subintervals and extrapolation.

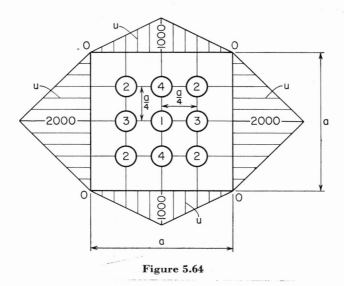

Figure 5.64

5.12 Determine by relaxation the steady-state temperature at the pivotal points of the plate of Fig. 5.65 if its sides are kept at the temperature indicated in the figure. Use the operator of Fig. 5.3b.

   Ans. $u_1 = 433; u_2 = 267; u_3 = 233.$

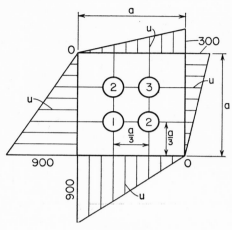

Figure 5.65

5.13 Determine by relaxation the steady-state temperature at the pivotal points of the plate of Fig. 5.66 if its sides are kept at the temperature indicated in the figure. Use the operator of Eq. (5.2.11).

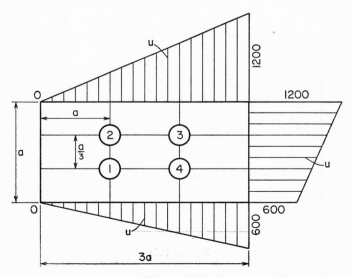

Figure 5.66

5.14 Start the solution of Problem 5.12 by block relaxation and continue it by under- and overrelaxation.

5.15 Start the solution of Problem 5.10 by block relaxation and continue it by under- and overrelaxation.

5.16 Use a graded net half the mesh size of that used in Problem 5.13 in the right third of the plate, leaving the mesh sizes unchanged elsewhere, in order to obtain a better definition of the temperature in this region.

5.17 Use a graded net of size $a/9$ in the lower left corner of the plate of Problem 5.12, leaving the mesh size unchanged elsewhere, in order to obtain a better definition of the temperature in this region.

5.18 (a) Solve by relaxation Problem 5.11 using the N-operator of Fig. 5.32. (b) Solve by relaxation Problem 5.12 using the N-operator of Fig. 5.32.

5.19 Determine the lateral deflection at the pivotal points of a square membrane of side L, assuming $PL^2/S = 16,000$, and $n = 4$ subintervals (see Sec. 5.6). Use the operator of Fig. 5.3b.

Ans. $u_1 = 1125; u_2 = 875; u_3 = 687.5.$

5.20 A simply supported square plate of side a is loaded with a uniform load q. Determine the deflection and the bending moment at the center of the plate, assuming Poisson's ratio $\nu = 0.3$. Use $n = 2$ and $n = 4$ subintervals and extrapolation. *Hint:* The differential equation of the plate $\nabla^4 w = q/D$ (see Sec. 5.19) may be split into two equations of the second order by setting $M = (M_x + M_y)/(1 + \nu)$* where M_x and M_y are the bending moments per unit of length on sections normal to the x- and y-axes. The equations in M and w are $\nabla^2 M = -q$; $\nabla^2 w = -M/D$. The boundary conditions for both w and M are $w = 0$; $M = 0$ on the boundary. Use the operator of Fig. 5.3b and solve the set of simultaneous equations in the pivotal values of w and M by Gauss's scheme.

Ans. $M_2 = 0.0406qa^2$; $w_2 = 0.00391qa^4/D$; $M_4 = 0.0457qa^2$;
$w_4 = 0.00403qa^4/D$; $M_{2,4} = 0.0474qa^2$; $w_{2,4} = 0.00406qa^4/D$.
$M = 0.0479qa^2$; $w = 0.00405qa^4/D$.

5.21 Determine by iteration the value of the function z, satisfying the equation $\nabla^2 z = 1$, if $z = 0$ on the boundary of a square of side a. Use the operator of Fig. 5.3b, $h = a/2$ and $a/4$, and extrapolate the value of z at the center of the square.

5.22 Evaluate z at the pivotal points of a square of sides $a = 4h = 2$, if $\nabla^2 z = x^2 y^2$ and $z = 0$ on the boundary. Assume the origin (point 2) at the center of the square and use the operator of Fig. 5.3b.

Ans. $z_1 = z_3 = -0.00391; z_2 = -0.00586.$

* See, for example, S. Timoshenko and S. Woinowsky-Krieger, *Theory of Plates and Shells*, pp. 92 ff.

5.23 Solve by iteration Problem 5.19 using the N-operator of Fig. 5.32.

5.24 Solve Problem 5.20 using the improved Poissonian operator of Eq. (5.11.4).

5.25 (a) Determine by relaxation the pivotal values of the function ϕ satisfying the torsional equation $\nabla^2\phi + 2 = 0$ and having zero values on the boundaries of the section of Fig. 5.67a. Use the operator of Fig. 5.3b.

(b) Repeat for Fig. 5.67b.

(c) Determine the torsional rigidity of the section of Fig. 5.67a (see Sec. 5.7).

(d) Repeat for Fig. 5.67b.

Use the trapezoidal rule for integration.

Ans.   (a) $\phi_1 = \phi_4 = 0.9756a^2$; $\phi_2 = \phi_5 = 0.9268a^2$; $\phi_3 = \phi_6 = 0.7317a^2$

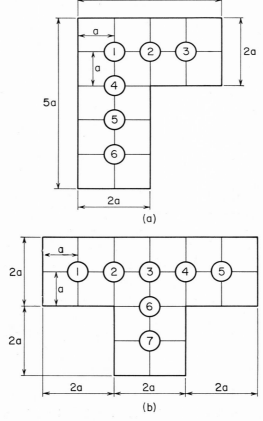

(a)

(b)

Figure 5.67

5.26 (a) Determine the values of the torsion function ϕ for the elastoplastic case considered in Sec. 5.8, assuming $\theta = 1.25\theta_0$ and $n = 6$ subintervals.
(b) Determine the corresponding value of M/M_0.

5.27 Determine the value ϕ_0 of the function ϕ at the center of a square of side a, if ϕ satisfies the equation $\nabla^4\phi = 0$ inside the square and the conditions $\phi = 0$, $\dfrac{d\phi}{dn} = 1$ on the boundary of the square. Use the operator of Fig. 5.3c and $n = 2$ and 4 subintervals. *Note: n is the outside normal to the square.*

Ans. $n = 2$: $\phi_0 = -0.1667a$; $n = 4$: $\phi_0 = -0.2191a$.

5.28 Evaluate to three significant figures the potential V at the pivotal points of Fig. 5.68, when the boundary values of V are as indicated in the figure. Use the difference operator of Fig. 5.29. *Hint:* The potential V satisfies the Laplacian equation.

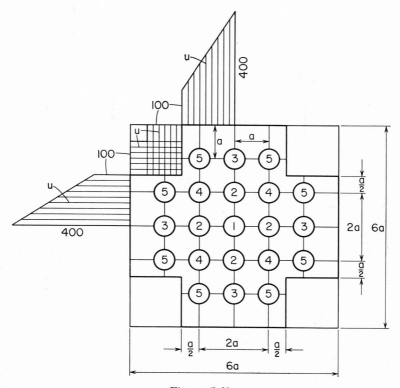

Figure 5.68

5.29 Evaluate the steady-state temperature at the pivotal points of the plate of Fig. 5.69, when the boundaries are kept at the indicated temperatures. Use the $\nabla^2 u$ operator of Fig. 5.29 at all points.

Ans. $u_1 = 4833$; $u_2 = 6056$; $u_3 = 8278$.

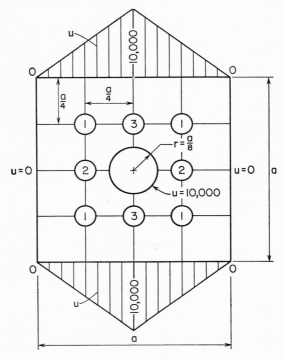

Figure 5.69

5.30 Determine the lowest frequency of vibration of an elliptic membrane of semiaxes a and $2a/3$, by means of a rectangular lattice with $h = a/3$ and $k = a/2$. Use difference formulas with errors of order h (see Sec. 5.10).

5.31 Determine the lowest frequency of vibration of a membrane whose boundary has the shape of Fig. 5.28, using the pivotal points of this figure (see Sec. 5.10). Use a ∇^2 operator with error of order h at point 4, and ∇^2 operators with error of order h^2 at the other pivotal points.

Ans. $\omega = (4.490/L) \sqrt{S/m}$.

5.32 The plate of Fig. 5.28 is a square of side L with two corners rounded off by arcs of a circle of radius $L/2$. Determine the temperature u at the pivotal points when the boundary has the temperatures indicated in the figure. Use operators for $\nabla^2 u$ with error of order h^2 at all pivotal points.

5.33 Determine by relaxation, the steady-state temperature at the pivotal points of the skew plates (a) of Fig. 5.70; (b) of Fig. 5.71, when their sides are kept at the indicated temperatures.

Ans.   (a) $u_1 = 99.6$; $u_2 = 139.0$; $u_3 = 160.9$; $u_4 = 152.2$.

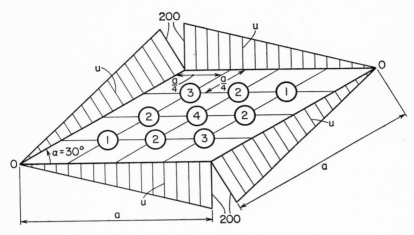

Figure 5.70

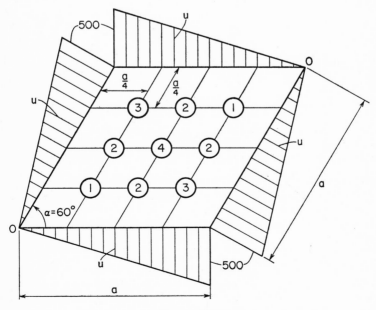

Figure 5.71

5.34 Determine the lateral deflections at the center of a skew membrane of angle $\alpha = 60°$ and equal sides a, when the ratio of pressure P to tension S equals 16,000. Use $n = 2$ and 4 subintervals and extrapolation (see Sec. 5.6).

5.35 Determine the lowest frequency of vibration of a skew membrane of equal sides a and angle $\alpha = 60°$, using skew coordinates with $n = 2$ and 3 subintervals, and extrapolation (see Sec. 5.9).

Ans. $\omega_2 = (4.619/a) \sqrt{S/m}$; $\omega_3 = (4.880/a) \sqrt{S/m}$;
$\omega_{2,3} = (5.088/a) \sqrt{S/m}$.

5.36 A simply supported 45° skew plate, with sides L and $\sqrt{2}\,L$, buckles under a uniform compression N per unit of boundary length. Evaluate the lowest critical value of N using $n = 2$, 3, and 4 subintervals and extrapolations (see Sec. 5.20 and Problem 5.55).

Ans. $N_2 = 24D/L^2$; $N_3 = 26.63D/L^2$; $N_4 = 27.15D/L^2$;
$N_{2,3} = 28.730D/L^2$; $N_{3,4} = 27.820D/L^2$; $N_{2,3,4} = 27.510D/L^2$.

5.37 Determine the pivotal values of the potential ϕ in the circular sector of Fig. 5.72, when its boundary values are as indicated in the figure. Use $n = 2$ and 3 subintervals. *Hint:* The potential ϕ satisfies the Laplacian equation $\nabla^2\phi = 0$.

Ans. $n = 2 : \phi = 155$; $n = 3 : \phi_1 = 138$; $\phi_2 = 171$.

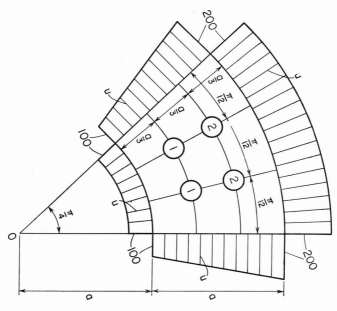

Figure 5.72

5.38 Determine the deflections at the pivotal points of an annular membrane of internal radius a and external radius $3a$, under a uniform pressure p and uniform tension S. Use $n = 2$ and 4 subintervals and extrapolation at the center line of the membrane (see Sec. 5.6).

5.39 Determine the lowest frequency of vibration of the membrane of Problem 5.38, using $n = 2$, 3, and 4 subintervals and extrapolation (see Sec. 5.9). Let $w = \omega a \sqrt{m/S}$.

Ans. $w_2 = 1.4142$; $w_3 = 1.4893$; $w_4 = 1.5153$; $w_{2,3} = 1.5495$;
       $w_{3,4} = 1.5487$.

5.40 The function $u(x,y)$ satisfies the equation $\nabla^2 u = 0$ in the interior of a hexagon of side a, and has the values indicated in Fig. 5.73, on its boundary. Determine by iteration to three significant figures the values of u at the pivotal points indicated in the figure.

Ans. $u_1 = 233$; $u_2 = 276$; $u_3 = 212$.

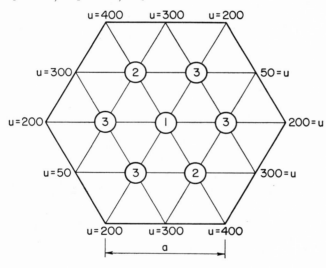

Figure 5.73

5.41 Determine the elastic torsional stress function ϕ, satisfying the equation $\nabla^2 \phi + 2 = 0$, at the pivotal points of an equilateral triangular cross section, using $n = 4$, 5, and 6 subintervals; ϕ is zero on the boundary (see Sec. 5.7).

5.42 Determine the lowest frequency of vibration of an equilateral triangular membrane of sides a, using $n = 3$, 4, and 5 subintervals and extrapolation (see Sec. 5.9).

Ans. $\omega_3 = (6/a)\sqrt{S/m}$; $\omega_4 = (6.532/a)\sqrt{S/m}$; $\omega_5 = (6.788/a)\sqrt{S/m}$;
       $\omega_{3,4} = (7.216/a)\sqrt{S/m}$; $\omega_{4,5} = (7.243/a)\sqrt{S/m}$;
       $\omega = (7.255/a)\sqrt{S/m}$.

5.43 Determine the lowest frequency of vibration of a regular hexagonal membrane of sides a. Use $n = 1$, 2, and 3 subintervals and extrapolation (see Sec. 5.9).

5.44 Determine the lowest frequency of vibration of the triangular membrane of Fig. 5.74. Use $n = 3$ and 4 subintervals and extrapolation. *Hint:* Derive the ∇^2 operator in triangular coordinates for $\alpha = 70°$, $\beta = 100°$, and let the deflection

$$z(u,v,w,t) = z(u,v,w) \sin \omega t$$

(see Sec. 5.9).

Ans. $\omega_3 = (4.701/a) \sqrt{S/m}$; $\omega_4 = (4.859/a) \sqrt{S/m}$;
$\omega_{3,4} = (5.062/a) \sqrt{S/m}$.

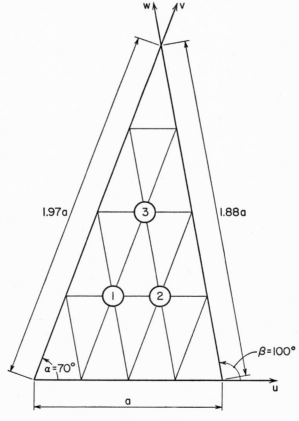

Figure 5.74

5.45 A simply supported equilateral triangular plate of sides a is acted upon by a uniform load q. Determine the lateral deflection at the pivotal points of the plate, using $n = 3, 4, 5$, and 6 subintervals and extrapolate the center deflection w_0 (see Problem 5.20).

Ans. $n = 3; w_0 = 0.00077qa^4/D$. $n = 4; w_1 = 0.00055qa^4/D$. $n = 5$;
$w_1 = 0.00036qa^4/D, w_2 = 0.00054qa^4/D$. $n = 6; w_1 = 0.000241qa^4/D$,
$w_2 = 0.000434qa^4/D, w_0 = 0.000627qa^4/D$. $w_{3,6} = 0.000579qa^4/D$.

5.46 A simply supported equilateral triangular plate of sides a buckles under a uniform compression N per unit of boundary length. Determine the lowest buckling value of N using $n = 3, 4$, and 5 subintervals and extrapolation (see Sec. 5.20 and Problem 5.55).

5.47 A simply supported hexagonal plate of sides a buckles under a uniform compression N per unit of boundary length. Determine the lowest buckling value of N, using $n = 1, 2$, and 3 subintervals and extrapolation (see Sec. 5.20 and Problem 5.55).

Ans. $N_1 = 4D/a^2$; $N_2 = 6.28D/a^2$; $N_3 = 6.77D/a^2$; $N_{1,2} = 7.04D/a^2$;
$N_{2,3} = 7.16D/a^2$; $N_{2,3,4} = 7.18D/a^2$.

5.48 Solve Problem 5.45 using the improved Poissonian operator of Sec. 5.15.

5.49 (a) Determine the temperature $u(x,t)$ in a bar of length L, insulated around its lateral surface, if its ends are kept at zero temperature and its initial temperature is $u(0,t) = 100x/L$. Use a mesh size $h = L/4$ and let t vary between 0 and 10 in steps of unity. Assume $K = 1$.

(b) Solve the same problem keeping the end $x = 0$ at zero temperature and $u_x = 10$ at $x = L$.

5.50 The square plate of Fig. 5.75, initially at zero temperature, has two opposite sides suddenly raised to a temperature of 10,000° and the other two

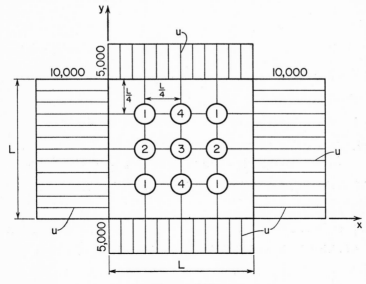

Figure 5.75

sides raised to a temperature of 5,000°. Determine the variation of temperature with time by the Bender-Schmidt method, using a mesh size $h = L/4$, for $n = t/k$ varying between 0 and 10.

Ans.

$n = t/k$	u_1	u_2	u_3	u_4
1	3750	2500	0	1250
2	4687	4375	1875	3125
5	6562	6718	5625	5468

5.51 Solve Problem 5.50 assuming an initial temperature over the entire plate equal to 10,000° and the condition $\partial u/\partial n = 10$ over the entire boundary.

5.52 Determine the value of α which will guarantee a steady temperature decrease in the Problem of Sec. 5.17 with the following boundary conditions.

(a) $u(0,t) = 0;$ $u(L,t) = a.$
(b) $u(0,t) = 0;$ $u(L,t) + 2u_x(L,t) = 0.$

Let $K = 1.$

5.53 (a) Determine the displacements $y(x,t)$ of a string with $m = 0.1$ oz/in., pulled by a force $S = 100$ lb if $y(x,0) = x(L - x)/L^2$, for $x = 0(2)10$, $t = 0(1)5$.
(b) Solve the same problem if the string is initially at rest and its left end has a displacement $y(0,t) = t.$

5.54 A uniformly loaded rectangular plate of sides a, $2a$ is built in along its short sides and simply supported along its long sides. Determine the deflection at the center of the plate, using $h = a/2$ (see Sec. 5.19). *Hint:* The boundary conditions along the simply supported edges are $w = 0; \partial^2 w/\partial n^2 = 0.$

5.55 A simply supported square plate of side a buckles under a uniform pressure N per unit of length of boundary. Determine the lowest buckling value of N using $n = 2$, 3, and 4 subintervals and extrapolation (see Sec. 5.20). *Hint:* The problem is governed by the equations* $\nabla^4 w + \dfrac{N}{D} \nabla^2 w = 0; w = 0, \nabla^2 w = 0$ on the boundary. Let $\nabla^2 w = z$ and use the operator of Fig. 5.3b.

Ans. $N_2 = 16D/a^2$; $N_3 = 18D/a^2$; $N_4 = 18.75D/a^2$; $N_{2,3} = 19.6D/a^2$;
$N_{3,4} = 19.71D/a^2$; $N_{2,3,4} = 19.75D/a^2$; $N = 19.74D/a^2.$

5.56 A simply supported rectangular plate of sides $2a$ parallel to x, and a parallel to y, buckles under a uniform compression N per unit of boundary length. Determine the lowest buckling value of N by rectangular coordinates, using $n = 2$, 3, and 4 subintervals and extrapolation (see Sec. 5.20 and Problem 5.55).

* See S. Timoshenko and S. Woinowsky-Krieger, *Theory of Plates and Shells*, pp. 378 ff.

5.57 A built-in rectangular plate of sides $2a$ and a, parallel to x and y, respectively, buckles under a uniform pressure N per unit of boundary length. Determine the lowest buckling value of N, using $n = 2$ and 3 subintervals and extrapolation (see Sec. 5.20).

Ans. $N_2 = 16.8D/a^2$; $N_3 = 26.55D/a^2$; $N_{2,3} = 34.35D/a^2$.

5.58 A simply supported square plate buckles under a uniform pressure N per unit length applied to two opposite sides. Determine the lowest buckling value of N, using $n = 2$, 3, and 4 subintervals (see Sec. 5.20).

Ans. $N_2 = 32D/a^2$; $N_3 = 36D/a^2$; $N_4 = 37.51D/a^2$; $N_{2,3} = 39.20D/a^2$;
$N_{3,4} = 39.46D/a^2$; $N_{2,3,4} = 39.54D/a^2$; $N = 39.48D/a^2$.

5.59 Solve Problem 5.58 by separation of the variables, letting

$$w = Y(y) \sin (\pi/a)x$$

and using $n = 2$, 3, and 4 subintervals.

5.60 A simply supported square plate of side a vibrates freely. Determine its lowest frequency by finite difference operators with errors of order h^2, using $n = 2$, 3, and 4 subintervals and extrapolation. *Hint:* The differential equation for the free vibration of a plate is $D\nabla^4 w + m\partial^2 w/\partial t^2 = 0$, where m is the mass per unit of area. Substitute $w(x,y,t) = z(x,y) \sin \omega t$.

5.61 A built-in rectangular plate of sides a and $2a$ vibrates freely. Determine its lowest frequency by finite differences using $n = 2$ and 3 subintervals and extrapolation (see Problem 5.60).

Ans. $\omega_2 = (12.962/a^2) \sqrt{D/m}$; $\omega_3 = (17.283/a^2) \sqrt{D/m}$;
$\omega_{2,3} = (20.740/a^2) \sqrt{D/m}$.

5.62 A rectangular plate is built in along its sides $2a$ parallel to x and simply supported along its sides a, parallel to y. The plate vibrates freely. Determine its lowest frequency by separation of the variables and finite differences for $n = 2$, 3, and 4 subintervals and extrapolate. *Hint:* Let

$$w(x,y,t) = Y(y) \sin (\pi/2a)x \sin \omega t$$

in the plate equation of Problem 5.60. Let $W = \omega a^2 \sqrt{m/D}$.

Ans. $W_2 = 13.175$; $W_3 = 17.132$; $W_4 = 19.373$; $W_{2,3} = 20.298$;
$W_{3,4} = 22.254$; $W_{2,3,4} = 22.906$.

Index